TRAIL-MAKERS
OF THE MIDDLE BORDER

By HAMLIN GARLAND

A Daughter of the Middle Border
A Son of the Middle Border
Ulysses S. Grant, His Life and Character

TRAIL-MAKERS

— OF THE —

MIDDLE BORDER

BY

HAMLIN GARLAND

Illustrated by

CONSTANCE GARLAND

NEW YORK

THE MACMILLAN COMPANY

1926

To the men and women of an older generation whose fireside chronicles form the basis of
my story, I dedicate this book. As they loved to
relive their pioneer experiences so I have taken
pleasure in recording them.

CONTENTS

BOOK I

Contents

BOOK II

THE TRAIL-MAKERS

BOOK I: IN PEACE

CHAPTER I

Boy Life in the State of Maine

I HAVE heard Richard Graham say that his earliest
memories were the sounds of his mother's voice and the
whirr of her spinning-wheel, mingled with the jocund sound
of the mountain brook which ran just before the farm-house
door. It was a swift stream, offering some danger to small
explorers, but it was also an allurement, for its ripples were
filled with a million glancing lights in summer, and in the
winter its banks were mysteriously beautiful with snow-
laden, overhanging shrubs and vines.

It came from the White Mountains to the south, and
vanished into equally alluring spaces in the vaguer north.
It had fishes in it and "Uncle John" used to draw them out
with a spear. Ducks and geese rode on its still pools in
springtime or nuzzled along its grassy margins in
September.

It was a never-failing source of interest to Dickie. He
went to sleep in his trundle-bed with its gurgle in his ears,
and woke to its laughter of a morning. As he grew older

he learned to swim in it, and in December, when its wider reaches were frozen into smooth ice, he skated upon it, or rather slid upon it, for he had no skates. It was the most cheerful and uncomplaining creature in his world, for Oxford County, Maine, was an austere place for children in 1837. Laughter had small place in any of its homes.

Deacon Graham, a small, grim-lipped man, handsome, with keen grey eyes, even teeth, and a voice of commanding power, was a typical New England elder. His chief interest was in the Church. He not only began each day with a prayer, but he invoked God's blessing each time he sat at meat. On Sunday morning he read a chapter of the Bible to his family and prayed long and loud, as was the pious custom of the time. There was no hypocrisy in this; it was sincere zeal.

His house was small and bare, for though a good carpenter he was singularly ineffective in a business way, and his wife, who was not strong, suffered many deprivations. She was a thin, dark woman with a sweet smile and a low-toned, musical voice. She came from the Androscoggin, and the sound of that word possessed a singular and poetic significance in Richard's childish mind, for his mother told him that the brook which came from the mountain ran toward the great river on whose bank she had spent her girlhood. He loved to hear her talk of her old home in the valley.

Richard's brother Addison, several years older than he, was more like a guardian or uncle than a brother, for he was a very serious boy, tall and spare like his mother. He loved books (as she did) and cared little for games. Deliberate of speech and motion, he never laughed, though he often smiled, and at times his words were quaintly humorous, while Richard overflowed with vitality and was always wrestling or racing. Addison seldom played and never hurried.

12

Boy Life in the State of Maine

From the time he was ten, the older boy was in service with a farmer, and the younger was called upon to do chores about the house before he was seven. Neither of them was allowed to go to school in summer and only for a few weeks in the winter. Life was serious business for them both, and yet they were not unhappy.

Oxford County, Maine, was on the north-east New England border-line and money, scarce even in the homes of the most prosperous farmers, was almost non-existent in the Graham home, for the deacon, conscientious and precise in all that he did, earned very little. Dollars eluded him, but shoes and hats and books were even more elusive; they could be obtained only by swift and continuous toil. However, children were not a liability but an asset in his scheme of life as in that of most of his neighbours, and he put both his sons out to work for wages as soon as they were nine.

It was a rigorous climate up there, close under the shoulders of the White Mountains. Winters were long. Snows fell deep in November and May was cold. In July, appalling thunder-storms broke in sudden shadow over the hills, washing the soil from the planted fields. The lands were steep and stony and the valleys narrow and winding. Only by incessant labour could the rocky slopes be made to yield a living, and yet a certain rude plenty was common. Most families had stores of apples and potatoes, and some made maple-syrup and kept bees. Rye and buckwheat flour were plentiful, but cane-sugar and white flour were considered luxuries.

Many houses stood high on the hills and teams of oxen were forever crawling up and down the rough roads, their drivers walking beside them, each carrying a goad, a long flexible rod in which a polished iron point was set. Richard began to drive such a span before he was nine years old and half his toes bore "stun bruises" by reason of the cruel walking beside his team.

He brought the cows down from the pasture each afternoon during the summer, and a scary job it was, for bears were often seen in the woods and "painters" or catamounts were reported on the cliffs. Once as he was driving homeward a load of Elder Robbins' hay just at dusk, a painter uttered a savage scream, and the oxen, whirling about in mad panic, broke the cart-tongue and overturned the hay. Scared as he was, the resolute boy succeeded in stopping the runaways and bringing them safely home.

Robbins reprimanded him soundly for this mishap and refused to credit his story of the fierce outcry. "It was all a piece of your dumb foolishness," he declared, and sent Dick supperless to bed.

Robbins, who was not only a grim man but a harsh taskmaster, paid a dollar a week and board for the boy's services. The board was not much to speak of, for Dick was denied any share in the delicacies which came occasionally to the table. Potatoes and skim milk often made up his evening meal.

The Robbins children, who were all grown up, had fled the house and Richard led a lonely life there with the two old people. Austere as his father's fireside was, he rejoiced in it by contrast, for his sister Susan, a delicate, black-eyed child, was its ruling spirit. Slight as she was, she dominated her father with quiet ease, and enjoyed such luxuries of food and dress as her brothers had never known.

She was of slender vitality and each winter her mother feared that she could not possibly endure the cold; but she did, and at seven became Richard's tiny companion on his way to school. They walked each day in all sorts of weather, although on certain mornings when the new-fallen snow was deep, Deacon Graham yoked up his oxen and took them both to the schoolhouse door, trusting to some neighbour to bring them home at night.

Schooling was a very simple matter for Richard. He had

only two books, a reader and a speller, and he earned his first slate by helping to build the fires for the teacher. By sifting and selling the ashes he earned enough to purchase one of the largest slates in the store. This was his first possession and he was very proud of it. (I have that slate in my desk at this moment and the date carved on the frame is 1839.) He was nine years old that fall.

Very far and still and remote seems that hill-encompassed valley in which Richard and Addison Graham spent their boyhood. It had no railroads, no telegraph, and very few carriages and horses. It was a land of two-wheeled ox-carts, long, crooked scythes, high spinning-wheels, and tin candle moulds. The chief events of the year were General Training Day and "protracted meeting" in the church. The hills and streams and trees were nobly beautiful, but the lives of the settlers, like their homes, were bare and drab.

It is certain that neither Addison nor Richard realized this austerity at the time. They only knew that some of the neighbouring homes were more cheerful than their own. Richard was especially fond of his Uncle Nat Bridges' home, whose fireside was the brightest spot in his childhood. Nathaniel was Harriet Graham's half-brother, and he and his wife, Pattie, were very fond of Richard and Susan.

It was in this uncle's home that Richard first heard of railways and the marvellous "ingines" which ran upon iron rails. "One is comin' up our valley," he said. Richard was too young to care about its name, but his brother asked, "Why is it named the Atlantic & St. Lawrence Railway?"

Nathaniel laughed. "Well, now, boy, you've got me. I don't know why 'tis so named. I guess because it's going to connect the ocean with Canady—if it ever goes through."

This railroad coming from the sea became the eighth wonder of the world to the people of Bethel and Overlook, but it was Addison, not yet fifteen, who knew the most about it and seemed most certain of its success. "It'll come," he said to his father, "and you and I will ride on it in less than five years."

He talked continually of it as it came creeping steadily toward Intervale, for it brought with it some part of the magical outside world, the world of cities and the sea. In his eyes burned a steady flame of quiet resolution. "Some day I'm going down to see it," he said to his companions.

One Sunday he called Dick aside and said, "Don't say a word about it to father, but I'm going to find a job on this railway. I'm told a boy can get two shillings a day driving a team, and I'm going to try it. Don't let on even to mother, but when next Sunday comes and I'm gone, you can tell her. I'll send back word as soon as I get settled, and bimeby if there's a chance for you, I'll let you know. You're too young to go now."

He went away as he had planned, and his family did not see him again till autumn. All summer long Richard hoped for a "call" but none came. On the contrary, Addison advised him to wait another year. "The work will be nearer and you will be older and stronger."

During that year the railroad was the most vital interest of the whole county, and when Addison came home in November, he was in demand as an authority concerning it. His bearing was so assured that his father ventured upon no reproof. It is probable that his restraint was due in some measure to the fact that Addison brought back enough money to provide groceries for the household during the winter, and when Addison said, "I'm going back in May," the deacon made no objection.

"I'm going with you," Richard declared, but to this his mother would not consent. "You are too young," she said, "the life of the camps would be too hard for you."

Dick knew better. He was a hardy boy, skilled with the axe and the scythe and unusually deft in all his movements; he had no fear of the hardships involved. Life on the railway would be preferable to the slavery of his position in the Robbins household. He resented his master's incessant nagging and he was tired of boiled potatoes, skim milk, and corn-bread.

Although Robbins never actually struck the boy, he took pleasure in depriving him of recreation. He denied him his Sunday visit to his mother; refused him holidays. Richard accepted work as an inescapable part of life, but resented his master's interference with his play-time. Filled with bitter rage, he made secret resolves to escape, and when one Saturday night Robbins again refused him permission to visit his mother, his heart overflowed with rebellious anger. "I'll go and I'll never come back," he vowed to himself.

Those of my readers who are boys, or who have been boys, will understand the hot resentment, the desperate temper in which he planned his departure that night. How he managed to keep awake, or how he roused himself at dawn, he was never able to explain, but at the first streak of light he awoke. Raising the sash of his chamber-window, he crawled out upon the roof of the wood-house, slipped to the ground, and set off down the road with all his possessions done up in a small bundle which swung in his hand like a Christmas pudding.

Clouds were curling round old Overlook, and the morning was murky, but the water of the stream cheerily sang as if in exultation over the boy's leap to freedom. It was cool and wet, and apple-blossoms were scenting the air, and the chant of early robins filled Dick's heart with joy. He was an adventurer at last, facing the wide, mysterious world. No longer a drudge, a "bound boy," he made off toward the east at a pace which soon left the shouting brook behind.

He had no shoes (those he had worn the previous winter were too badly cracked to be of service), and so he pattered tenderly over sand and gravel, fording the creek from time to time, and cutting across well-known fields to save distance, until he reached the main thoroughfare which ran down the valley toward Portland. Thereafter he kept to this road, not knowing the country well enough to venture on cut-offs. The world was lit with new glory as the sun rose, for each mile led him into strange lands and toward a mythic sea.

His exultant self-confidence lessened a little as the hours passed and leg-weariness set in, but he had no thought of turning back. He grew hungry (he had not dared to take anything from the pantry for fear of arousing suspicion) and he feared to ask for food until he had reached a point much farther from his master's house. Swift-footed as a dog, he trotted for several hours. No one paid especial attention to him until, along about eleven o'clock, as he was passing a small church, some boys called out, "Hello, sonny! Does your mother know you're out?"

He was tempted to sail a rock at them just to let them know that he was a youth of courage, but his better judgment decided against an act of war and he trotted on.

It was too early in the season for even a boy of his experience to find anything in the way of forage, and so at last it became necessary to stop at a farm-house to buy a piece of bread. He owned a few pennies and proudly expected to pay his way, but as he had no idea how long it would take him to find his brother, he was very reluctant to part with his money.

By noon he was so hungry that he was almost desperate. He studied each of the houses he passed in the hope of seeing some elderly woman to whom he might safely apply. At about two o'clock he came to a cross-roads tavern, on the porch of which sat several men in Sunday dress. As Dick approached, one of them, a young and handsome man, called, "Hello, bub! Where you bound?"

Dick did not reply and another and older man laughingly said, "By the look of his bundle he's on his way to Boston."

His raillery incensed Dick and he was hurrying by, when the first speaker called to him, "Wait a minute, my lad. If you are going as far as Snow's Corners, I'd like you to carry a letter for me. I'll pay you a shilling for the job."

There was something winning in the stranger's voice, but his offer was still more arresting. Whatever else might be said of Richard, he was neither thick-skulled nor lazy, and when a chance to earn an honest coin offered, he took it. "I don't know how far 'tis to Snow's Corners—but I'm goin' to the railroad camp."

"Not today?" the stranger inquired with a note of surprise.

"Yes, sir, I got to get there. My brother is workin' for the railroad. I must find him."

"I see. I see. How far have you come?"

Dick hesitated. "Lock's Mills."

"That's a long walk for a lad. You must be tired. Come up and sit down while I write my letter."

His tone and glance were so friendly that Dick was won. No man had ever spoken to him in just that sympathetic way. Slowly mounting the steps, he took the seat which was placed for him.

"I suspect you're hungry as well as tired," said his host. The kindness in his words touched the lad. Tears came to his eyes. "Yes, sir, I am. I'm awful hungry."

"I guessed as much. Come with me and we'll see what can be done for that hunger."

Dick followed his guide through a big room where six or eight roughly clad workmen were seated, on into the kitchen where an old man and a young woman were busily washing dishes.

"Jake," called Dick's friend, "give this boy something to eat. He's going to run an errand for me and feels the need of fuel in his fire-box."

The old man had a sour and worried look, and it was evident that without an advocate, Dick would have fared badly. Muttering something about the nuisance of "feedin' a boy 'tween meals," the Kitchen Colonel set out some cold pork, a slice of bread and butter, and a glass of milk. "Now fall to and be quick about it," he growled.

Dick was willing to hurry. In ten minutes he had filled his fuel-box and was back on the porch ready to take orders. His host said, "I want you to hand this letter to the tavern-keeper at Snow's Corners. You'll reach there about dark tonight. Tell him that Walter Ackerman sent you, and that I want you to stay all night. He'll take care of you. I think you can reach the advance camp of the graders by noon tomorrow, although it's a good stiff tramp."

In less than five minutes he had obtained all of Dick's life history, but he made no attempt to discourage him in his course. "This is your start in the world," he said with a look on his face which moved the boy even more than his voice had done. "Who am I to turn you back? I left my father's house in Massachusetts twenty years ago in much the same way. Follow your brother. Don't drink, don't gamble, keep good company, and you'll become a leader of men," he said in conclusion.

With this magic formula in his ears, Dick set forth, feeling inches taller and all of a year older than when he had first met this man's glance. The tense excitement of the morning was gone. From Walter Ackerman he had gained a shilling and the conviction that luck was on his side.

This new-found confidence was still so strong that when an hour later a team came rapidly up behind him and a voice called out, "Want a ride, boy?" he was not much surprised. He accepted it as another and deserved good fortune.

The driver proved to be a brown-bearded, middle-aged man seated in a spattered, leather-canopied four-wheeled gig. "Climb in, son," he cheerily said.

Without a word Richard mounted to the seat, and the

man started his ponies with a slap of the reins. "I live in Snow's Corners. How far are you going?"

"To the railway camp," replied Dick.

"That's quite a trip for a boy of your age."

"I know it is, but I can reach it tomorrow. I have a letter to give to the tavern-keeper at Snow's Corners."

The man's interest went no further. He began to doze, his head toppling about on his shoulders in a most alarming way. Occasionally he opened his eyes, smiled, took a look at the road, and fell again into uneasy slumber. He appeared tired as well as sleepy.

At last Dick said, "Shan't I drive for you?"

"You may. All you need to do is hold the lines. The horses don't need much guidance. They'll take us home. Just keep the main thoroughfares."

After giving the reins to Dick, he folded his arms, leaned back, and closed his eyes. His face was pale and worn, and the boy, certain that he was a doctor, was glad to relieve him. He recalled his mother's dependence upon just such a man of medicine during Susan's sickness a year or two before.

He was careful not to interfere with the choice of turnings which the horses unhesitatingly made, for he knew by the pointings of their ears and by the rhythmic plod of their feet that they were on their way home and were sure of their ground.

After nearly two hours of this rapid trot they came to a church, a tavern, and a row of houses surrounded by apple trees and lilac bushes. It was a lovely village, more finished, more comfortable than Dick had ever known, and the yard into which the horses turned contained a large white house.

Roused by the change of motion, the doctor awoke. "Here we are!" he exclaimed. "You've done a good job, you and the ponies."

"Is this Snow's Corners?"

"It is and this is my house. That's the tavern opposite. Suppose you deliver your letter and come back and have supper with me?"

"I'll unhitch your team first."

"Very good. All you need to do is unhook them. They'll tell you where they belong. When you've finished, come to the house and, if I'm asleep, as I'm likely to be, Miss Swan will look after you."

After unhitching the horses and stabling them, Richard crossed the road and left his letter with the tavern-keeper who said that he would hand it to the proper person.

The doctor's invitation had been not only kind but commanding, and yet the boy, fearing "Miss Swan," was tempted to go on. The doctor's trust in him finally decided his action. Returning to the yard, he sought the side door where a small sign bore the words:

Doctor Boynton
Office

The door stood open and as Dick looked in he perceived the doctor already asleep on a couch. His hands, slender but tanned with much open-air driving, lay on his breast with a startling suggestion of death. As the boy hesitated, a tall, long-faced, elderly woman appeared in an inner doorway and crooked her finger at him. "Go round to the kitchen door," she signalled.

This he did. She met him with unsmiling visage. "You're the boy the doctor spoke about, I suppose."

"Yes, ma'am, I am."

"Well, come in and wash up and I'll get you something to eat, such as it is. The doctor is so nigh dead for sleep that he can't even *see* his vittles. He's had an awful run of dipthery up to the falls. He ain't had a real good sleep for a week."

She talked along in this way without any need of a word

from Dick, except when she asked where he lived and where he was going.

It was a little disappointing to have her pass over his reply with an indifferent "Aha," "I want to know," or "Do tell." She was not greatly interested in anything or anybody aside from Dr. Boynton. Her world centred about him. He was not only her nephew but "the noblest man in the country and as good as any in the state of Maine."

However she fed her guest bountifully and pleasantly. "No use waking the doctor," she remarked as she did so. "Somebody's just sure to come galloping up and destroy his night's repose. I'm goin' to let him sleep right where he is. He told me to take care of you and that's what I'll do. He said you was to sleep here tonight and you'll find a bed in the room at the head of them stairs." She indicated a narrow door leading to the upper storey.

Remembering his mother's admonitions, Dick sought the horse-trough and there bathed his burning feet, and beat the dust from his shirt and trousers in careful preparation for the clean bed which he foresaw was waiting for him in the room above.

As his weary body sank into the soft deeps of the "feather tick," his spirit smiled. What a day it had been! It seemed a long time since he had slipped out over the roof of the Robbins wood-shed. The water was singing past his mother's door just the same as ever, and little Susan was saying her prayers to the sound of it, wondering why Dickie did not come.

When he woke, the robins were singing and the morning light flooding into his room, which was a large chamber lying just above the kitchen. Its furniture was of pine, painted that everlasting blue which people used so generally in those days. A rag carpet lay on the floor, and three ancient cane-seated chairs stood against the bare walls, but to the boy it was all spacious and fine.

Dressing with Richard was a simple process. It consisted in putting on his trousers and running his fingers through his hair. Stealing softly down the stairs, he found his way to the stable where the horses, greeting him as if they knew him, called upon him to feed them. This he did, and as he was busily currying one of them, he heard a merry whistle. Looking up, he saw the doctor sauntering across the yard, his hands in his trousers pockets, bare-headed and joyous as a bobolink. It was evident that he had enjoyed a good night's sleep.

"Hello!" he said as he saw Dick at the horses. "You're an early riser."

"Yes, sir. I went to bed early."

"Did you? Well, so did I." As he watched the grooming of his horse, he smiled. "I'm thinking of keeping you," he said slowly. "I need just such a boy. How would you like to live with me and be a doctor?"

Dick shook his head. "I wouldn't like it," he replied. "I'd rather drive a team on the railway."

The doctor was amused but persisted. "I'm serious about this offer. If you'll stop here and look after Miss Swan and me, I'll give you six dollars a month."

This offer stunned the boy and for a moment he stood looking at the speaker with round, astonished eyes. "I don't believe I better. My brother's expectin' me," he repeated.

Dr. Boynton did not press him further. "You'll have breakfast with me, anyhow," he said, and to this Dick agreed.

Before the doctor had finished his steak, a messenger came for him, and Richard hooked his team into the gig and brought it around to the door.

The doctor was pleased. "Dick, you've spoiled me!" he said as he came out to the carriage. "Whenever you want a job, come to me. Good-bye. Good luck."

Almost before the carriage had passed through the gate,

24

Richard took up his bundle and set off down the road in quest of the railway, which was for him the magical goal.

It was a glorious day for adventure. The warm sunlight, the blossoming trees, the springing grass starred with pink and blue and gold, the voice of the brook, and the melody of birds, filled the small pilgrim with happy courage. He sped on without thought of stopping or turning aside. His confidence in himself and his belief in the world were redoubled by this meeting with Dr. Boynton.

CHAPTER II

The Railway and Boston

THE first sign of the railway, and one which Dick did not at once identify, was a row of square pegs running through the meadow on his right, but when, farther down the valley, he saw men with ploughs and scrapers piling dirt into a long ridge, he understood. He had reached the field of his labour. He had sighted the advance-guard of the road-makers.

From a shanty near by a smoke was rising, and though he feared that a barefoot runaway boy might receive but a sour greeting, he decided to stop and inquire his way.

It was the cook-house of the gang, and the only person in the place, a short, red-faced man in an incredibly dirty leather apron, was stirring something in a big pot which gave off such a delicious smell that the lad was faint with desire of it. He had been travelling desperately for nearly five hours and his breakfast was a dim memory. It was

26

plain that this was a part of the railway outfit, and that the mid-day meal was almost ready to be served.

The cook, on seeing Dick, nodded genially and said, "Good day to ye, me fine gossoon. How is the walkin' the day?"

"First rate," replied Dick, and then he added quickly, "Can you tell me where to find my brother, Addison Graham?"

"I can not—more's the pity," the cook answered in a kindly spirit. "Is he on the work, I donno?"

"He's teamin' for the railway," Dick answered proudly.

"Is he now! Well, he may be somewhere down the line. Sit ye here and wait till the men come in, some wan of thim may know yer brother. What was his name ag'in?"

"Addison—Addison Graham."

"A fine name indade. It brings back me school-days intirely. And phwat is yer own name?—'tis equally literary, I'll be bound."

"My name is Richard, but folks all call me Dick."

The cook again stirred the pot. "Well, now, Dick, have ye starch enough in yer legs to snatch a drop of water for me out of the spring beyant?"

He indicated a wooden pail with the toe of his boot, and the direction of the spring with a jerk of his thumb.

Catching up the pail, Dick made off without hesitation, hoping to earn at least a doughnut. Experience had already taught him that ready and skilful service gave, at least, assurance of food. In this case it promised more.

On his return, the cook handed him a plate of stew and a hunk of corn-bread, and began to dish out the meal for the men who could be heard coming into camp with their teams. "I nade a broth of a boy like you," the cook said reflectively. "I nade a dish-washer. I'm heart-sore with pot-wrasslin'. Stay with me and I'll see that ye are handsomely paid."

This, the second offer of employment in two days, added

to Dick's feeling of security. The world needed his services, that was evident, but he firmly declined. "I must find my brother. He wants me to work with him."

The truth is Dick had no intention of washing dishes for a living. His ambition was fixed on driving a team of horses. He was out to rise in the world. With a bowl of hot stew and a piece of johnny-cake in his gizzard, he was ready to go on, but a sense of gratitude kept him till after the hands had eaten.

They were a silent and weary lot. Much less interesting than he had expected them to be. Building a railway was evidently nothing like as exciting as he had imagined it. They all listened to his explanation of how he came to be there, but only one man made reply to his question.

"Ain't never been no Addison Graham in ary camp that I know anything about," he said decisively.

Dick became still more disappointed in the method of building railroads as he helped wash the dishes. He had expected to see a snorting engine nosing up close behind the graders and track-layers, all engaged in heroic bustle. In imagination he had pictured a long line of busy men and teams, making the dirt and rails fly, whilst a throng of citizens stood about watching and cheering. Instead of that, building a railway seemed very much like working out a poll-tax.

In the second camp, he found Addison in a small cottage which was a kind of office. He was seated at a table with some books before him, and as Dick entered he looked up in surprise and silently studied his brother. Slow to speak under any condition, he gave Dick time, in the present case, to say, with a defensive smile, "Well, here I am! What can you do for me?"

Addison's first thought was of his mother. "How are all the folks?"

"They're well, I guess. I didn't see them this week."

28

"How do you happen to be here? Did father give his consent? What about Deacon Robbins?"

"I didn't stop to find out. I just slipped out o' the back window, and skittered down the road as fast as I could go—and I'm never going back."

"I suppose you want a job?"

"That's what I'm here for."

"I guess we can arrange it. We need help." He said "we" with a quiet air of pride which made Dick ask, "What are you doing here?"

"I'm book-keeper. I've been keeping 'time' for almost two weeks."

Addison's learning was always a source of pride to Dick, and he was not at all surprised to find him in a position of responsibility. "Where is the engine?" He called it "injun" as most boys did; men called it "injine," but Addison called it a "locomotive," and explained that it was at work down the road a few miles.

"I want to see it run," said Dick with a note of disappointment in his voice. "I want to ride on the train."

"You'll see it running along here in a few weeks," Addison assured him, "and we'll both ride on it."

The camp in which Dick found work stood near a village called Conway Center, and part of the men lived there. The crew was small, but as full of talk of railroading as if it had been an army. One man came from Portland, another from Portsmouth, and the overseer was a Boston man. Dick rejoiced in their company. He had moved out of his narrow valley beneath the Overlook into the wide air of the world of steam.

His work, while tiresome, was not severe and he liked it. The men were kindly and in a few days he was so much at home among them that Addison sent a letter to his father advising him of Dick's presence. "Better let him stay here. I'll see that his wages are sent home."

Dick consented to this arrangement but with some reluctance, for he had begun to plan other uses for his money. He wanted a pair of boots, boots of such quality as the surveyors wore.

The purchase of these and a new jacket a month later formed the milestones in his progress toward manhood, and shortly after that came the supreme event of his summer, a visit to South Conway to see the railway train.

The scene was all that he had expected it to be and more. The crowds of people, the iron horse puffing out clouds of smoke and dragging four great stage-coaches hitched together and filled with officials, was of dream-like splendour. The engine, marvellous as a dragon, was terrifying even at a distance, and when it drew near Richard's knees trembled. In spite of his brother's reassurance, he fled up the bank, with the others, an action which made the engineer laugh, but an old gentleman standing near spoke a comforting word. "It *is* scary. It don't seem exactly the kind of thing that the Lord intended men to create. I can't quite get used to seeing a bunch of metal moving around by way of a little hot water. Seems too much like an unlawful creation on the part of human beings."

It was all more wonderful than General Training Day. Ladies, gaily dressed, were standing in groups, or sitting in carriages near by attended by gentlemen in tall hats and high-shouldered coats. The boys learned afterwards that the congressman, the Honorable Hannibal Hamlin, was there, but they didn't know anything of his presence at the time; they were much more concerned with the engineer, who seemed to them the most intrepid as well as the most skilful individual they had ever known. The calm dignity with which he let loose the machine's infernal power was exalting.

"Some day," Dick said to Addison, "some day I'm going to ride away on that train to Portland."

The Railway and Boston

"Portland!" replied Addison with a note of scorn. "I'm going to Boston."

Boston! With that remark a new seed was planted in Dick's mind, a seed which would one day flower into heroic action.

As winter came on the work of grading ceased, and Addison returned to Overlook. He urged Dick to go to school, but to this the lad made objection. "I'm going to chore for Dr. Boynton at Snow's Corners," he declared.

His return to the homestead brought a renewal of the awe in which he held his father, but the weight of the silver dollars in his pocket restored his courage. His look and a new tone in his voice made the deacon hesitate about pressing him too far. His mother met him with a kiss. Brought up in repressive New England ways, she was shy of caresses. It had been years since Dick had felt the pressure of her lips and his heart was touched by her tears.

His father's chief grace was a sonorous and musical voice, and the utterance of his son's name gave his greeting a grave and distinguished character. Richard's resentment melted under the charm of it. With all his shortcomings, Robert Graham was a man of note. Though small, he carried himself with natural dignity. He was absolutely fearless, and in all matters of conscience, was like a lion.

It chanced that soon after his return, Dick saw his father in his most heroic mood. A Free Soil meeting had been announced and a gang of men made known their intention to tear down the poster from the Town Hall door. Hearing this, Robert Graham hurried to the spot and Richard, filled with admiration of his diminutive sire, followed him into the crowd, and as near the steps of the hall as he could get. The deacon, almost lost in the press of his towering antagonists, calmly set his back against the poster and confronted them, his face set in a rigid defiance. Dick was close enough to catch his father's words as he undauntedly declared, "This poster stays just where it is until *we* decide to take it down."

Although checked by his resolute face and ringing voice, several of his antagonists were moving upon him when his brother John, a big man and a formidable fighter, mounted the steps and took a place beside him. "I guess, neighbours, you'll have to let this poster alone." There was menace in the calmness of his tone and the opposition halted. One by one the Free Soilers gathered and the meeting "took up" at the scheduled time.

Richard's respect for his father was restored by that incident. When the inevitable clash came and his father demanded his obedience, the boy, knowing that Dr. Boynton would house him for the winter, asserted his new independence. "You can't bind me out again, father. If you do I'll run away so far you'll never see a cent of my wages."

Graham's voice grew hard. "By law your wages belong to me till you're of age."

This interview might have ended in a physical struggle and complete estrangement had not Harriet Graham quietly interceded. "I guess you'll have to yield a point, Robert. Let Richard keep half his wages till he is eighteen. You'll lose him entirely if you don't."

Low-voiced as she was, there was strength and courage in her face and in her tone. The deacon gave reluctant consent, and Dick went away to Snow's Corners elated by his victory and with augmented admiration for his mother. For her he was ready to do anything.

For two summers Richard and Addison worked for the railway, and in winter Addison taught a country school whilst Richard returned to Dr. Boynton's to take care of his horses and cut firewood. He attended the village school a part of the time, but books did not interest him as much as the coasting and the skating. Restless as a young wolf and caring nothing for the cold he was never at rest except when he slept.

It was a grim country, this county of Oxford. It was in truth the north-west frontier of New England, and Addison whose blood was thinner suffered under the hardship of the long walks to the schoolhouse, and when an acquaintance asked him to go to Quincy, Massachusetts, he consented gladly. It was almost like going to Boston.

His going turned Richard's ambitions toward the city. Hitherto Portland had been his goal, but now he was fired with a nobler ambition. "Get me a place to work and I'll come along," he said to his brother without a thought as to how his mother would feel when both her sons were gone. The golden dome of the Massachusetts State House now allured him. It glowed in beauty like the turreted clouds at sunset. It was the centre of his world.

Harriet Graham was a Spartan mother. Although prematurely aged, her brain remained clear, her will-power undiminished. Realizing that Overlook was a narrow field for an ambitious boy, she made no opposition to Richard's going. She only asked him to wait until he had attained his full stature. In this request she was reinforced by Dr. Boynton, who was still hoping that Dick would decide to stay with him.

At last in the spring of his seventeenth year, Richard announced his decision. "I'm going to Boston tomorrow, mother. Addison says he has a job for me and the sooner I go the better."

"I've been expecting you to say that," she quietly replied. "I shall make no objection. I am as anxious to have you get on in the world as anyone can be and you shall go with my blessing."

The deacon, however, was opposed. "You're needed here. Your mother should have the comfort of one of her sons."

"Now, Robert," she warningly called, "Richard must have his chance in the world as well as Addison. Our boys are good boys with quick minds. I see no reason why they shouldn't do as well in the city as Elias and Ethan Shaw. Many of the merchants of Boston are the sons of country folk. The city has done them good. It can't be as bad as it is made out to be."

This settled it and Richard planned to get away at once. Trains were running regularly now from Bethel to Portland, and his plan was to go partly by rail and partly by steamboat, thus experiencing all the wonders of travel by steam.

He knew nothing of the sorrow and anxiety which kept his mother awake that night, for she concealed, even from her husband, the sense of desolation which shadowed her as she realized her bereavement. She did not deceive herself. She knew that neither of her sons would ever return to live in Oxford County. They were moving on into wider horizons, and she had no wish to bar their progress.

Richard took the train at Lock's Mills, which was only a few miles from his father's home. He was a handsome youth, tall, fair-skinned, and graceful, but in spite of the best intentions of his mother, and the undoubted skill of his Aunt Patty, his clothes were manifestly home-made and the amused smiles of two girls who were riding to Portland made him feel, as he looked, the country boy.

The train in which he rode into the world that day would cause a shout of merriment to an Oxford County boy today, but it was very impressive to Richard, and the conductor who had charge of it, or who appeared to have charge of it, was a refulgent figure in Richard's eyes.

In the beginning of the traffic a sad conflict of authority had arisen between the coachman (that is to say, the engineer) and the conductor who was in effect the footman. The driver naturally declared himself the man to start or stop the string of coaches. As the descendant of the stage-

34

driver he was disposed to be autocratic in his authority.
"I'm the man in charge," said he.

To this claim the conductor (or guard) argued that no
man away at the head of the train could be trusted to tell
when the passengers were safely aboard. "You are to wait
my signal," he said, speaking for the future. "You are the
driver, not the conductor."

This discussion ceased to be academic when the driver
started his engine just as a passenger, a prominent stock-
holder, had one foot on the step. Highly indignant, he
demanded redress, and the conductor, who chanced to be
a man of unusual readiness with his fists, went to the door
of the engine, snatched the driver from his perch, and gave
him such a mauling that the question of authority was never
again in dispute. Thereafter all trains started and stopped
on signal from the conductor. The "driver" had been de-
throned by the "footman."

Exactly in proportion as Dick acquired a sense of safety
in railway travel did he begin to dread Portland, the great
city whereto he was rushing at fearful speed. How to find
his way from the railway to the docks troubled him. He
began to wish that he had arranged to complete his journey
by train. He would have changed his plan, even after leaving the coach, had it not been for a passenger who kindly
agreed to show him the way to the *Massachusetts*, which
was the steam packet which sailed every other day for
Boston.

The wonder of this vessel subdued the boy even more
painfully than the train. It was much more splendid than
his vision of it had been. He went early to his bunk, at the
suggestion of his kind friend, in order that he might avoid being sea-sick, and so as the water was smooth he slept soundly
and saw but little of the ocean, for when he awakened
next morning, the boat was steaming into Boston in full
view of the city to which every New England lad aspired.

The gleam of the dome of the State House and the tall monument on Bunker Hill were the first objects pointed out to him. The city in general was like a broad garment crumpling over the hills—a wide-spread robe patterned in red, which reached to the edge of the bay whereon many vessels both great and small were in motion. Sea-going ships with towering masses of snow-white sails were setting forth on new voyages, whilst others lying at their docks were being unladen. Some seemed resting whilst flocks of other smaller ones, "fishing smacks" some called them, were moving outward with tilting spars.

It was a glorious and stirring picture, and the boy standing at the rail, his grey eyes set wide, absorbed every detail as if he were never to see its like again. The sailors shouting and singing, the sound of capstans, the rumble of trucks on the wharves—all these sounds mingled with the smell of the sea, the glitter of the waves, and the bustle of the ship's company around him.

Once off the boat, the sounds of the sea were lost and the voice of the streets, a deep rumble with an occasional whistle and clanging roar, overwhelmed him. With his bundle slung on his shoulder he took his way up the narrow street toward the State House, as inexperienced a youth as ever trod its pavement, inquiring his way to Quincy from time to time.

The noise of the traffic increased as he proceeded, for the streets were paved with rounded boulders, over which the heavy drays bumped and clattered with prodigious uproar. The iron tires howled, the hooves of the horses click-clocked, whilst the clang and clatter of lighter vehicles added sharply to the tumult which fell upon the country boy's ears like the sound of thunder upon a rabbit. He could not think, he could only see, so immersed was he in this benumbing ocean of sound.

By the time he had reached the corner of the Common, however, he had recovered enough of his native quality to admire the great Percheron horses which certain of the rich merchants owned and employed in draying. He had never seen such animals before, and he studied them closely—their magnificent brass housings, the massive chains which connected their collars with their chariots and their decorations aroused his admiration. It interested him to see that the drivers directed their teams without reins, and that the horses were hitched one before the other, making a train of three, and in some cases five, huge, hairy-fetlocked beasts with enormous shoulders and massive tread.

With an eight-mile walk before him he dared not linger on the way. Glorious as the city was, it was also a place of danger. A forest had less terror for him than the streets of a town.

The splendid horses helped him to regain self-confidence. To see them calmly and good-naturedly picking their way gave him comfort. It was good to see with what secure ease they planted their huge feet and swung their ponderous trucks around the corners. With what straining of muscular limbs they heaved their carts up a hill! So long as they obeyed their masters they were secure and happy, and when the clear voice of a driver rang out, Dick decided that if he could ever be commander of such a team his ambition would be satisfied.

Quickening his steps he soon passed out of danger. His stupefaction gave place to ease. Elm-bordered lanes, small yards, chickens and flower-beds restored him to joyous confidence. At a point across the bay he could look back on the shining State House dome. "Some day I'm coming back to live in Boston," he declared silently.

Addison greeted his brother with smiling glance and his voice was full of quizzical humour as he said, "Well, so you've made the plunge!"

It is well to admit, at this point, that to Addison belongs

the credit of Richard's success. He led the way. He not only found a place for Dick to live, but he secured for him a job. As driver for one of the teams with which the granite company supplied the builders of the city with stone, Dick achieved his ambition easily and quickly.

The sense of exaltation with which he took his way into Boston the first day may seem foolish and a little pathetic to some of my readers, but it must be borne in mind that this boy regarded his new job as a station on the road to a shining goal. What that goal was he did not define; perhaps it changed from month to month—but he was on the road!

Whilst his great horses swung along with steady, monotonous stride he had time to study his surroundings, and this he did, to such good effect that in a few weeks the streets to the south and west of the city were as familiar to him as to any of the drivers. On Sundays he eagerly explored such parts of the capital as his leisure permitted.

"I intend to know Boston like the back of my hand," he said to his brother, and in less than a year he was competent to act as guide to any part of it. His ambition now was to gain employment in the city. He liked Quincy, but he wanted to be able to say, "I live in Boston."

CHAPTER III

The Lure of the Sunset Regions

ONE day in the spring of 1848, while young Richard Graham was delivering a load of granite blocks for the foundation of a new house on Roxbury Hill, Enoch Lawrence, the owner of the place and a renowned Boston merchant, came by. As he passed he called out cheerily, "Good morning, Richard."

"Good morning, Mr. Lawrence," Richard replied with an intonation which indicated a clear, composed mind. He was a handsome boy of eighteen, tall, broad-shouldered, and fair-skinned.

Lawrence was a short man with a grey beard, a gentle, kindly soul whom the boy venerated as a nobly successful business man. The fact that the great merchant knew him by name was a pleasant surprise.

Enoch, who made a point of knowing the name of every clerk or teamster in his employ, was a natural aristocrat whose unassuming dignity won, at the same time that it awed, his employees. As he questioned, Richard told him quite frankly how he came to leave his home in Maine, and what he hoped to accomplish in the city. Lawrence studied him with interest. The care with which the boy had driven his team among the trees of the lawn had won his approval. His liking led him to say with a half-smile and a shrewd sidewise glance, "How would you like me for a boss?"

Richard stared at him a moment before replying, "What do you mean, sir?"

"How would you like to drive one of my teams?"

"I should like it very much, sir, only I should be sorry to say good-bye to this one." He patted his wheel-horse as he said this.

Enoch's tone was sympathetic as he replied, "I value that loyalty, Richard. The good teamster loves his horses. That is why I should like to see you in charge of some of mine. Think it over, and if you feel like making a change come to my office on Monday morning, and I'll see that you have one of the handsomest of my spans."

Richard's hesitation was short-lived, for the Lawrence teams were famous among Boston drivers. They were all perfectly matched, dapple-grey Percherons, with coats like satin, whose polished brass housings, massive silver chains, and numerous ivory rings set them apart from all other draught-horses. To be the driver of such a span appealed to the boy as a proud position, a promotion to be instantly accepted.

That night he wrote a letter to his mother in order that she might rejoice in his good fortune, and this must be taken as evidence of his high excitement, for he was a most reluctant writer and postage was high. "Next week I'll be driving one of the grandest teams in Boston," he stated with perfect confidence in the merchant's promise.

Early on Monday morning he presented himself at the great man's door and was at once admitted, for Enoch had instructed the man outside to send the youth in without delay.

To enter the private office of this renowned merchant was (to a boy from Maine) like gaining audience with a king, and yet he entered without an awkward gesture. The room in which Lawrence sat was carpeted, and contained a massive desk, a row of bookshelves, and two or three oil portraits. A vase of flowers adorned his desk, and the morning sunlight filling the window above his venerable and shapely head quite dazzled the boy's admiring eyes.

"Good morning, Richard," said Enoch pleasantly. "I've just been thinking about you. Take a seat."

His kindly tone and the lines of his face expressed a reminiscent wistfulness. Something in the tone, the face, and the bearing of his visitor had reminded him of his own youthful encounter with the city more than forty years earlier, and he was deep in the tender joy of recalling these experiences when Richard appeared. With the air of having plenty of time to expend, he again pointed to a chair. "Be seated. I want you to tell me more of your home and your plans."

Richard, although deeply moved, was not hesitant. He described his home and related his hard experiences as a bound boy briefly, but enlarged upon his work for the railway. He stated the arrangement with his father, and when he had finished Enoch remarked, "I hope you have kept to your bargain, and that you are regularly sending your wages back to your mother."

"Yes, sir, I am sending something every month, and I shall keep this up although I am past eighteen. My brother helps, too, and mother's more comfortable, I guess, than she's ever been before."

Enoch looked away musingly. "I can imagine how she misses you. When I left my mother in Vermont nearly fifty years ago, I fully expected that at some time she would come to live with me. But it didn't work out that way. She died before I had a home to which I could safely bring her." He paused here as if to steady his voice, and then added, "I hope you write to your mother often?"

Dick looked down at the floor. "I'm not much of a letter-writer," he admitted. "But I wrote to her last night. I told her that I expected to work for you."

"What are your extravagances?" asked Enoch with abrupt change of tone.

"What do you mean by that, sir?"

"How do you waste your money?" he smiled. "We all have different ways of being prodigal. What is yours?"

Richard regained his poise. "I guess the theatre is my main extravagance," he explained with a smile. "I go pretty often, but I sit up in the gallery. It don't cost so very much, and I enjoy it best of anything I can afford to pay for."

"I like that in you," said Lawrence, who perceived in Dick a scion of his own stock. "You're a boy after my own heart. You'll make your way, of that I'm certain. There's only one 'out' about you. Your schooling has been neglected. It isn't entirely your fault, for you've had a pretty severe boyhood, but you should remedy this lack as soon as possible. It will prove a serious handicap unless you do. You must find time for study. I shall have an eye on you, and I shall do all that I can to promote your best interests. Take this card to the foreman of my stables, and he will set you to work."

Richard's eyes glistened as he thanked the good man, and he hurried to secure his new job with exultant haste.

The three great horses which the foreman put into the new driver's keeping were the noblest of their kind. They walked forth with the pride of chieftains, their glossy necks arched high in kindly, conscious power, and Dick was transported with pride. He gave such attention to their grooming

42

that their coats soon became of such dustless satin smooth-
ness that a lady's kid glove would not be soiled by contact,
and the brass buckles of their jet-black gear shone like
pieces of burnished gold. He laughed with candid delight
when people in the street paused to remark upon the beauty
of his outfit.

He taught them to obey his whistle as well as his word,
and when in the midst of a crowded, thunderous street, they
swung to right or left in answer to his chirping call, he
glowed with boyish pride. He was perfectly content. He
had attained his goal.

Although his days were completely filled with the use and
care of his horses, his nights were free. He had time for
study, but he did not improve it. He was too active, too
companionable to read. Education was not a necessity in
his work. Night school seemed an injustice, for it cut
into his chief amusement, the theatre.

He loved the play. Every gallery seat in Boston soon
became known to him, but the Howard Athenæum was his
favourite resort. From the grimy wooden benches of the
peanut gallery he looked down on Junius Brutus Booth in
many a classic rôle. Booth was king of the stage at this
time (a strange, moody, marvellous, almost legendary character), and Dick, his whole-hearted admirer, was quite
willing to fight in defence of him.

Accepting all the tales which concerned the tragedian's
half-mad absorption in the characters he impersonated,
Richard in common with other lads was persuaded that
Macduff stood in actual danger from Macbeth in the great
battle scene. That the actor who fenced with Booth did
so at the hazard of his skin was implicitly believed by every
gallery god. They related with awed voices how in one of
these stage contests, the mimic Macduff, having broken
his sword, was forced to leap into the pit to save his life.
Credence of this tale gave delightful suspense to every

43

performance in which a duel took place. They all hoped to see Macduff leap into the audience, but he never did.

Richard especially loved Booth as Richard III, and when the great actor came limping on the scene with one shoulder hunched high above the other, he and the other boys in the gallery whistled and pounded the floor and cat-called in such storm of greeting that the tragedian (in no wise displeased) turned his face upwards, and snarled with wolfish malignancy at the gods in their heaven. He was, for Richard, the actual monster of the text, and when with a scream of rage he uttered the king's fretful lines, "In the naarth? What do they in the naarth when they should serve their sovereign in the west?" the youthful teamster shivered with delight. The player fitted his conception of the tyrant.

There were not many theatres in Boston in 1848 and the Oxford County lad saw all the great actors who came. He applauded Charlotte Cushman and Julia Deane, and thrilled with awe as Edwin Forrest roared the lines of the Gladiator or stalked about the stage as Othello. Forrest was a big man with short side-whiskers, an orator rather than an actor, and the inferior to Brutus Booth so far as Richard's judgment was concerned.

This teamster loved oratory. In Faneuil Hall he heard Daniel Webster and Rufus Choate as well as Wendell Phillips. By great good fortune he and Addison were both present on the historic occasion when, in order to give emphasis to his words, Phillips went through the motions of lashing a slave with a whip. He became Richard's ideal speaker as Booth was his ideal actor. Entranced by the music of the orator's voice and the beauty of his face, Richard at once became an abolitionist.

On another occasion he heard Ralph Waldo Emerson of Concord, a calm, cold, slender man, who seemed not to care whether anyone agreed with him or not. Richard was not especially impressed by this address, but Addison was deeply moved, for this was a brave soul speaking his mind against slavery, unmindful of the storm which his words aroused.

Fierce passions were aflame in Boston, as everywhere in the nation, and Free Soilers were holding defiant meetings in public places, while the papers were in constant debate concerning the Mexican War and the spread of slavery. Without being at any time a reader, Richard could not avoid political instruction. The daily newspapers were of slight interest to him, but he found great interest in public discussions.

With nothing namby-pamby about him, he was a youth of good habits. He could fight like a tiger, if necessary, and he loved all kinds of athletic sports, especially those in which hardihood was involved, but he had no taste for gin and wasted no time in roistering. He carried himself like an athlete, and his fine head, piercing grey eyes, and shapely hands and feet denoted good blood. He moved quickly, gracefully, and with precision. Crowds, construction, movement delighted him. His eyes were like cameras which neglected nothing. He saw everything and forgot nothing that he saw.

His knowledge of the city and his temperate habits pleased Enoch and in the autumn he put him in charge of the barns. For nearly a year he held this position, although he would have preferred to drive a team of five horses. Confinement was irksome to him.

One day in the spring of '49, the merchant again sent for him. "Richard," said he, "we need an assistant shipping-clerk and I have decided to put you in that position."

Richard's face darkened. "I've been in the open air all my life, Mr. Lawrence; I don't believe I can stand being shut up in a warehouse. I'd rather run a dray."

Lawrence smiled. "There's considerable activity connected with your new job. You're too fine to be a teamster all your life, Richard. I want to promote you. I would give you entire charge of the shipping-room, only you are not able to keep the books and do the figuring. If you want to go higher you must study."

To this Richard could only reply, "I've tried to study, sir, but I can't hold myself to it. I'm not like my brother in that."

He had in Addison a fine example of a student happy in his work. His comfortable room in a South End boarding-house was always supplied with books and most of his spare hours were spent in reading. He now held a responsible position in a great shoe-house and like Richard believed himself settled for life in Boston. Both were getting good salaries and the future promised even greater prosperity for them both.

Upon their contentment, into their quietly prosperous world, two powerful currents of allurement suddenly poured. One of these arose from the discovery of gold, a tale from far-off California which changed the whole nation's outlook toward its newly acquired Mexican territory. The winter of 1848 and the spring of '49 wrought an immeasurable change in Boston complacency as in the life of thousands of other cities. The spirit of the pioneer revived. The papers began to print stories of the "free gold" at Sutter's Mill, and the faces of millions turned toward the West. By the middle of June the excitement amounted to a craze. Men literally went mad with desire of those far-off golden sands. The *Transcript* was full of this hysteria. Mining companies were advertised, the sailing of vessels announced, and the departures of "caravans" described. Citizens on the street corner meeting one another asked, "When are you going to California?" and the common answer was, "By the next caravan."

The Lure of the Sunset Regions

Richard was precisely the kind of youth to be attacked by this disease. His essentially adventurous spirit flamed out in action. He was all for throwing up his job and sailing for San Francisco at once, but Addison, cautious, practical, checked him. "Wait a while. Don't be led away by these reports. They may all be a hoax. I am a good deal more interested in the new state of Wisconsin than I am in California."

"Why Wisconsin?" asked Richard.

Addison handed him a letter. "Here's a letter from mother. She says the emigration fever has broken out in Oxford County. After much backing and filling, Uncle Nathaniel Bridges has sold his farm and is going out to help build up Wisconsin. Aunt Patty's brother Hiram is mining lead out there, and has been urging them to join him. Mother wants you to consider Wisconsin. It isn't so far away as California and she thinks it safer. I'm getting information on the soil and climate. Don't do anythink rash. Wait a while."

Harriet Graham was a good letter-writer. Her words came easily and her pen ran smoothly. She enjoyed correspondence and her missives to her sons had something of the news journal in them. "I hope you will not go to California; it is so far away. Everybody here is talking about the new state, Wisconsin. Nathaniel and Patty have about decided to go to Green County where Ethan Roberts and your Uncle John have already settled. John is delighted with the country and wants us all to join him. California seems a very serious undertaking, and if you insist upon pioneering, I would rather you went to Wisconsin, where your uncles are."

Richard was affected by the tone of this letter, for his mother was not given to expressing emotions of any sort. He read between the lines of this appeal such profound alarm that he gave up all thought of California. He said to Addison, "Would you consider going to the Wisconsin lead mines?"

Addison pondered. "I might. I'll think about it. As mother says, it's a serious problem."

In the letters which passed between him and his mother, it became evident that a kind of madness had settled upon the neighbourhood, and that she was touched by the same disease. Her husband, fine and intelligent as he was, was in a poor situation. Persistent and bitter in his war against rum and slavery, he had not only increased the number of his enemies, but had wasted his time in controversy, and Harriet, arguing that in a new country he would find a more tolerant community, one in which his skill as a builder would count, urged migration. "If Richard will go to Wisconsin, father and I will go with him," she finally wrote to Addison.

By this time Richard thought of little else than exploration. Boston lost interest. He took no joy in his work. He began to read of sailing the Great Lakes and of building homes in Wisconsin, this new, romantic, and remote state. "If we can settle father out there," he said to Addison, "in a country where every man is building and where labour is in demand, I guess we'd better do it. He's just about run ashore where he is."

The more he read of Galena the more alluring it became. Tales of fields from which lumps of pure white metal worth hundreds of dollars were dug up with a spade, and luscious descriptions of prairies on which a man could amass a fortune with a few crops of wheat, filled him with such hot unrest that he could talk of nothing else.

During the winter, thousands of New England farmers were reported to be selling their ancestral acres for half their worth, in order to join the tide of Western settlement. In this exodus, the Boston papers very naturally discovered cause for alarm. Their editors united in an effort to discourage a migration "which threatens to deplete every township in the state, and to carry away the most vigorous and adventurous of our young men."

Nevertheless, now and again, in spite of all the efforts to prevent it, something favourable to the coast or to the prairies appeared in the *Transcript*, either by way of a letter from a successful settler or an editorial which (in opposing "the madness which has seized upon our citizens,") gave further publicity to the glowing reports of crops and mines.

One letter which profoundly affected Addison described a visit to the lead-mining district. "Some day," the writer predicted, "Galena will be a great metropolis. It is only about fifteen years old and is, at present, a muddy and ramshackle village, but it is a river port and in the midst of lead deposits. It is certain to be a great inland capital."

This report confirmed all that Ethan Roberts had written and Addison was moved to say "A new town like Galena would be a good place for a start in merchandising."

Thus it happened that during the winter of '49 the New England farmer who could hardly find money enough to pay his taxes was reading tales of golden sands and flourishing prairies in the West. Every Eastern state was involved. A new and marvellous empire came into being. Maps of the North-West widened the nation illimitably. The imagination of ambitious youth reached out and laid hold upon those distant free lands. Illinois, Iowa, Minnesota were, after all, parts of an ever-widening republic. That the Mississippi Valley had been claimed by the French counted for little with Congress. "It is our manifest destiny to govern from sea to sea," the orators on the Fourth of July declared, making much of John C. Fremont's inspiring conquest.

A play which came along in the spring exerted a most amazing influence on the city of Boston.

49

It was called *Mose in California*, a hastily built and farcical piece which cleverly capitalized the craze. One scene represented Mose leaving for the gold-fields singing the words of a popular song:

> Oh, Susan Annah dear,
> Oh, don't you cry for me,
> For I'm off to California
> The gold mines for to see.
> And there I'll dig the mountains down
> And drain the rivers dry,
> And fill my pockets full of gold,
> Susannah, don't you cry.

This scene, which represented a ship leaving the dock, was tremendously impressive to the gallery gods, and so was a third act which showed a mining-camp in California with Mose sitting on a mound of gold-dust and crying, "Bread! Bread! Give me bread!"

It was a foolish piece, but Richard confessed to a stirring in his blood as he watched the gold-seekers going gaily aboard. It brought his longing for adventure to the point of action. "I'm going West. I've got to go—I can't stand any more of this business of loading bales and boxes on a truck."

Meanwhile the war against slavery was growing more intense every day, and the question of its introduction into each new state was vital. William Lloyd Garrison and the young poet Whittier had become shining figures in Addison's world, but Wendell Phillips remained Richard's idol. The graceful form, clean-cut features, and merciless wit of the great abolitionist created in the boy an admiration which was almost worship. Phillips spared no one. He offered no compromises. He fought with pitiless blade, willing to sacrifice friend or foe on the altar of his faith. By comparison, Clay, Webster, Choate, all seemed compromising professional politicians. Phillips was an aristocrat as well as an evangelist. He had nothing to gain by his stern crusade. He was a moral paladin.

James Russell Lowell's "Bigelow Papers" with their comments on the Mexican War, amused both Addison and Richard, but they did not take them seriously. Like Fremont, they were believers in the westward march of the republic, and were all for annexing the land which joined it. "Fremont, the Pathfinder" was the most romantic and splendid figure in the West; a soldier, serving the nation with decision and power at a time and place where decision and power were of vital concern. He was adding territory to the nation at the moment when Wendell Phillips was insisting that slavery should be abolished in every state.

As the summer waned, the editorials in the *Transcript* became more insistent upon the hardship and danger of pioneering. Articles delineated in detail the grim tragedies of the Overland Trail. Gruesome stories of death by thirst in the desert, and of cold and hunger among the snows of the Sierra mountains, put a chill into the fevered hearts of those who had been hot to take the Sunset Way.

During the winter months those who had failed in the mines of California also began to be heard from. "Don't come out here expecting to pick up gold in chunks," they wrote. "Ninety per cent of the men on the spot are only making a poor living. Many are suffering privation." These reports did not check the tide of emigration; they merely turned it into new channels. Many who had been planning to cross the plains decided to settle in the Middle West instead.

Richard, with no doubts, no hesitations, pored over Peck's "Gazetteer," finding such descriptions of Wisconsin in the pages that he could hardly wait till the season of migration should open.

"Valleys filled with wild bees abound," one account declared. "Streams in which fish swim are everywhere," but above and beyond these descriptions gleamed something subtler, a radiance which the boy could not describe, a light which shimmered in the West like the impalpable gold of evening—a mist shot with purple streamers, and as he walked the hills of Milton, he imagined himself a pathfinder in the green savannahs of the Sioux. He heard a calling, far and sweet, a melody which the wind sang in his ears with insistent appeal.

This emotion was expressed in a song of the border which a book of travel caught up and reprinted, a song which Dick had never heard at home, but which one of his friends often sang to him, a ballad which expressed, better than any praise could do, the mighty urge which was transferring an army of men and women from the hills and valleys of New England to the woods and prairies of the sunset.

The first verse began in this wise:

> "Cheer up, brothers, as we go
> O'er the mountains westward ho,
> Where under boughs of mistletoe
> Log huts we'll rear,
> Where herds of deer and buffalo
> Furnish the cheer."

The chorus was an exultant one:

> "Then o'er the hills in legions, boys,
> Fair freedom's star
> Points to the sunset regions, boys,
> Ha, ha, ha, ha!"

"The sunset regions." There was a phrase which sank deep into Richard's mind, transmuting all his musings into poetry. It enabled him to turn his back on the splendours of Boston, leaving behind him the theatres, the music, the ships, the holiday crowds, the orators of the city. Strange alchemy! This song, simple as it seems now, made the distant wilderness more alluring than all the glories of civilization, filling the boy's mind with a fantastic, unreasonable hunger—a madness which had peopled the wilderness of Europe, a lure which led men forever toward the sunset regions of the world.

CHAPTER IV

The Westward Journey

ONE evening in May, Addison came to Richard's room and said in the tone of one who is both surprised and amused, "Well, Dick, the procession is about to start! Nathaniel has decided to leave for the West on the twenty-first. He writes, 'I've harvested my last crop of rocks.'"

In this phrase, "crop of rocks," may be found the explanation for a large part of the New England exodus which Nathaniel had joined. Returns to farmers were meagre, even for those who tilled the valleys, and for those on the hill-farms the soil was cruelly unrewarding. The oft-repeated jest, "Have to sharpen my sheep's noses sos't they can git at the grass between the stuns" carried a touch of bitter truth in its humorous description.

Nate loved his birth-place and his many friends, but he was tired of hacking a living from the flinty slopes. In the light of the reports of Wisconsin soil, rock-picking in Maine had become an intolerable drudgery. The word

The Westward Journey

"prairie" held out to him, as it did to thousands of his kind, a release from stone walls and a promise of harvests such as the best acres of his home county could never produce. To be free from hills, to plough an unbroken furrow in a level field, had become an obsession with him.

"I'm going where I can clap a hoe into the ground without striking fire," he stoutly declared. "I want to own and drive a team of horses the way John Bridges is doing. All my life I've crawled up and down these hills. I began life with stun bruises on my toes, and I've carried stun callouses on my hands all the rest of the time. Right here I quit the job of watching for rocks to hop out of the ground. I sold my farm for just about what the barn cost me, but no matter. I'm going where land is not only good, but cheap."

His robust young wife, while less imaginative, was one of those women, few in number, who are natural pioneers. Aunt Patty, as the boys called her, was by temperament a joyous adventurer. Handsome, strong as a man, and of confident temper, the plan for going West was the promise of a grand excursion to her, whereas to Harriet Graham it was an appalling break-up, a tragic necessity.

The fact that this delicate woman was willing to consider pioneering at all is proof of the overwhelming force of the passion which had already carried so many of her neighbours out of the lovely valley, away from homes in which they had lived all their lives, commanding them to far quests. Harriet was not well, and the mere thought of travel was painful to her. As a woman of unusual dignity and refinement, she dreaded the loss of her home, her friends, and her church, but her frail body housed a spirit of indomitable courage. Having come to the conclusion that to migrate was for the good of her sons and her husband, she put aside her weakness and confronted the ordeal with serene glance.

Of the mental struggle which preceded this decision, she gave no sign. No hint of the pain, the confusion, the despair of the actual break-up reached her sons. She merely put down, very carefully and minutely, the date of her departure and the hour of her arrival in Boston.

"We shall have few impediments," she explained. "We can't afford to pay freight, and besides we have sold all of our furniture that would sell. Your father is taking his chest of tools, for he is certain that no such tools can be found in the West. We are selling at a sacrifice, for many other families are offering their goods at almost any price. All the hill farms are being deserted. Your Uncle John Bridges, who is settled in Green County, Wisconsin, is sure that we can all make our fortune out there. Nathaniel is equally confident. He is our leader. He is going with us as far as Detroit. It is a very sad time for me. It seems like saying good-bye to everything and everybody. The men don't mind it so much, even your father is cheerful in the face of it."

When this letter came, Richard went immediately to his employer and said, "Mr. Lawrence, I shall want my 'walking-papers' on the first."

"Why so, Richard? Are you leaving?"

"Yes, I'm going West."

"Going West? What part of the West?"

"Southern Wisconsin."

"Wisconsin? Why Wisconsin?"

"My father and mother have decided to go there, and I'm going with them."

"You're making a mistake, Richard. You're in line for promotion here."

"I know, but I can work for myself out there."

"Aren't you working for yourself in working for me?"

"Not in the way I mean, and besides, I don't like indoor work. It doesn't agree with me."

Lawrence looked at him keenly. "You've lost some of your tan, I'll admit, but you are a pretty vigorous youth in spite of that. I'm sorry you are going. I had it in mind to promote you again. However, if you've got your heart set on seeing the new country, there's nothing to do but let you go. You're giving up a great deal in giving up Boston." He smiled as he added, "I shall consider it only a summer excursion. I'll keep a place open for you till October. You'll be homesick for Boston and working your way east by that time."

His words stiffened Richard's resolution. "I'm going for good, Mr. Lawrence. You won't see me in Boston for a good long while—but I'm much obliged for your offer just the same."

To Addison he reported this scene. "I like Mr. Lawrence. He's been good to me, but I'm not going to handle boxes and check bolts of cloth all my life."

Enoch was really concerned about the boy. It seemed a foolish move. This migration to a raw, new state was madness, but nothing he could say in praise of the city availed to change Richard's resolution.

On the morning when the Oxford County party was to arrive by way of Portland, Richard and Addison went down to meet the boat. It was a delicious spring morning and the bay, glittering under the sun and flecked with sails of vessels standing out on their shining Old World ways, appeared to mock all plans for inland exploration. "Why go West?" the City said. "Here is life. Here is wealth. Here is every opportunity for happiness and fame."

Nevertheless, these young visionaries, like thousands of others, were about to turn their faces from the storied East in order to share the task of peopling the West. To men like Enoch Lawrence it was a sorrowful illusion. Only those whose hearts responded to the calling winds of unploughed spaces and the lure of trackless forests could share the emotion of these home-seekers and take their way into lands unpeopled and remote. In this spirit Massachusetts had been won from the savage. In such psychology the West was being settled in its turn.

At last the steamboat came sliding majestically into port and clustered on her forward deck stood the Grahams and other Oxford County adventurers for whom the boys were waiting. Aunt Patty, wildly waving her handkerchief, was the first to be distinguished, but Richard had eyes only for his mother who stood quietly beside her grim and silent husband. Nathaniel, his hands and feet encumbered with baggage, called a jocular word as he leaned over the rail. "Here we are—horse, foot, and dragoons."

They all came down the gang-plank bewildered but self-contained, a state of mind which Mrs. Graham expressed when she said, "Now, boys, we are in your hands. Take direction of our enterprise."

She was wearing her best dress and did not in the least resemble an emigrant. She had little to carry, pitifully little, but Patty possessed several boxes and bundles which she herded with anxious care. "I'm not going into the wilderness without some of the things I love and need," she explained. "I wanted to take a chest of drawers but Nathaniel said it wouldn't pay."

She was happy as a bobolink, whereas in Harriet's voice lay a plaintive note which neither of her sons had ever heard before, a tone which enabled them to realize some part of the doubt, the fear, the sorrow through which she had passed. She was so frail of body, so sensitive of mind to be starting on a journey whose vicissitudes would try the most robust, and at the end of the long, wearisome journey, her resting-place could be, at its best, only a rough cabin in a strange community. That she failed of Patty's exultation her sons perceived, but her glance was steady and her words confident. Her own desires were wholly subordinate to those of her sons.

Like thousands of other wives, she was a forced emigrant. Her childhood had been spent in Portland, and her youth in Oxford County. Her life-history was interwoven with the religious and literary traditions of New England, and the pain of breaking with familiar scenes and parting with lifelong friends had been especially bitter in her case. Nothing but the conviction that her husband and sons would enjoy the larger life and share in the greater prosperity of a new state, sustained her.

What an almost mortal agony that parting with her friends had been! We of today can not measure the sense of loss, the passionate grief, the agony, the despair which accompanied such an uprooting. It had in it something of the solemnity of death, for such separations were recognized to be (as in truth they were) tragically final. If I could, I would put my readers back into that day, into the small village, so that they might sense the heroism involved in Harriet Graham's decision. There is no parallel to it today. Distance does not exist today as it existed then. None of the Overlook neighbours expected to see the Grahams again. They were passing to a far and savage world.

After a serious conference in a near-by eating-place, Addison announced that he had decided not to accompany them. "I'll wait another year. With all our savings combined, you have hardly enough to complete your journey and set up housekeeping. I am earning good wages here, and it appears advisable for me to hold my job until you are settled in your new home."

Harriet recognized the good sense of this decision, although she was greatly disappointed. "Very well," she quietly said, "we will go on without you."

They left at once on a railway train bound for Hoosac,

and although suffering from loss of sleep and the physical hardships of the journey, Harriet made no complaint. Richard assumed the care of her, and his aunt, though much worried by her parcels, took charge of little Susan, whose velvety-black eyes mirrored the world in their deeps. She, too, accepted the various phases of the journey with quiet resignation.

Nathaniel Bridges was the direct opposite of Harriet. Tall, bronzed, blue-eyed, smiling, he presented a handsome figure, alert and capable. He was a natural home-builder, handy with hammer and saw. Adequate in any emergency, sanguine and resolute of temperament, he had no doubts of the future and no regrets for the past.

The train contained other "movers," and a feeling of comradeship, a common understanding of the hardships to be shared, aroused a general desire to comfort and support those less hardy than themselves, a spirit which was well expressed by Nathaniel when he said, "Now, Harriet, you let us who are well-cushioned take the bumps."

For most of these migrants, the journey on the train was a delightful novelty. To them the weeks of travel to reach their destination had no terrors. The change of vista, the new sights, new people, gave constant pleasure. Once on the road they permitted no backward glances.

The railway, except for a short space over the Hoosac Mountains, ran trains to Troy. From Troy to Buffalo a canal was reported to be still competing for traffic, and at Buffalo, steamboats invited to further migration into the ever-widening waters of the Great Lakes.

Travel by canal was the cheapest possible method, so the Grahams took passage that way, glad to escape the ox-cart and the covered wagon.

Posters, pamphlets, gazetteers describing the beauties and the wealth of the new lands west of Lake Michigan, met them at Albany. Letters from Milwaukee, printed in the papers, contained this question, "Why groan and sweat at heaving rocks in the East, when you can raise forty bushels of wheat to the acre in Wisconsin on land without a stone?"

To this the editors replied, making common cause against those who would depopulate the East to build up the West. "Don't be fooled by statements of land speculators," they warned. But the movers only smiled. Naturally the builders and rulers of the older states would decry a movement which stripped Eastern hills and valleys of their hardiest, most enterprising citizens. The editorial emphasis upon the loneliness and the lack of common comforts, and their warnings concerning wild animals and savages, only caused Dick and Nathaniel to say, "I'll bet the fellows writing that stuff wish they were going too."

It took two days to cross the Hoosac Mountains and reach Schenectady, long days of dirty, wearisome travel, and poor Harriet Graham was nearly at the end of her endurance when she reached the canal-boat. "I couldn't have stood another day like yesterday," she confessed to Richard.

As they had chosen the canal route because it was cheaper than the railway, so now for the same reason they took passage on a "line boat" rather than on a "packet" in which meals and beds were furnished. The vessel was a low, narrow barge with only one deck, which moved at a rate of three miles an hour and they were forced to camp out as best they could, making way for the "expresses" which swept grandly by at a trot—that is to say, four miles an hour—with their deck passengers smiling compassionately down upon the line-boaters, much as the passengers in the Mohawk Valley Railway coaches wondered at those who still endured the pace of a packet.

On the emigrant boat meals and beds were of the passengers' own providing, and Richard detailed himself as forager for milk and bread along the way. It was not a bad way to travel. No one lacked a place to sleep and no one went hungry. The worst of the hardships, for the women, was the lack of privacy, but Patty, undismayed by any deprivation, "kept house" on the boat with amazing skill. Upon her fell the larger part of the "contriving"— the "providing" was left to the men.

The weather was glorious and as the canal-boat entered the Mohawk Valley, the lazy progress seemed the perfection of travel. Sunlit meadows, green hills, and banks of wild roses adorned the banks by day and moonlight gave mystery as well as beauty to the hills at night. Richard, with none of the doubt of his father and equally free from the regrets which troubled his mother, welcomed each day's beginning with keenest appetite. The noiseless advance of the barge made the songs of birds and the sound of the wind in the trees a part of each evening's peaceful history.

As this region, lovely as the land of their dreams, unrolled before their eyes, the marvel is that they did not all leave the boat and make their home there. They did not consider such a plan. Had the land been fairer than it was, they would have failed to see in it the beauty which it possessed, for the paradise toward which they had set their faces was a still more dazzling ideal. This country was at once too settled, too near at hand to tempt them. With desires fixed on a more romantic world beyond the Inland Seas, they persisted in their progress. The Mohawk, like Boston and Overlook, was already a song that was sung to Richard. He had only one regret; he wished that they had taken one of the swifter packets.

CHAPTER V

The Great Lakes

RICHARD'S chosen companion on the canal-boat was a young Vermonter named Clinton Helmstock, also on his way to the Galena lead mines. He was a year older than Richard and nearly twenty pounds heavier, a handsome youth, smiling, confident, ready of speech, and on frankly amiable terms with every passenger. The women especially liked him, for he was natively chivalrous. With him women were beings to be honoured and protected, an attitude which had in it, perhaps, something of manly arrogance, but it kept him from doing an injustice to those whom he considered weaker than himself.

Richard shared this feeling. Although possessed of something like Clinton's easy manners with maidens, he was in no sense a philanderer. He had met several attractive girls during his stay in Boston, but with none of them had he been other than a frank, good friend. Lacking nothing in essential manliness, neither of these boys inclined toward the rowdy side of life. Richard could fight and did fight on occasion and he could and did swear like a pirate when deeply angered, but he was not coarse of speech. Clinton did not use tobacco or liquor at this time, and something in their similarity of tastes made them chums.

Clinton, with an excellent record at school in a village academy, was older in bearing as well as in years, but Richard's experiences in Boston offset much of this difference in book-education. Neither of them lacked a knowledge of the evil in men and women, but they had never made vicious persons their associates. Youths less robust and self-reliant might have been called effeminate, but there was nothing weak or sentimental in either of them.

I touch on these points at this moment for the reason that while they paired off with two young English girls who came on the boat at Schenectady, it was all in the spirit of wholesome youth. The girls, whose names were Clara and Josephine Edwards, were not at all as reserved as English girls were supposed to be. On the contrary, they laughed and chatted with the boys in joyous freedom. Perhaps the explanation of this pliancy of manner lay in the fact that on the spindle side they were of Irish stock.

They confided that their mother was dead, and that they were on their way to join their father who owned an "estate near the city of Mil-wau-kee." "We are going by stage from Detroit to Chicago. Daddy is to meet us in Chicago." She pronounced it *Chic*-ago, and believed it to be a city entirely surrounded by red men.

They were accompanied by their uncle, a quaint, middle-aged Irishman, and by a vigorous young English woman who was on her way to join her husband on a farm near Racine. She acted as "chaperone," a word of strange significance to Richard.

Neither of the girls had ever been out of England before,

and every mile of their westward journey held something wonderful or amusing. It was all gloriously exciting to them. Realizing at once that Clinton and Richard were essentially gentlemen, they seized upon the opportunity to learn from them all about Wisconsin, and Clinton, almost as ignorant concerning the land to which they were bound, was nevertheless quite ready to answer any question. When he knew nothing of the subject he invented information. They soon dicovered his prevarication, but did not resent it. On the contrary they derived amusement from his humorous exaggerations. He was delightfully gay and unexpected, like everything else in the New World, and Richard, though less amusing, interested them with his stories of Boston, and his descriptions of his native hills.

The girls talked of the "Hall" which their father had erected on the shores of "a sylvan lake," and quoted from his letters in which he spoke of his horses and his hounds, with quiet satisfaction. Clara said, "We are taking our saddles and our riding-habits. We intend to ride every day hunting wolves and foxes."

Clinton had his doubts about all this. "It's a wild country out there. I'll be disappointed if it isn't, but I don't know about those foxes and the wolves."

"Oh, indeed there *are* wolves, and there are red Indians. Daddy says they are 'peaceable beggars.' He has killed many bears and he says there are wildcats and raccoons in our forest and that they disturb the fowls."

"Wisconsin can't be too wild to suit me," said Richard. "That's why I'm going there."

Josephine, who was two years older than Clara, tried very hard to assume the dignity and authority of her years, a post rather difficult to maintain in the face of Clinton's banter.

Neither of the girls was pretty in the sense in which Richard used the word, but they were pleasing. They had lovely complexions, fine eyes, and a grace of bearing which gave them distinction. Their voices possessed a quality which the boys could not define, and the fact that they came from a land which was almost legendary added to their charm. Richard said, "I can't believe that you girls have come from England, so far away."

"So far away!" exclaimed Josephine. "England isn't far away. America is far away."

"Well, you'll find Wisconsin still farther away. What do you expect to do out there, beside hunt wolves?"

"Oh, we shall keep house for daddy, and plant flowers and go boating on the lake."

"How long do you expect to go on doing that?" asked Clinton.

This seemed to surprise and confuse Clara, and Josephine took it upon herself to answer. "I'm sure I don't know. Daddy expects us to make our permanent home out there."

"Well, you won't keep house for daddy very long," said Clinton. "Not if the men of the neighbourhood there have any sense."

Josephine evaded this. "I could be a school-mistress. Mrs. Graham says that school-mistresses are in great demand in a new country like Wisconsin."

"So are housekeepers," persisted Clinton, "and when I make a strike in my lead mine out in Galena, I'm going to send for you."

All this was immensely amusing to Clara, but Josephine, while enjoying it, was a bit in doubt about its propriety. However she accepted it as characteristic American banter, for Clinton's clear eyes and Richard's sunny smile had no guile in them.

Mrs. Whatford, the woman who had the girls in charge, was less catholic in her judgments. She complained to Uncle Tim about the company his nieces kept. "We should have gone by the express boats," she said. "I am quite sure that Mr. Edwards never intended his daughters to travel on an immigrant ship like this."

Uncle Tim was not disturbed. It was evident that he had had his orders, for (as he privately explained to the boys) Edwards had spent all his money in buying land and building houses. "He's a bit of a gambler," he added significantly, "and has a lofty idea of himself. He thinks he's founding a great estate out there, but he'll go broke, I'm thinkin', before he gets his kennels and stables in order."

They were now gliding softly through a level country across which they could discern the spires of Buffalo, the Great Lakes port, and all the women were greatly worried by the necessity of changing boats, for they had heard much of the conscienceless "runners" for competing transportation companies, ruffians who made Buffalo a "den of thieves." One writer had described them as a "mob of howling, remorseless hyenas," and while Clint and Richard were not precisely afraid of them, they braced themselves for the encounter, assuring the girls that they would be protected.

The throng of dock-hands, barkers, and cab-drivers was not as intimidating as they had expected it to be, but it was there, and the spirit of greed and insolence was so apparent that the girls were appalled. Like hawks after stray chicks, or foxes after lame geese, the ticket-sellers, stage-coach agents, teamsters, hotel-runners, pickpockets, and gamblers swarmed about each bewildered new-comer, pushing and pulling, shouting: "This way for the Short Line!" "This way for Niagara Falls!" while persistent, flashily dressed individuals crowding close to the shoulders of the girls repeated, "Hotel? Hotel for the night?" with a tone which was in itself an insult.

It was a man of this type who felt the force of Clinton's fist, and nearly brought them all into the police-court. An evil-eyed fellow laid his hand on Josephine's arm. More indignant than alarmed she tried to free herself while her uncle ordered the man away. The ruffian replied with a grin, and this so infuriated the small Irishman that he dropped his baggage, and was rushing at the thug with the courage of a bantam cock, when Clinton intervened with a blow which toppled the ruffian over a box on the ground where he lay for a moment, looking up at the youth with a wondering stare. As he slowly rose he asked with ludicrous persistency, "Who hit me? Where's the man who hit me?"

Uncle Tim replied, "Oim the man that *will* hit ye, if ye lay hand on me niece again."

The fellow looked at him in contempt. "You! You couldn't knock me down with an axe!"

At this point Clinton confronted him. "I'm the boy that smacked you? Want another?"

A crowd of roughs encouraged the rowdy. "Go in and smash him, Hank! Do him up!"

The man hesitated (there was something formidable in the poise of the young fellow's body) and his hesitation gave Dick time to place his mother and Susan in charge of Nathaniel, and to take his place at Clinton's side. "Come on, you fellows," he called cheerily.

Exactly how this battle would have come out must remain a question, for a policeman shouldered in. "Who's hit who? Phwat's goin' on here?"

Tim, with fearless glance, stepped out and confronted him. "Oim the man, Tim O'Shannahan," said he. "That dirty spalpeen was molesting me niece and this bye," he indicated Clinton, "a friend of mine, took a fall out of him."

The officer, a man of discernment, perceived in Timothy a fellow-countryman as well as a man of courage. "Just which man was it, Mr. O'Shannahan?" he politely demanded.

Tim looked around, they all looked. The offender had

slipped away, too wise to face authority. The crowd shifted quickly and soon no one remained but the travellers who clustered about the policeman while Timothy told his story in great detail and with most convincing Dublin accent.

At last the officer found opportunity to say, "All right, Mr. O'Shannahan. Yez can go, but no more fightin', mind!"

Keeping together, the home-seekers found their way to the wharf where a magnificent vessel, the *Commodore Perry*, was waiting for them. No outward-bound ship in Boston harbor had ever given Richard the thrill which came to him as he realized that this boat was bound for Detroit, the Straits, Lake Michigan, and Milwaukee!

The character of its freight as well as its passengers declared the Sunset Empire to which it belonged. Some of the men walking its decks were on their way to Kansas, California, and Oregon. Others were ticketed for Springfield, Chicago, and St. Louis—all new and grandly romantic cities, cities whose very names were poems to Richard and his companions. He felt himself a part of a tremendous movement, a soldier in the march of a nation. (Will it ever come again on this continent—that spirit of exploration and settlement, that exultant faith in the future which moved these men and women in the mad days of '49?)

It was deep night when the *Commodore Perry* began to move, and while they were all standing on the after part of the deck watching the lights of Buffalo recede, Clara expressed her joy in their escape from the city. "I wish you were going all the way by stage as we are."

"I wish so too," replied Dick, "but mother could not stand that. The boat is best for her."

"What do you intend to do in the new country?" she asked.

"I don't know. Make a home for father and mother first of all. Then I'm going to buy a farm for myself."

This ambition seems modest enough, and yet, if that

English girl had not caught the spirit of America hitherto, she must have felt something of the courage of this lad who was going almost empty-handed to a new and wonderful state and planning a home for his parents before thinking of one of his own.

The *Commodore Perry,* palatial as it seemed to the boys in contrast to the crowded canal-boat, was small and slow. However, to Mrs. Graham it was especially grateful, for it offered a full night's sleep in a fairly comfortable berth and regular meals. Like every other conveyance going west, it was crowded with movers.

When Clinton and Richard met next morning, nothing but water lay to the north and east and west, but on the south the shore of Ohio, covered with an almost unbroken forest, could be seen. It appeared that they had already entered upon the lonely lands of the Huron and the Miami. Possessed of a certain ideal, with minds preoccupied by visions of the prairies, these Yankee Jasons would have sailed through the gardens of the Lord without thought of pausing by the way. Wisconsin being their land of the golden fleece, any shore less distant was powerless to detain them.

All day they sailed, touching now and then at some small, new town, and part of the time out of sight of the shore. When night again fell, the ship was nosing her way into a brisk westerly wind, heaving and tossing on a sea which made many sick. Clara was one of these, and for that reason Richard did not see her again till the boat was steaming into Detroit.

This town, so famous for its French and Indian history, was at first sight a sadly disappointing, small, and shabby village, but a closer study developed the flavour of its frontier character. Red men, trappers, lumbermen, fishermen, fur merchants and soldiers mingled on even terms in its muddy streets, while confident pigs and grazing cows gave evidence of comfort as well as of a good-numoured rural tolerance of nuisances on the part of its citizens.

Here the families I have been following separated. The Edwards girls and Clinton, together with Nathaniel Bridges and his wife, Patty, took the stage for Chicago, whilst the Grahams continued north by way of the Straits to Lake Michigan and Milwaukee, although Richard roundly declared he would rather go by waggon.

He meant this. There was more adventure in the stage-coach. It offered more of traditional pioneering, and held, besides, further companionship with Clinton, for whom he had developed a warm affection. It was hard to lose him and Clara at the same time. They both promised to write, but Richard realized, with a pang of regret, that the chances for seeing either of them again were not many.

The friendship which had sprung up between these young Yankees was based upon something which neither of them could define, a mutual confidence and understanding which had been almost instantaneous. Richard trusted Clinton as not many brothers do, and Clinton parted from his new-found friend with a candid sorrow.

"We'll meet in Wisconsin," he declared. "I'll walk across the state to find you. Good luck!"

"I hope you strike a chunk of lead as big as a horse," replied Richard, but the parting threw a cloud over his departure into the North. It was only a momentary shadow, but it was very real while it lasted.

Nathaniel and Patty took passage with a freighter and entered upon a slow and painful progress across the state of Michigan. Patty refused to leave her precious bags and boxes, and Nat, with smiling acquiescence, said to Harriet, "Tell 'em we're coming—along with Christmas!"

Patty was disturbed by Harriet's white face and feeble movements. "I do' know but what I ought to go along with you, Harriet. You look dreadful peaked."

"Don't trouble about me," replied Harriet. "I'll pick up on the boat, and besides, I have Richard," she added, laying her hand on his shoulder with a gesture of love and pride.

Serene as she appeared and brave as she really was, Harriet faced that long ride up Lake Huron and down Lake Michigan with a distinct sinking of the heart. Each new stage of the journey put Oxford County farther away and deeper in the past. She knew now that she was never to see Overlook again.

CHAPTER VI

The Promised Land

THE steamboat on which the Grahams sailed in coursing the Great Lakes was not especially seaworthy. When the winds were brisk, it rolled and tossed heavily. Harriet Graham was confined to her berth during a large part of the voyage, and poor little Susan was in even worse case, for she had developed a persistent fever which took away all joy in the trip. Richard became her nurse, and in his anxious service missed many of the strange towns and picturesque cliffs along the shore.

As the days passed, Deacon Graham's lips settled into a sour pout which indicated not only his disgust of the vessel, but his waning faith in the whole nonsensical enterprise. It was in this mood that many of the other passengers rode down Lake Michigan, which chanced to be very rough and cold and bleakly grey.

At last, at the close of the noon meal, the captain said: "By five o'clock tonight you'll see Milwaukee," and upon

73

this promise even the most disheartened voyagers began to place faith. The bustle of preparation for landing set in. The breeze, though still from the west, had taken on a softer touch, and as the steamer's course brought her nearer the shore and the waves smoothed out, the clear green waters hinted of welcoming shores. At three, wooded banks were in view, and at four the word ran round the deck, *"Milwaukee is in sight!"*

To the Grahams, as to many others of the company, the word "Milwaukee" was not merely the romantic name of a far-away city on a "grand, unsalted sea"; it was the radiant portal of the promised land. All who were able to stand assembled on the forward deck in order to scrutinize the slowly developing haven. The long and tedious journey was at an end. The work of founding homes in the new state was about to begin.

Seen from the ship, the town presented itself as a collection of frame houses arranged in rows along a low and pleasant plateau. A few trees, native oaks, stood to the north, but for the most part the buildings, bare as wooden blocks, perched bleakly on the plain. Nevertheless, flimsy as the village appeared, it was thrillingly welcome to Harriet Graham as well as to other travel-sick adventurers from Maine and New Hampshire.

Eager to disembark, Richard gathered together the few boxes and bundles which made up their baggage, and when the boat touched the wharf, he took Susan in his arms and carried her down the gang-plank, leaving to his father the task of steadying his mother's uncertain steps. It was not in the least like the triumphant arrival he had anticipated, but there was in it a blessed sense of relief.

Poor little Susan! Too sick to be interested in anything, she lay in her brother's arms like a baby, her thin face and big black eyes arousing the pity of the passengers, several of whom had come to love her for her patience and sweetness. Even the rough dock-hands and teamsters, as they made way for Richard, had sympathetic words for her.

While standing in momentary hesitation, not knowing where to rest his burden, he was approached by a man of middle age with a whip in his hand, who asked in kindly tone, "Need a carriage, son?"

Attracted by the stranger's face and voice, Richard replied trustfully, "Yes, I do. My sister is too sick to walk and my mother is not very strong."

The teamster peered into Susan's face. "Poor little gal! I s'pose she's been sea-sick."

"Yes, it was a rough voyage."

"Folks expectin' you, or do you want a hotel?"

"We have no folks nearer than Green County and we can't afford a hotel. Don't know of a boarding-house, do you?"

"You bet I do! Just the place for you. You climb into my carriage and I'll take you all there, bag and baggage. Won't cost you but a dollar all told."

With Susan still in his arms, Richard entered the ancient, low-hung carryall, for which the driver apologized. "It's an old ark of a thing, but it's all the easier for sick people to get into."

Once safely aboard the vehicle, the Grahams had time to look about them at the people who had come down to see the steamship come in. Some of them were welcoming friends, others were merely sightseers.

The main part of the town lay to the north, and as they climbed the muddy street and came into the central thoroughfare, Richard found in it signs of the wilderness which he had come so far to see. The sidewalks swarmed with adventurers from many lands. English, Irish, Swedish, and German immigrants mingled with home-seekers from New York and New England. Prairie schooners (great wagons covered with canvas) alternated with loads of hay and drays of lumber. The buildings were mostly built of yellow pine, fresh from the stump, but a few warehouses of brick gave evidence of a firm faith in the future. All faces were smiling and all voices gay, for the citizens were mainly young, and all were confident.

The boarding-house to which Richard and his family were driven was neatly painted on the outside, but presented a sad clutter of disorder within. The landlady, a worried, querulous, elderly woman, led them to a room at the back of the house and curtly said, "This is the best I can do for you. You'll all have to camp down here. I'm crowded to the shingles and hain't got time to slick up, to say nothin' of waitin' on sick folks. Make yourselves to home."

The room had two beds, but they were both unmade, and the floor was littered with cast-off rags and newspapers. However, it offered rest for the travel-worn mother and child, and was, therefore, welcome. In a few moments Susan was resting on a couch which had at least the virtue of standing still. Poor child! She had been so long on dusty cars and heaving boats that to lie horizontally without being bumped or tossed about was a blissful release.

Mrs. Graham, almost at the end of her strength, sank into a chair, saying, "Richard, I've had enough of moving. I want to stay 'put' for a while."

"All right, mother. We'll stay here till you are rested."

After setting the room in order for her, he hurried out to taste the air and explore the town, so eager to get a view of the new land that he took one of the streets which led away toward the west, and hurried on till he had put the village entirely behind him, halting only when, from a low ridge, he confronted the unbroken level horizon-line.

The gentle wind, sweet with odours of blossoming meadows, came to him from the illimitable reaches of prairie lands whereon the Indians still hunted the buffalo. And he thought, "Somewhere under that sky lies our farm." This was the land whose legendary fertility had lured him and his people from their ancestral acres in the Androscoggin Valley. In the beauty of that sky he read the promise of happiness.

At this time only one short railway had been built west of Milwaukee, but a plank road led to the southwest toward Chicago, which was a small, ramshackle town on the edge of a marsh and near the end of Lake Michigan. St. Paul, three hundred miles west and north, was a military outpost. The entire North-West was still the hunting-ground of the Sioux, a copper-colored people whose numbers no historian had as yet been able to compute. After having been successively under the rule of France, Great Britain, Virginia, Ohio, Illinois, Indiana, and Michigan, Wisconsin was at last a state.

Realizing that every mile toward the west carried him away from the old, the civilized, the prosaic, out toward the savannahs which lay as God's hand had shaped them, Richard's exaltation returned. The explorer awoke in him. He longed to continue on and on into this glorious, enticing, unknown region, but as the sun sank and the sky turned grey, he reluctantly retraced his steps, knowing well that his sorely-tried mother was depending upon his aid. The question of a home for her and for Susan must be answered at once.

The talk in the boarding-house that night was all of towns whose very names suggested exploration—Dubuque, Prairie du Chien, Portage, La Crosse—and one of the men at their table had come more than a hundred miles to market a load of wheat. He confidently predicted a railway, however, and was full of praise for his county. "It's the finest soil in the world," he said, with a fervour that was almost solemn.

Something homely and sympathetic in this man led Richard to confide in him. "We're from the state of Maine," he said, "and we have relatives in Green County, but our money is running low and we can't afford to stage it. What will you charge to carry my mother and sister as far as Monroe? Father and I can walk."

The settler liked the boy and answered, in true pioneer spirit: "I won't charge you a cent for your women, and as for your walkin'," here he grinned, "I want to tell you we men will *all* walk—in spots! Our roads out here have some pretty sudden holes in 'em, and the sloos—just to advertise how deep the soil is—are bottomless."

"From the look of the wheels on all the wagons I guess that's a fact," Richard replied, catching the spirit of his banter," but maybe we can help in prying you out of the mud. Anyhow, we'll be much obliged for the lift, and if we can work out the passage we'll do it."

"Don't worry about that. I'm going your way, anyhow, and I'll be glad of your company. I kinda hate to travel alone. We men will ride when the going's good and your womenfolk, of course, can ride all the way. Your mother don't seem very stout to me."

By stout he meant strong, and when Richard told him that his little sister was feeling pretty weak and might not be able to leave her bed for several days, the farmer's weather-beaten face grew thoughtful. "That's bad. I'd planned to start back tomorrow. However, I can wait a day or two and if she gets rested up by Saturday, you let me know and we'll set out for home."

With what mingled hope and doubt Harriet Graham "set out for home," can only be imagined. There is no record of her emotion, but that this offer of a ride was most welcome to Richard is certain, for without it he and his father would have been forced to remain in Milwaukee, an alternative which would have made his life a wholly different story.

The settler, whose name was Dudley, arranged a bed in

The Promised Land

the bottom of his canvas-covered wagon, and as soon as Susan seemed able to travel, they all set forth on their journey toward the sunset regions with the persistence of insects led by an ungovernable instinct, while the sick child, lying silently on her pallet, gazed at the canvas roof above her head with wondering eyes.

It was a glorious morning, cool and sweet, and in spite of all disheartening conditions, Richard resumed his westward march with an elation which was as baseless as it was genuine. Even his mother's anxious brow smoothed out as she reacted to the beauty of the new world opening out before her. The radiant grassy slopes, the wild roses, the lush meadows aflame with phlox, the musical piping of red-wings, the tinkling bells of bobolinks and the boundless reach of the horizon exalted her, moved her almost to tears. "It is all for the best," she said. "It must be that the Lord is leading us to green pastures and still waters."

Occasionally they passed level fields of wheat, or purple-brown squares of tilled land in which the springing, light-green blades of corn appeared, and beyond all ran the distant sky-line which spoke of endless virgin empire waiting for the plough. Wooded ridges alternated with open glades. Lakes of clear, sweet water gleamed amid rounded, velvet hills. Streams flowed with lazy ripple across the trail. At times they caught glimpses of red men in canoes or in wigwams on the shores. To Robert Graham and his son this was the perfection of the pastoral, the fulfilment of their dream.

Alas! As they proceeded they began to realize the bitter truth which lay beneath Stephen Dudley's jocose remarks. Fair as the landscape appeared its roads were treacherous. Recent rains had filled every ravine with water and each slough was a morass. Bridges were primitive, and the turnpikes, newly ridged, were so soft that the horses laboured through them like flies treading black molasses; at times the wheels became solid disks of mud, and Richard and his father were forced to set their shoulders to the end-gate in order to help the wagon from the quag.

Sitting at her daughter's side, and clinging to one of the hickory ribs which held the canvas cover, Harriet Graham lost her exultant humour. The motion of the vehicle was a torture, not only on her own account, but by reason of her anxiety for the sick child, and at last, calling her husband to the side of the wagon, she said, "Robert, I think we've made a mistake. Susan can't stand any more of this rough usage. We must stop and rest."

Thereupon the three men withdrew a little and discussed the situation. "We are more than fifteen miles from Milwaukee," said Dudley. "The road is getting better. If your girl can stand another hour's drive we'll reach Shard's. Shard is an old friend of mine and will take care of you as cheap as anyone I know. Furthermore, there's a young doctor located in the town."

With the promise of rest and medical aid, Mrs. Graham consented to go on, and as the road became smoother, the landscape so sunny, so odorous, so jocund with bird-song reasserted its charm. Her forebodings faded and she began to hope the child might be able to ride out the journey to her brother's house.

Shard's Hotel, a two-story barrack, stood so close to the road that the drivers in passing would knock at the door with the butts of their whips. On two sides of it, making a cross-roads village, stood a cluster of fifteen or twenty cabins, all as flimsy as chicken-coops, and yet something magical, something which prophesied success, ease, and happiness was in the air. The boundless wealth of the soil was apparent even before Shard, a hearty, loud-voiced boomer, began to boast of it.

Susan had not suffered from the journey as severely as

her mother had feared, and when Dick carried her into the hotel and laid her on a cool, clean bed, she smiled. Although her face was still deeply flushed and her hands hot and dry, she did not suffer.

The doctor who came in to see her was young and plainly without experience. Calling her malady "a touch of ague, nothing serious," he comforted the mother.

Susan slept well that night and seemed so much better when she woke in the morning that Harriet consented to go on, although she would gladly have stayed on another day.

At noon they stopped at another roadside tavern for dinner, and while his elders were at meat, Richard remained beside the wagon to keep Susan company. He had pinned up the corner of the wagon-cover, and stood talking to her, when another wagon similar to Dudley's drove alongside. The driver, a small man with a chin beard and watery eyes, was flanked by a broad-shouldered woman with grey hair.

Peering round the canvas hood of her wagon, she called out, "Hey, son, are you the hostler?"

"No, I'm a mover," Richard replied with a boyish pride in the fact.

"Where ye movin' to?"

"Green County."

"I want to know if ye be! Well, that's where I live. That your team?"

"No, it's Mr. Dudley's team. He's inside eating dinner."

"Reckon we better eat here too," the beldame remarked to her companion in the tone of a commander, and in climbing down over the wheel she presented to Richard a rear elevation in which strength decidedly predominated over grace. He had never seen quite such a bear-like female figure.

Once on the ground she approached the boy. "What ye got in there? Dog or human?"

"My little sister. She's not well enough to go inside to eat."

"Sick, is she? What's the matter with her?" Without waiting for an invitation, the strange woman approached and peered in at the child with intent interest. Starting back, she exclaimed, "For God-a-mighty's sake!" Then, striking her hands together as if to brush something vile from her fingers, she said, "Boy, do you know what you've got in that wagon?" Without waiting for a reply, she shouted to her husband, "We can't stop here! They've got a case of smallpox in that wagon!"

With amazing agility she climbed back into her place. "Drive on!" she commanded with decision.

Her action up to this time had amused Dick, but at the word "smallpox" he ceased to smile.

Smallpox was the most feared of all contagions in those days. The very sound of its name was a funeral-knell. Whole towns had been depopulated by it. Ships had sailed into Boston harbour like floating charnal houses, filled with dead and dying, and although the boy had never seen a person suffering from it, his mind filled with alarm, for he, too, had seen on Susan's face certain inflamed spots which the experienced stranger had instantly recognized as signs of the plague.

While he stood thus, appalled by her accusation, a girl came out of a house across the street. To her the woman screamed, "Keep away from that wagon! They've got smallpox in it."

"What wagon?" asked the girl.

The harridan pointed at Richard. "That boy's wagon. There's a case of *smallpox* in that wagon."

Stephen Dudley appeared in the tavern door. "What's all the row?" he asked.

An excited citizen addressed Stephen. "Is that your wagon?"

"It is."

"Well, you hop into it and get out of here. This woman says you've got a case of smallpox in it."

The woman yelled back, "You bet I did and I know! I looked in. I lost three children with it. You can't fool me. You've got a girl all broken out with it."

Dick drew near his father. "I guess she's right, father. Susan is all spotted with red sores."

Mrs. Graham came slowly down the steps, her face tense and white. The stranger's words had brought to a focus all her vague distrust. She had been troubled all day by the child's appearance, but relying upon the young physician's report, had said nothing of her fear. With her back to the group of people on the porch of the inn, she explained, "It can't be smallpox. We had a doctor examine her last night. He said it was only a touch of ague. My daughter has not been exposed—so far as I know."

By this time a group of excited people had collected on the opposite side of the road, and from them a spokesman developed. "All the same, we ain't takin' no chances. You climb into your wagon and git!"

"Come on, mother," said Dick, taking command of the situation. "Let's go on."

The woman who had made all the trouble laid whip to her horses and drove away.

Stephen paid his bill with a face which was an open page to the landlord. He was not scared, but he was beginning to understand. "I'm afraid it is smallpox," he confessed, "although that young fool of a doctor called it fever and ague."

"Well, I don't blame you," said the landlord. "But the sooner you go, the better I'll like you."

Stephen climbed to his seat and motioned Graham to join him. With a smart cut of the whip he started the horses.

Dick swung in over the end-gate, and as the wagon neared the first group of villagers, they scattered like a flock of chickens, some of them holding their fingers pressed against their nostrils, others with handkerchiefs to their mouths. All this would have been comic had it not been for little Susan who had heard every word of the woman's harangue, and now lay frightened and motionless beneath her cover.

Harriet lifted an appealing glance to her son, a message which he understood. "It is true! Susan has the smallpox. What shall we do?"

Not a word was spoken till the town was well behind, then the deacon turned. "Harriet, I don't believe it. It's all nonsense. The child has a fever—that's all."

"No, Robert," his wife replied. "I fear the woman is right. The child has been exposed. However, it appears to be only a light case." She said this to comfort Susan. "Mr. Dudley, what would you advise us to do? Where can we find shelter?"

Stephen's kindly face took on a troubled look. "I don't know," he answered hesitantly. "People are terribly afraid of smallpox out here, and I don't know exactly what to do. The child ought to have a doctor, and yet we can't stay here. They'll run us out. I guess the only thing to do is drive on. Our chances on getting into a tavern are better ahead than they are behind."

To this Richard agreed, and they drove on, discovering very soon that news of them, warning of them, had been scattered along the road by the old woman. Mothers called their children indoors, and men on the highway kept to windward of them as if Dudley's vehicle were carrying some poisonous gas.

"That old fool has made it her business to warn every house along the road," said Stephen. "And the worst of it is we can't overtake her. She enjoys spreading the news.

The Promised Land

She'll keep ahead of us all day and our chances for getting lodgings are mighty slim. However, our best plan is to keep going till we reach Brownsville. There's a doctor there, and I know some people who will take us in."

"We can't ask you to do that," protested Harriet. "You are anxious to reach home and you should go on. You can either drop us at some road-side tavern, or carry us to Brownsville. There is nothing else for us to do but go with you—if you will let us."

To this Richard and his father agreed, and Dudley drove on, watching with increasing anxiety the westering sun. "We must reach shelter before dark," he said decisively.

CHAPTER VII

Harriet's Home in the West

RICHARD'S pleasure in the new country was utterly gone. The winding trails, the open country, the up-start towns, had lost their charm. The sloughs and the unbridged streams had become not merely barriers but sources of actual danger. The thought of his mother and Susan spending the night in the open without food or roof was disturbing. "Our only hope is in our experienced driver," he said to his father.

Robert was all for returning to Milwaukee. "We should never have left there," he grumbled.

Stephen insisted on going on. "We can't go back now," he declared firmly, and in this decision Richard supported him saying: "Our chances for shelter are as good going as returning. Surely somebody will take pity on mother and Susan."

They kept on and strange to say Susan's condition improved. The humour breaking out upon her skin had re-

duced her fever. She appeared brighter than when they
started and encouraged by this change, Richard urged
Stephen to push on. "We'll find shelter somewhere along
the roadside."

The land grew lonelier as well as more level as they
turned to the southwest. Throughout long stretches of the
road, they saw no houses and the winding trail faded at
times till it was hardly more than two deep paths running
side by side through the meadow grass. From the doors
of the rude pine shanties or still richer log cabins, settlers
clothed in garments shaggy as the bark of hickory trees,
hailed Dudley, asking for news, while their frowsy children,
shy as quails, swarmed about the door. Once or twice
Richard caught sight of a girl at work upon a kitchen porch,
barefooted and bare-armed. The lives of these people appeared very primitive and very brave, and as the old woman
had not traversed this road, no one betrayed fear of the
Grahams. At last Dick said, "Let's ask some of these
folk to take us in."

"We couldn't do that without telling them all about
Susan," replied his mother. "If they knew the truth they
would never let us enter their doors."

"You're right!" declared Stephen. "Our only chance is
Brownsville. I'm banking on some people I know there,
and when we get to the edge of the town, I'm going to
leave you all behind and go in afoot and tell these old
neighbours of mine just what we have. I'll tell 'em the
whole story and I'm confident they'll help us out. If not
I'll come back and we'll go on to my home."

They reached Brownsville about six in the afternoon, and
the first view of it was pleasing. It contained several hundred houses and was built on both sides of a gentle river
running between low, wooded hills. It was more attractive, more like New England than any of the settlements
they had seen, and while obviously only a few years old,

its little wooden church and a new schoolhouse gave evidence of human and understanding folk.

Stephen halted on the hill-side just before reaching the outskirts of the town. "Now you people stay here while I go on ahead. I won't be long."

Anxious as they all were, the home-seekers could not fail of taking comfort in the scene before and below them, for it was delightfully typical of the first stage of border development. Cow-bells tinkled from the grassy glades among the hazel bushes, and saws and hammers sounded from the growing frames of golden pine. Calves bawled, pigs squealed, and hens clucked, while over and beyond this busy swarm, the sunset clouds were piled in lofty domes, so dense, so like great fields of snow, that Richard fancied himself looking out upon the great Continental Divide of which he had read, and which so few Americans of that day had ever seen.

Notwithstanding the beauty of the valley, the sight of his brave and patient mother sitting beside little Susan caused a return of the boy's doubt.

Was it a mistake, after all? Should they have remained in the home valley?

He thought next of kind Enoch Lawrence, but the memory of his last words: "I'll keep the place open for you, Richard. You'll be back along about November," so far from filling him with home-sickness, brought back his courage. "I won't give in. Even if father and mother and Susan all go back, I'll stay here, somewhere."

His father considered the whole venture a costly and foolish affair and said so, predicting disaster. "I never more than half believed in it," he protested bitterly. "It's all a wild-goose chase," and Harriet at the moment not only admitted this but could find nothing to say in justification of her plan of action.

They had been waiting nearly half an hour when they

caught sight of Stephen coming across the valley accompanied by two elderly citizens, and followed, at a distance, by a dozen or more men and boys. Something in the approach of the two groups was ominous, for as they neared the bottom of the ridge on which the wagon stood, the two leaders halted, and Stephen came on alone.

His face was wrinkled with trouble and his voice faltered as he said, "We got to go back and go round. They won't even let us drive through the town."

This roused Dick's hot blood. "If the team was mine I'd see about that!"

His father was also in fighting mood. "Will they turn us out like dogs? Drive on. The street is public. We have a right to it."

One of the men nearest them motioned with his hand and shouted, "Turn around! Go back! You can't come into this town!"

The throng of men and boys had joined the spokesman and farther away excited groups of women and children could be seen. Apparently the news had spread and the entire village was in a panic of fear and repulsion.

Deacon Graham got out of the wagon and started down the hill to argue the case, an action which sent some of the crowd scurrying backward, but one of the citizens brandished a stick and called, "Halt! Stay where you are!"

His attitude was so threatening that Mrs. Graham urged her husband to desist. "Don't go down, Robert. We must go back. They are right. They are only defending their homes."

While Dudley and the deacon stood thus conferring, Richard's attention was called to a singular figure approaching from the rear. A huge old man with a plough on his shoulder was coming down the road. He had no hat on his head and his thick grey hair stood up from his rough-hewn, kindly visage like a fantastic war-bonnet. He did not appear to see anything in his path, for his eyes were on the clouds. He was about sixty years of age.

For the moment Dick forgot the inhospitable citizens below, so singular, so powerful, and withal so attractive was this tall figure stalking dreamily down the path.

As he came opposite the wagon he suddenly awoke out of his trance, and in a musical voice and with a decided Scotch-Irish accent, called out, "Good even to ye, neighbours."

Stephen smiled, "Good even to you, brother McLane."

The big man put down his plough and approached. "Is it you, Stephen Dudley? How are ye the while, Stephen?"

"Well, but sore perplexed, Mr. McLane."

"In what way?"

"These people," Stephen waved his hand toward his passengers, "are from the East. I met them in Milwaukee and I'm taking them to Spring Valley where they have kin. They've a sick girl with them and the mother is none too stout, and we all need shelter for the night, but your fellow-citizens down yonder are all for turning us back. They won't let us enter the town."

The patriarch straightened till he towered almost a head above Stephen, who was of goodly frame.

"Why not?"

Stephen hesitated. "They have been told that our sick girl has smallpox."

"Has she?"

"I don't know, Mr. McLane, but I'm afraid she has."

"Let me see her," commanded McLane. As he greeted Richard with kindly glance, the boy noted that his deep-set eyes were grey-blue and that his high, narrow brow was marked by noble lines. His face was rugged, but his mouth showed kindliness. All in all he was one of the most attractive and picturesque old men Dick had ever seen.

Harriet's Home in the West

"Good even, mistress," he said to Mrs. Graham. "Ye have a sick girl? Let me see her."

Mrs. Graham raised the side of the cover and the stranger peered in at Susan, who gazed up at him in alarm, an emotion which quickly changed to confidence at the sound of his voice. "Poor child! I can see you need help—and you shall have it!" Dropping the wagon-cover he motioned to Robert Graham. "Come with me—you, too," he added, addressing Dick. "Stephen, you follow on with your team."

Richard and his father, in obedience to their new-found friend, started down the bank past the forgotten plough. Graham and McLane walked together and a strange pair they made, for the deacon, striding with a dogged jerk of his head, hardly reached the shoulder of his bareheaded guide looming above him.

The citizens below drew together as if for conference, and when McLane neared them he called out, "What is the meaning of this? Is it true ye forbid these people to pass along the public highway?"

One of the men explained, "They've got smallpox, Mr. McLane."

"Suppose they have. Will ye turn them back into the forest? It's true there's a sick girl in the wagon and a mother who looks to be but a wisp herself and they must be cared for. They shall not be turned back. I go bail for that."

Tears rose to Richard's eyes and his throat filled with gratitude as the old man went on: "Ye know me—ye know my sons. When the McLanes set their minds upon a thing, men do well to heed them. Clear the way! The man who would stop these people must stop me. I shall find shelter for them."

The throng retreated, hastening their steps in order that the pestilence-laden wagon might not come too near them, but one of them, a man walking beside McLane, argued the case of the citizens. "What can we do, Hugh? We can't contaminate our own homes. We bear no ill will to these people, but we must defend our wives and children from the pox."

The man's tone softened McLane's indignation. "I have a plan," he answered. "You know that empty cabin just beyond my house? They can camp in that and I'll attend to them."

In the centre of the town another stand was made, and the mayor, a long, lean, determined individual, demanded that the wagon keep on without pause. "What business have you, Hugh McLane, in helping to bring these plague-stricken people into our town?"

"What business?" demanded Hugh. "The Lord's business. Would ye leave women and children to die in the highway?"

"Self-preservation is the first law of nature, father McLane," said another man. "We must protect——"

"Is that the Christ spirit? Did He avoid the leper?" demanded McLane, his face uplifted. "A curse will be on your town if you drive these people out."

The lawyer shrugged his shoulders. "These people are more dangerous than lepers."

Around this speaker a group of equally determined citizens gathered, demanding that the wagon turn back, and as McLane confronted this compact group, two young men of heroic stature came rapidly across the street. One was a bearded, smiling man of about thirty years of age, the other, a strikingly handsome youth with grave dark eyes and the beginning of a moustache, was about Richard's age. Pushing their way through the crowd which gave way for them as if they were chieftains (which they undoubtedly were) they took positions beside the old man.

"What's the matter, pap?" asked the older man in a musical voice which had the hint of a laugh in it.

Harriet's Home in the West

Hugh explained with quick, incisive phrases, and as he spoke the two new-comers turned and faced the crowd. "Pap is right," said the one whom the bystanders called Bill. "These people must be housed. They shan't be turned back if we can prevent it—and I rather think we can."

"Clear the way!" commanded McLane with a sweep of his arm. "Come on," he said, addressing Dudley and Graham.

With the three McLanes walking the middle of the road, Dudley followed along the way they had cleared, while Harriet, filled with wonder at this intervention on the part of the McLanes, rode in silence.

As the wagon proceeded, the citizens scurried into their yards. No one remained near enough to catch a glimpse of the sick girl, but Richard read in the expressions of many of the spectators a desire to help. They were only protecting their children from a scourge. Their repugnance had nothing personal in it.

After having passed entirely through the village, the McLanes turned into a cleared field, where a low, unfinished log cabin stood. Its walls and roof were complete, but it was without doors or windows. All about it stumps of trees testified to the skill and industry of the man who had made the shelter. It could have been taken as the typical cabin of a pioneer, for it had been hewn out of the forest on whose margin it stood.

At the door of this poor dwelling Hugh turned to his sons. "Boys, go home to your mother and tell her we have a sick girl here. Tell her these people will need some supper. I will stay and make them comfortable for the night. None must come anear us till we know what the ailment is. If it is smallpox—I shall stay here with them."

At his direction, Dudley took his team off the wagon and drove away, while the Grahams went into the shelter of this rough cabin. Hugh himself carried Susan in and held her in his arms while a rude bed was made for her upon the floor. At his direction blankets were hung up at the windows and doors, and when his sons came back half an hour later, he ordered them to bring chairs, quilts, and other necessaries. At his command they put these down at a distance from the cabin.

In the course of an hour the Grahams were as comfortable as the circumstances would permit, and Hugh said, "Now, Richard, we're all in for a quiet time. Yon big stump is our dead-line. No foot must cross it either comin' in or goin' out. I put that matter in your charge. If the child has smallpox ye'll all have it. As I have had it once I have no fear of it again. I will camp with ye and see what happens."

It was in this way that the Grahams and the McLanes met. Harriet's first home in the promised land was a pest-house! Her family circle a quarantine! What she thought will not be recorded here, but as she looked round on the rough log walls of her house which contained nothing but four wooden chairs, two beds laid on the plank floor, and a table of pine, her heart must have failed her utterly.

Robert was dazed. He obeyed their noble rescuer with the readiness of a child, and by the time William had brought their supper to the dead-line, he was in the mood to say grace to mother McLane for what she had sent.

94

CHAPTER VIII

Richard Helps Harvest

DURING the evening Robert Graham, with Yankee inquisitiveness, drew from Hugh the story of his wanderings which were typical of many of his neighbours. Born in Virginia of Scotch-Irish stock, the old trail-maker had reached Wisconsin by way of Maryland, Pennsylvania, and Ohio, stopping from five to ten years in each state. He had made each of these removes in a covered wagon drawn by oxen, with his every-ready rifle providing game for his pot.

It soon appeared that despite his border experiences he was a deeply religious man, a "Second Adventist" in faith. Just what this faith was Richard could not tell, but it provoked a snort of derision from his father, who was disposed to make his dissent and disgust still further manifest, but Harriet restrained him, perceiving in McLane's face and voice a sincerity of devotion and a poetry of creed which she would not have disturbed.

"We have no church in the West," Hugh said, as he spoke almost in apology for his coming to this new state. "I did it for my sons. They wanted more land than we could buy in Ohio, and so—here I am. I have five sons and five daughters, all near me save one who is gold-seeking in California."

In spite of his contempt for Hugh McLane's beliefs, Robert in giving thanks to the Lord, spoke of "our noble Samaritan" and his voice rang out in that studied eloquence with which he always addressed the Supreme Being, but Richard was certain that Hugh McLane was not listening to his father's words. His lips were moving in a prayer of his own.

In spite of his excitement, his anxiety, the youth went to sleep on his hard bed and slept so soundly that he heard nothing until his father touched him on the shoulder and said, "Time to get up, Richard."

For a moment he was too bewildered to realize where he was. McLane was out in the yard, and the rhythmic sound of his axe could be heard. Harriet, who was sitting up in her blankets combing her hair, smiled wanly and said, "Mr. McLane says Susan is out of danger. We should be very thankful for that, but I fear we shall all come down with the plague."

Richard arose without speaking. He felt languid and miserable, but hoped it was only weariness and would pass away during the day. He did not know that Hugh had watched over Susan all night, but he did know that he had been active in their behalf, for a little later David and his brother Luke came to the dead-line with food and dishes, and their mother, a sturdy woman with a serene face, brought soap and towels and a looking-glass. She insisted on coming in to help. "I'm not afeared," she declared. "I've had it."

This her husband would not permit. "You might carry

the poison back to the children," he said. "One of us is enough. Furthermore, you must not touch a pot or a pan till I have scalded it."

Several times that day, these kindly neighbours not only brought furniture, but windows and doors which Robert set in place, and so before the close of the second day, the little cabin was fairly comfortable. Hugh acted as cook as well as nurse, for Mrs. Graham was hardly able to stand on her feet, and her husband was not of much service in such matters. The sight of that shock-haired giant scouring pots or bending over Susan's bed filled Richard with wonder. Such combination of strength and tenderness he had never known.

Three times each day thereafter, David or Luke deposited on the stump at the edge of the clearing such food as Hugh considered suitable, and Richard looked forward to their visits with eager interest. They were so handsome and so unlike anyone he had ever known. Luke a year or two older than David looked like his twin and Richard admired them both deeply.

No one else dared to approach the cabin, and many of the farmers who were obliged to pass put their horses to the gallop as they reached the clearing. Richard laughed even in the midst of his resentment, as he watched this absurd performance. That the fear was very genuine, he had no doubt, but it seemed a needless precaution. How could smallpox fly on the wind?

At Robert Graham's request, David rode away to the west to find Nathaniel Bridges, and convey to him the news of Susan's misfortune, but old Hugh privately said to his son, "Tell them not to come here, now. They can do little to help and the danger is great. We'll let them know how we come on."

He was right, of course. Nathaniel did not come, but he sent such money as he could spare and promised to drive over as soon as it was safe. Patty wrote to say that they had arrived safely, but Hugh would not permit Harriet to send a letter in reply. " 'Tis a subtle disease," he said. "A letter might carry the seeds of it."

Susan recovered rapidly, but no sooner was she able to sit up than her father took to his bed. Strange to tell, Harriet, the weakest of them all, escaped the contagion, but a week later Richard was stricken. In his case, however, the scourge seemed to have lost some of its virulency. Nevertheless he was very miserable. Harriet, worn to a shadow, remained outwardly serene. Her dream of a pleasant home was shattered. It had no more substance than a bubble which has broken in the wind. Without the aid of Hugh McLane she would have utterly despaired.

These were dark days for Richard. "If only I had been content in Boston," he said to Hugh. "It's all my fault. I urged my people to come."

" 'Twas so ordered, my boy," replied the old man mystically. " 'Twas all a part of the world's plan, and besides, railing agin' the past does no good."

Richard's regard for his nurse was now almost worshipful. The huge, gnarled hands, the tender, deep-sunk eyes of the giant had become very dear to him. It was in a sense miraculous that they should have fallen into the keeping of such a man.

Harriet Graham acknowledged this blessing. "Without his help," she said to Richard, "Susan and I might both have died."

As his patients became stronger, McLane found an occasional hour to sit on a bench outside the door, and there the neighbours often saw him, deep sunk in thought which was almost a trance, his face shining with the light of some inward vision. Richard sometimes heard him chanting the prophetic lines of Isaiah, or the wondrous revelations of John. In other moods he sang hymns which pictured "The

Sweet Fields of Eden," finding in those far-off amaranthine lands a poetic satisfaction which the near-by landscape utterly failed to give.

He had little time to read, but now and again at Harriet's urgent request he took the Bible in his hand and recited her favourite passages. The text was not really necessary to him, for he held in memory most of the New Testament and all of the prophetic older gospels. To him the Bible was a library of drama as well as a book of song. It supplied his highly imaginative soul with the poetry for which it longed. He read no other books.

Richard listened to these prophecies with the look of one refusing to be comforted. Imprisoned in this hut, unable to care for himself, he felt as weak as a babe. The glory of his sunset regions had faded to a grim reality. The joyous expedition of May had ended in disaster. His vague dreams of wealth and happiness had shrunk to the sad actualities of his own thin arms and feeble feet. No promise of life "on the other side of Jordan" was compensation for his disaster.

Had it not been for the serene patience of his nurse he would have fallen into despair. In the presence of such unselfish devotion, such faith, and such tender humanity, the boy's impatient fury was restrained and gradually his faith returned. He had only one ambition now, and that was to house his mother and sister against the winter. All his golden hopes were faded to this concrete task. He thought much of Clara and Josephine and the happy days of travel on the boat, but that part of his adventure seemed far away, and, to complete the separation, no word came from Clinton.

At last the time came when Richard and his father were both able to sit up and watch Harriet and Susan moving about the room. Although still very weak, Harriet's slender hands contrived to relieve Hugh of the cooking. Slight as she was in body, her soul was unconquerable. As she saw her husband and son make daily gain in strength, she regained her serenity.

Hugh insisted that all of their bedding and such of their clothing as could not be put through hot water should be destroyed, and hence it is almost literally true to say of the Grahams, as some of their neighbours remarked, they began life in Brownsville as naked as the day they were born. Had it not been for the McLanes, I do not know how the family could have survived, for no one was willing to employ Robert, although all danger of contagion was passed.

The pressing need of the hour, food and raiment, being met, the question of a permanent shelter came up, and when John Bridges rode over to offer a place under his roof, Harriet was ready to go but Hugh advised against leaving the village. "The people of Spring Valley will be afraid of you," he said. "Stay where you are for the present," and to Richard, William shrewdly said, "Why don't you buy this log cabin? No one else wants it now. You can get it for a song and sing the song yourself."

This was good advice, and Richard took it. He wrote to Addison for money to help pay for the plot, and to Nathaniel and Patty, who helped as best they could. Thus it fell out that Richard began his Western career with two bare hands and two feeble legs. However, he was of a buoyant nature and with the return of his physical strength, recovered his cheerful outlook. "Don't worry, mother, we'll make our fortune yet."

One of Harriet's reasons for remaining in Brownsville, perhaps the chief reason, was her love for the McLanes. Her gratitude for what they had done for her made her unwilling to leave until she had in some way compensated them for their kindnesses.

By the first of August, Robert was at work, and the cabin, cleaned and furnished with at least the essentials of frontier housekeeping, was rudely comfortable. Gradually

Richard Helps Harvest

the village lost its fear of the men as carriers of the disease, although no one entered the cabin.

As soon as Richard was able to leave the house, David brought a suit of clothing, so that the youth went forth to help Arnold Robey harvest his grain, clear of all contaminating poison. Robey, who was McLane's son-in-law, understood the case and was not alarmed.

That first week was at once a joy and a punishment—joy in his release from prison, and a commitment to labour such as he had never undertaken before. The beauty of the land was enhanced by his sharpened senses. The weather was glorious summer, and the grain-fields quite as golden as the circulars of the agents had declared them to be. Never had he seen such abundance as this black soil had produced. In his walk along the river road to Robey's farm, he recovered some part of the enthusiasm, the hopefulness with which he had left his place with Enoch Lawrence.

Robey, a tall, stoop-shouldered man of thirty-five, studied the city-bred youth with quizzical glance. "Don't believe you'd better jump into harvesting too brash, just yet," he advised in his nasal drawl. "Guess you'd better kindo *ease* your way into it. You look pretty white."

Richard's courage was high, but he had sense enough to know that he was not yet a "full hand."

For nearly two years he had lived the life of a clerk in Boston, and now, after a severe illness, he had contracted to enter upon one of the severest tasks of Western farm life. Harvesting in those days was carried on by skill and endurance. Reapers were unknown, and the grain scythe with its fingers of hickory, a contrivance called a "cradle," was swung against the standing wheat by means of strong young arms, and the stalks thus laid in gavels were gathered together and bound by a "raker and binder" who followed close behind. Neither of these tasks was possible to Richard during his first week, but he could "shock"—that is, set the bound sheaves into "stooks"—but even this proved a severe test of his endurance. Long before the noon hour that first day, his hands were swollen and full of briers, his back aching, and his legs trembling with fatigue.

Robey encouraged him by saying, "Don't hurry and don't worry about your condition. They say the pox is a great cleanser of the system. You'll come all right. Take it easy for a few days."

He got through the day by stern resolution, but a worse moment came the following morning when, at dawn-light, he was called upon to rise. He rolled from his bed with a sense of utter defeat, so sore that he could scarcely move. To hold his knife and fork was a trial, so swollen were his hands.

The men joked him but were sympathetic. "You've got too hard a job. You ought to have my place. Just to accommodate you, I'll trade," said one of them. "I've got the easiest job I ever had."

This was a favourite joke of his, for he was one of those slab-sided, iron-muscled, deft workmen who find all jobs easy. He was especially renowned as a cradler and the test of the other men was whether they could rake and bind after him. His name was Starr.

Richard looked at him with calmly estimating gaze. "Give me a week Mr. Starr and I'll rake the heels off you," he retorted, in boyish resentment of the older man's boast.

Jane Robey liked and pitied the lad sincerely and was careful to see that he had the first drink of the milk which she brought out at ten o'clock. At meal-time she made certain that he shared in every dish. She had the McLane kindliness of soul and took his part when the men became too rough with him. To her he was not only a lad convalescing from a dread disease; he was a city dweller, and of finer quality than the other workmen.

Richard Helps Harvest

In a few days his hands became calloused and his muscles hardened. He came to his work each morning with increasing zest, and before the end of the week he said to Robey, "I'm ready to rake and bind now."

"Better wait till Monday," his kindly boss replied.

Richard was careful to keep clear of the reaper's job. He knew what it meant to swing that great scythe all day against the wheat. There was no severer task upon the farm, nothing which equalled its physical stress. The strain upon the muscles of the back and hips was so great that even "Eastern" Starr was glad of every pause to whet his blade or take a drink. At times they all drew together in the shade of a tree to rest, but these periods were determined by the leader.

At lunch-time jocular remarks and pithy stories were exchanged, and Richard heard much of a singular character whom the men called Hooper. At first he thought him a real person; later he had moments of thinking him just an imaginary individual to whom each man ascribed the anecdotes which he himself had composed.

For instance, as the men came back across the field with their cradles on their arms, "carrying the swath" as it was called, Robey said, "Hooper used to say it paid to reap the long way of the field. 'I once cradled a hundred swaths a mile long before breakfast,' said he, 'and on my way back, killed a deer stuck in a snow-bank.'"

William told another tale of Hooper. "He was a great marksman. Once while hunting he came upon two deer standing on a knoll facing him. 'I had only one bullet,' said he, 'and the two deer were standing side by side. How could I get 'em both? I couldn't bear to lose ary one of 'em, and just then I noticed that right prezactly half-way between 'em was a sharp rock. I fired at the aidge of the rock. The bullet split, the two pieces hit the two bucks and down fell both of 'em.'"

The absurdity of this so amused Richard, that Robey brought forth a third exploit. "That's not so wonderful as his story of the pigeons. You see he was out hunting with his rifle, and came under a tall tree with a long, straight limb reaching out from the top. On this limb fifty pigeons were roosting. 'I wanted them pigeons,' says he, 'but how was I to get 'em? I had only my rifle. Then I hed an idee. I tuck aim at the middle of the limb and fired. The bullet slit the branch quick as lightnin', the laigs of the birds dropped into the crack, the crack closed up with a snap, and there I had 'em—the hull string and bilun of 'em.'"

After the haw-hawing ceased, Richard asked, "How did he get 'em down?" Robey grinned widely. "He was always a leetle unsatisfactory about the ending of his yarns. He most generally quit at the most exciting part."

"I always liked his speech at the camp-meeting best of all," said Robey. "You see the old feller had got converted and while giving his testimony, as they call it, he got going like this: 'Oh, yes, my bretheren and sisteren, I've been a bad man, an *awful* bad man. I've been a liar and a drunkard. I've been the worst drunkard anybody *ever* see; why, I've drunk *whisky* enough to float a steamboat from here to Ohio.' 'Tut, tut! Brother Hooper,' said the parson, 'you're exaggerating again!' 'I know it, elder, I know it,' groaned the old rascal, 'exaggeration's my worst fault, and I've wept *barrels* of tears over it.'"

This story gave Richard a great deal of amusement, although he could not believe it. Robey declared that it was entirely true, for he had been present and heard the old scalawag's confession.

Not all the talk was humorous, or trivial. Sometimes at noon or at night, while they were sitting round the smudge to keep off the mosquitoes, the men talked of the new state of which they were a part and of which they

Richard Helps Harvest

wcre very proud. They made much of the promise of railroads and the plan for making Madison the capital. They were all young (not one was over thirty) and all were confident of the future. In the atmosphere of such bouyant youth, Richard's desire to own a farm sharpened. He resolved to buy the forty acres adjoining the plot on which his little cabin stood, and at once wrote to his brother describing it, and asking for money to make the first payment.

On Saturday afternoon, believing himself capable of demonstrating his skill as a raker and binder, he said to Robey, "On Monday, I am going to set in behind Starr. He'll have a chance to show his best paces."

Starr smiled. "All right, son, I see that you are not the Boston dude I took you for, but I think I'll manage to worry you a little."

CHAPTER IX

The Musical McLanes

RICHARD learned a great deal about the McLanes during his week at Robey's farm, and all he heard increased his interest in them, and on the following Sunday afternoon he went to call on them for the first time. Their house, a wide-roofed structure, part logs and part planking, stood on a level piece of "second bottom" land just below the village. It was a raw, unpainted building, but its windows overlooked the river, and vines had begun to soften its ugly porch. Unlike any other house in the village, it had a huge chimney at either end and suggested a Southern rather than a New England homestead.

As he approached the door, Richard heard singing, a chorus of young voices so strong and sweet that he was astonished and somewhat intimidated. Not wishing to interrupt, he stole softly up the path, and took a seat upon the edge of the porch to wait for the end of the song.

Through the open door he could see David and Wil-

The Musical McLanes

liam each playing a violin, while seated between them at a table, a handsome, black-haired girl was beating with small hammers upon the strings of a dulcimer. Behind her and facing the door stood a young girl, hardly more than a child, with lifted head, uttering voice like some ecstatic bird, serenely unconscious of herself and of her audience.

She was a sturdy figure, with a fine head and beautiful brown eyes, and her voice, a pure soprano, high and sweet and singularly mature, rose above all the others with a beauty which remained individually distinguishable while harmonizing with them all.

The words they sang were new to him and he caught only the refrain:

"The Chariot, the Chariot! Its wheels roll in fire,
As the Lord cometh down in the pomp of His ire.
Lo! Self-moving it rolls on its pathway of cloud."

Entranced by the music and lacking the courage to announce himself, Richard remained outside during another song and would gladly have stayed there throughout the concert but William discovered him, and insisted on his coming in.

Upon entering the door, Richard saw old Hugh sitting in an arm-chair on one side of the room like a patriarch among his tribesmen. He offered a kindly greeting. "Take a chair, Richard. Sit ye down. We're right glad to see you on our threshold."

David presented the newcomer to his sisters, Deborah, Rachel and Isabel. Isabel was the young soprano, Rachel the contralto and Deborah was the girl who played the dulcimer. They were all musicians, as Richard afterwards learned and many of the villagers shared in the festivals of song which came whenever they were together and had leisure. However much their neighbours might criticize their methods of farming or question their easy-going habits as housekeepers, their skill as hunters and musicians won respect.

Richard had never seen their like. They were at once Southern and Scotch and as sharply differentiated from their fellow-citizens as immigrants from some far-off ocean island. Their dark eyes, their beautiful voices, their ready laughter and their cloudy changes of mood were inexplicable to their self-controlled New England friends.

Of the skill with which David played the violin Richard had heard much, but no one had described to him the singular quality of his music, for no one could understand it. When he played and the girls sang they became mysterious, sombre, remote. They suggested captive exiles, dreaming of happier unforgotten gardens toward the sun. In truth they were Celtic poets, haunted by tragic yet poetic, undefined memories.

While their visitor listened in silence, they sang on voicing glorious old Scotch and Irish ballads, or joining in hymns which the slaves of Maryland had composed. Among other melodies they sang some of the pioneer border tunes, melodies which David had caught and transposed to suit their needs. One of these choruses was "Sunset Regions," a song which Richard's mother often sang, but the tune differed from the one she knew. It was more measured in its swing, more like a march, and when Isabel's soprano and Luke's tenor blended in the refrain—"Then o'er the hills in legions, boys! Fair freedom's star points to the sunset regions, boys"—Richard forgot his disasters and rose again to the daring, the allurement, the glory of American pioneering.

This song had led the McLanes across Pennsylvania, Ohio, and Illinois. It voiced an urge which they could not otherwise express. Some of these words, coming from the mouths of hunters like Luke and David and William, had

the thrill of a bugle. All Richard's doubts were swept away. With confidence restored, he faced his future, resolute of soul.

Old Hugh took no part in the "profane" music, not even in the ballads, but Richard observed that he kept time by drumming with the tips of his fingers on the arms of his chair. Unable to conceal his interest in the violin (he had been a master player in his youth), he loved to handle it. In spite of his religious scruples, he occasionally accepted the bow on the pretence of showing David how an old tune went, and when he laid the fiddle beneath his chin with the grace of long practice he became the minstrel again. All these graces were vanities, but they were very dear—so dear that he could not shut them out of his life.

Each time they sang, Richard fixed his gaze on Isabel, in whose dark eyes a brooding shadow rested, an expression which interested and puzzled the boy. Sadness on the face of one so young was wholly unaccountable. It set her aside from all her companions, but Richard, perceiving the same look on David's handsome face, discovered that this brooding melancholy was a family trait, a quality shared by even sturdy little Franklin. It was a kind of Celtic reaction to the deeply penetrating power of beauty in nature or in song—an inherited memory of ancestral pain.

Mother McLane, though lacking the singular quality of her husband and the charm of her children, was by no means commonplace. Beloved for her abounding kindliness and her unhesitating hospitality, tireless, cheerful in adversity, reticent in the midst of merriment, she had but one desire—that of seeing her children happily married and her sons prosperous. She seldom rested and never complained.

All her girls resembled their father and all were handsome. Deborah, the third daughter, with her snapping black eyes and her pitiless tongue, was something of a terror to Richard and to the young fellows who came to call upon her, but Rachel, a slim, lovely girl of sixteen, and Belle were gentle and rather silent.

Isabel appealed to Richard more strongly than any of her sisters, not only through her voice, but by way of her shy smile and her big brown eyes. She was tall for her years and carried herself with unusual dignity, and yet, much as she interested him, he thought of her only as a gifted child. Deborah and Rachel were the young ladies of the family.

David and Luke were of the same type, tall, dark, with handsome, straight, clean-cut noses and eyes which drooped at the outer corners, a touch of the Oriental quality which added to their beauty. They could play upon any instrument they knew and they each had a genius for remembering every tune they heard.

Altogether, Richard considered the McLanes the most enthralling family he had ever met. They typified the adventurous West, they expressed its allurement. Most of the villagers were good, familiar types, but old Hugh and his sons came from a wider, more hospitable home. They were minstrels rather than clerks. Their books were books of song. Their words had no malice, their jests no sting.

Richard went back to his work on Robey's farm that night in a more resolved and happier frame of mind. His visit to the home of the Samaritan who had rescued him from the pit of despair had put new courage into him. The sound of David's violin and the lilt of Isabel's voice went with him. He worked now with the expectation of revisiting that alluring home at the end of the week.

A second visit enabled him to see more of the household, for he took supper with them. The living-room was not only larger than most houses offered, but its brick chimney and open fire-place set it apart from all others in the village. It presented something of the charm of a Scottish hall with that of a New England kitchen. It was a plain, bare room with low ceiling and plastered walls, and the chairs were of wood with splint bottoms, straight-backed for the most part, but Grandsire Hugh had his own "cheer" as he called it, broad-seated, ladder-backed and painted grey with red bands at the turned joinings.

The only books were the Bible and a few flat, yellow pasteboard-bound volumes, "The Golden Circlet," "Songs of Praise," and "The Family Choir." On the wall depending from deer horns were long rifles and their accoutrements, and standing in the corner two violin boxes leaned on end like small coffins. On a low table rested the dulcimer, a small, flat, stringed instrument, with its cork hammers beside it.

That meal was to Richard a further revelation of the character of the McLanes. Hearty, smiling, noisy, and jocular, they drew up to the long table without ceremony other than a moment's pause while the patriarch whispered grace. Richard found the food and talk entirely to his liking. They were good-humoured in all they said, and kindly in all their actions. "A jolly lot," Stephen Dudley had called them from his Connecticut standpoint.

Mrs. McLane insisted on waiting upon them till David forced her into a seat, and during the meal she remained as silent as her husband, though in a different way. He was silent because his mind was fixed on something far away, she because she would rather listen than talk. She loved to hear her sons and daughters "go on" and her smile was sweetly wise.

She had given birth to twelve children. She had cooked and sewed and nursed almost every day of her life. She had never known privacy, nor comfort, nor leisure, and yet her face was not merely serene; it was proudly happy. She worshipped her handsome sons and adored her pretty daughters. If she considered her case at all (which I doubt), she considered herself a most fortunate woman.

Harriet Graham, speaking to her son of the McLanes, said, with a clearer understanding than Richard could achieve, "They are the happiest family of my acquaintance —the most harmonious. Your father considers them shiftless and disorderly and so they are, but they are the best neighbours in the world."

In a sense they were not typical of the border. Only in their strength, their daring were they akin to their surroundings. In their natural refinement, their love of music, their harmonious family relationship they were more distinguished than their fellow-pioneers were able to realize.

As careless farmers they were objects of contemptuous comment. "As fiddlers and hunters they are wonders, but no man can fiddle and farm equally well." As riflemen, they were reputed to have the skill of Daniel Boone. It was said of William that with his long, heavy rifle he could clip the head of a chicken at a distance of seventy paces.

Arnold Robey told Richard that at a "turkey shoot," the previous fall, David and William were both ruled out "to keep 'em from getting all the birds."

In contests of strength and agility they were all equally formidable. David could outdo any man in the country in broad-jumping, and his record, it was said, was phenomenal. Luke was a champion vaulter and runner, and William, while not as swift on foot as Luke and David, was of greater strength. No man in all the region had been able to surpass his lifting power, or to put him on his back. His form, though far beyond the normal height and weight, was graceful, and his gestures swift. His step was as light as that of a red man, and his hands as deft as a cat's paws. He, too, played the fiddle and sang bass in the choir.

The Musical McLanes

The presence of these Scotch songsters made a holiday of any task. Harvesting was a game with them. Dexterous with axe and rake as with the rifle or the fiddle-bow, they led in the field. Each of them could swing the cradle with untiring ease and to rake and bind after another reaper was sport for them.

As they passed along the roads they scattered merry greetings and quaint jests. Gay, sweet-tempered, wholesome and temperate, they not only won universal liking, they helped to make this new land the joyous country the Grahams had imagined it to be.

As October came on and the evenings grew cold, the McLane house took on increasing charm. Its open fireplace was the centre of a throng of young people every Sunday night, and when other engagements kept Richard from sharing in these meetings, he felt cheated.

Hugh took no part in the services of the village church, but he made no objection to his daughters' singing in the choir on Sunday morning, provided they sang his favourite hymns at home. "A thousand years, my own loved Zion," and "The Chariot!" were among those he loved best of all, and the grandiose chanting of Zephaniah and the epic marching and thundering of Micah were ever at the tip of his tongue. At moments of leisure these lines came from his lips in musical, exultant chant. He was at heart a Scottish bard, a medieval minstrel whose action as woodsman and pioneer had failed to express or satisfy his soul. For emotional outlet he turned to the sultry splendour of Hezekiah and the Apocalyptic visions of John.

Mrs. McLane, while sharing in some degree her husband's faith, was too practical, too much the housewife to dream. On her the routine of the home depended. Like her daughters she enjoyed the service of the village church and none of her sons, save William, took more than a kindly interest in the vague discourse with which Old Hugh occasionally favoured them.

Isabel, too young to take more than a child's concern in the matter of her father's harangues, gladly joined with him in singing the hymns he loved and they made a charming picture as they wistfully repeated the lines "On the other side of Jordan in the sweet fields of Eden," or exultantly proclaimed, "The Great Day, so long foretold!" No doubt she thought of the Jordan as a river in Ohio, and for Hugh, Zion was not the dry desert region of the East, but a land somewhere under the sunset. No matter, these anthems voiced some part of their mutual longing for the mystical and the beautiful.

The more Richard saw of this singular family, the deeper his interest in them became. Without them, life in Wisconsin would have been far less alluring. Harriet Graham shared his enthusiasm, especially for David and Isabel. Of the family in general she said, "They have in them something of Bible times, something patriarchal," and Richard understood her to be speaking in their praise, which she was.

CHAPTER X

The Turkey Shoot

FOR nearly three months Richard worked for Robey, making a hand at harvesting, stacking, and ploughing the land for the next year's crop, acquitting himself in such manly fashion that he won the respect even of the redoubtable "Eastern" Starr, but as the soil froze and activity on the farms began to slow down, he found himself confronted by the question of employment for the winter. Having contracted for the plot of land adjoining his cabin, he must earn money to pay for it, and as the village had few industries and offered little even to its carpenters and masons he turned with interest to "the Pineries" of which the men of the village increasingly talked.

The township in which the Grahams had found lodgement was situated on the verge of the prairie in the extreme south-western corner of the state, whereas the famous pine-lands boundless and dark, lay far to the north on the upper waters of the Wisconsin River.

"The Gate-way to the Woods" he was told, "is Stevens' Point. From there on there's nothing but forest. No one except a few hunters knows anything about how far it extends."

It was a most romantic region, that northern wilderness, and from several of his companions on the farms, (men who had spent a winter up there as choppers or teamsters) Richard heard much of "Big Bull Falls," "Mosinee Mountain," and "The Dells."

"There are a few mills but no towns above Portage," they reported. "It is just an uninhabitable wilderness filled with Injuns, wolves and bears," all of which appealed to Richard with disturbing power. He resolved to see it, to explore it with Clinton.

Several of the younger men of the village had begun to plan a winter in the woods, not so much for the wages the lumber camps offered, as for the reason that the life promised adventure, and something of danger. Naturally Richard shared this desire to explore. "That is what I came out here for," he said to his mother. "I'm going to see this forest country."

To have a part in its life was now his ambition and he fully expected David or Luke to join him in this enterprise. To his surprise, neither of them would consider it. "I don't like the life of a logging camp," David said. "Besides, Luke and I each have a team and can earn better money freighting," and William added, "Winter is my time for hunting."

Disappointed in not having either David or Luke for a companion, Richard wrote to Clinton. "You promised to join me in some project. Come along this way about Thanksgiving time, and we'll go up into 'the Pineries' together. It's said to be a grand country up there, and I want to see it. Besides I need a job."

To this Clinton replied, "I'll be with you."

The Turkey Shoot

The more Richard learned of those illimitable pine forests and the swift rivers which came out of them, the more intensely eager he became to explore them. The only maps known to him were those of his schoolbooks which presented only the vaguest outlines of interior Wisconsin, but Luke who had spent one winter teaming to Portage, was able to fill in some of the blank spaces. "The whole upper part of the state is covered with trees," he explained, "there are no roads, and the cutting is all done along the banks of the Wolf or the Wisconsin. Each camp runs from twelve to thirty men. Choppers get about twenty dollars a month and board. It's hard work and a rough way to live. I prefer to team."

Richard was not disheartened by this statement.

The truth is, he could not bring himself to spend the winter in Brownsville. It offered so little to a youth who had come west in search of romance. That he should be found mapping a trail to the north was inevitable. "I can't hole up here," he protested to his father. "It's like wintering in Intervale, Maine, and besides you'll need all I can earn."

Harriet said little but she was disturbed by his plan. He was only a boy, not yet twenty-one, and the life of the camps was reported to be hard and rough. Tales of drinking and brawling, as well as of the relentless severity of the labour alarmed her. Suppose he should be sick? She did what she could in her quiet way to change his course, all to no result. When his face hardened into certain lines, she understood all too well that further argument was useless.

She faced the winter with dread, for the cabin, notwithstanding its "chinkin" and "bankin" was a poor defense against such cold as her brother and his family jestingly described. "Compared with winter back East, it's about six of one and half a dozen of t'other," said John

Bridges. "You won't mind it after you get a little more fat on your bones."

To this Harriet made no reply for she had given up all hope of regaining her health. Although not in acute pain, her vitality remained low. Her mind was active but her feet were hesitant.

True to his promise and greatly to Richard's joy, Clinton turned up at the Graham cabin one night about the middle of November, bursting with physical energy and full of enthusiasm. "I have the promise of a job for us both in a camp not far from Big Bull Falls," he at once announced. "My idea is to start early and walk from here to Stevens' Point. I'm told we can catch a ride into the camps most any day on a freight wagon." Here he smiled, "Moreover I want to go round by way of the Edwards place and see Josephine. It's a little out of our way, but I promised her I'd come and bring you if I could. They'll be glad to see us, I'm sure of that. I got pretty well acquainted with them on our way to Chicago."

He said this lightly, but Richard, reading in his tone a very definite purpose, assented to the plan with instant readiness. Tireless on foot as a hound, and rejoicing in the opportunity to explore the new state, he was ready to make the detour although his sickness and the busy summer through which he had passed had somewhat dimmed the faces of the girls he had met on the boat. He still retained enough of his liking for Clara to be pleased at the thought of seeing her again. He would not have planned such a call alone, but with Clinton to lead the way, a romantic glamour lighted the project.

Clinton told his story of the stage ride from Detroit to Chicago, with humour. "The roads were a holy terror, especially as we got near Chicago, which is the muddiest hole with the worst side-walks you ever saw. All the same I enjoyed the trip. The Edwards girls stood the mud and bad grub like little Majors. Your aunt and uncle are trumps! We came up to Galena together. Patty never whimpered at any hardship. In fact, she stood it better than most of the men. She's a born pioneeress, that woman!"

Harriet McLane liked and trusted this handsome Vermonter, and when she learned that he and Richard were planning to go into "The Woods" together, she was greatly relieved. "He's older than Richard, more experienced in many ways, and seems fine and dependable," she said to her husband.

"Richard couldn't have a better partner. It relieves the situation for me."

That night Richard took Clinton over to call upon the McLanes, and introduced them (with an air of proprietorship which amused Clinton), feeling certain that they would like him and that he would be interested in them. Clinton was open in his admiration for David and his father. Luke and William made a less vivid appeal. Isabel he regarded as a child.

David asked about lead-mining and Clinton frankly owned to a failure. "It is a played-out game," he said. "It hasn't paid anybody for several years and most of the prospectors have gone to farming; others are turning to the lumber business."

David and Luke had much to say of a combined "Turkey Shoot and Barn-Raisin'," which had been arranged for Thursday of that week. "Dad's one of the judges at the shoot, and William is the captain of the crew that is to raise Harry Adams' barn. We meet early in the forenoon for the shooting and eat dinner at the Adams place. After supper we 're goin' to have a dance at Arnold Robey's."

Clinton was keenly interested in this typical day of Western sport, and on the way home proposed putting off the start to the pine woods. "I've always wanted to see a turkey shoot, and McLane says he's going to have this carried out in the true backwoodsy way. I like your McLanes. The girls are beauties and David is a wonder with the fiddle."

The place of meeting for the shoot was on a gently sloping, grassy hill-side near a grove of oak trees and on that morning the air was keen as steel. As the boys walked up the sloping grass-blades, stiff with frost, crisped under their feet. They were the earliest arrivals, but shortly William and David arrived to measure the ground and lay out the target-range.

Arnold Robey came next, bringing two bundles of live turkeys with their legs tied together. These he carried to the pit of loose loam in which they were to be buried one by one, with only their necks protruding. Bertram Noble brought an equal number which were to be tied to a stake at a more distant spot.

By the time the sun had melted the crystals from the grass, a throng of men and boys had gathered, impatient for the contest to begin. No women appeared, a fact which seemed very strange to Clinton. On speaking of it to the McLanes, David said, "The girls never come. I don't know why. They think it's hard on the turkeys, I reckon."

With the arrival of old Hugh, the tournament began. The first number on the programme was the test of individual marksmanship. Each man had brought his own target (a spade-shaped piece of wood), marked with his name so that no chance for dispute might arise. Each of these was fastened, in turn, to a tree under direction of Robey, and when a contestant had finished shooting, his target was brought back to Hugh who studied the hits and announced the score. In such an arrangement, the best man was certain to win.

When all had taken their turn, William's target was

put up and with calm precision he fired five shots. "Dick, bring my target," he said to Richard.

On approaching the target, Dick was surprised to find but one rather large hole. Each bullet had centred! It would be an exaggeration to say that they had all entered the same hole, but they had all struck so near the centre that a dollar would cover the scar. Such was William's keenness of eye and steadiness of arm. To him went the prize.

In shooting at the live turkeys, he was almost equally successful. The birds which were buried in sand, with only their heads showing, made very slender marks, and yet both William and David won three out of every five shots. To William had been awarded the quarter of beef which was the prize of the target-shooting, and he would have carried off most of the turkeys, had the judges permitted it. "Now, William, you've had your share," they protested.

Clinton was almost as pleased by these awards as Dick. "I wish I could shoot like that, but I never can. To shoot like that you've got to grow up with a gun in your hands. You've got to *think* gun all day and every day."

The barn-raising which came next was a familiar process to both Clint and Richard, but they enjoyed it all the more for that reason. It was not a large barn and the bents were soon in place and pinned fast. A great deal of cider was consumed, but as nothing stronger was furnished by their host (who was a staunch temperance advocate), no one was the worse for it. William contributed the turkeys for the dinner and the meal was a feast. All the women of the neighbourhood assembled during the afternoon, and at night the young people danced on the rough floor of the new building with the starlit sky showing through the rafters. This was only to dedicate it, however, for it was too cold to be comfortable even with outside garments on. The smaller space of the kitchen was more alluring.

The fiddlers were of the usual elbow-jerking sort and some of the young people who knew David's skill, urged him to play for them. To appease them he borrowed one of the instruments and took the place of the owner for one reel, but he did it with a smile, and Richard could see that in imitating the mechanical jigging of the other performers he was drawing the line between fiddling and playing the violin.

He did not dance and neither did William, but Luke was graceful and light on the floor. Richard took his turn in every "set" although most of the dances were new to him. Clinton at once assumed leadership. Roughly dressed as he was (he had brought only his working clothes to Brownsville), he carried himself with the easy assurance of a city man among farmers, and something of this self-possession appeared in Richard's manner. His Boston experience gave him a distinction which Luke, handsome as he was, could not claim.

"Why don't you and David shake a foot?" asked Clinton of William. With a twinkle of his fine black eyes, the giant replied, "I'm too heavy, and as for Dave—I do' know. He's always been queer about dancing. He says he don't like it—too much like showing off—like a turkey-cock, I guess."

Isabel was at the supper-table and later Richard saw her looking on, wistfully, at the dance but she did not stay long. Too young to be considered a dancing partner, she went away with her mother, dreaming of the time when she, too, might put up her hair and be counted a young lady.

There were several girls of fourteen who took part in the dance, but Hugh and his careful wife considered Isabel too young for such experiences. "Time enough for that after you 're sixteen," they said.

It was long after midnight when Clinton and Richard

walked back to the Graham cabin. "It has been a regular Western pioneer day," Clint remarked. I'm glad I've had it. If all they tell me about the woods is true we won't see another woman till spring. We're going a hundred miles above all settlement, and once in camp we'll have no time for anything but the axe."

"I don't mind," responded Richard. "I'd rather do that than pound nails here. It'll be sport getting there, anyway."

"If we don't get lost; there are no roads across country. We'll have to find our way."

"All the more fun," retorted Richard. "We'll know what the state looks like."

CHAPTER XI

The Logging-Camp

A FEW days after this, the two New England boys set out on their wondrous journey into the north. Each carried a small pack containing a clean hickory shirt, a heavy woollen shirt, a razor and comb, and two pairs of socks. They had no overcoats and but one pair of boots, but they boasted of an indifference to cold and wet, and laughed when they were warned to expect snow-storms and muddy trails. "If it snows we'll get under a tree. If it's muddy in the road we'll walk on the grass," Clinton retorted.

Once outside the town, Richard observed, "Our first objective is Madison, the capital of the state, and as the road is not very direct I propose we cut across lots."

"What a journey that was!" exclaimed Clinton in after years. "Part of the time we were in a wooded country without roads or bridges and with few houses. At night we rested in all sorts of beds, usually as guests, for in those days every household considered it a pleasure as well as a duty to lodge passing strangers. Mails were few and irregular and newspapers weeks behind the times, therefore any well-informed traveller was a welcome visitor. From passing strangers, like us, these lonely settlers obtained a glimpse of the outside world."

One story of their entertainment which I have often heard Richard tell, will serve to illustrate the primitive hospitality of the ruder cabins along the way. "One day after a tedious afternoon's walk in the rain, we came to a new shack in the middle of a sandy flat. The building which was two storeys in height, looked promising, and Clinton said, 'Here's for food and a bed!'

"His knock brought a slatternly woman of twenty-five or thirty to the door. She was sandy-haired, long-visaged and bony, but she said, 'Certainly! Walk right in. My man has gone after the cow but he'll be back in a jiffy.

" 'Set by and rest your face and hands. We don't make a practice of keepin' folks, but we sometimes do so, bein' that we're a kind of half-way house between settlements.'

"Having made us comfortable, she set about supper, questioning us as she worked. 'Where ye from? Are ye goin' into the woods? How are the camps in Green County?' With a wink at me, Clint answered her with whatever came into his mind, but the joke was on him when the man of the house came in, for his wife insisted on Clinton's telling the stories all over again!

"The meal was served on a table built of slabs and consisted of boiled potatoes, biscuits spotted with saleratus, salt pork, and what the woman called 'cawfee.' It was. As soon as we sat down she said to me, 'Will you have long sweet'nin' or short sweet'nin'?'

"Not knowing exactly what she meant, I answered, 'long sweet'nin'.'

"Thereupon she brought a jug, and poured a thin stream

of black molasses into my cup. Cutting this sticky ribbon in two with her dirty forefinger, she licked it clean and passed it on the Clint. 'Would *you* wish long sweet'nin'?' says she.

"Clint, who didn't relish the idea of the finger she had licked, decided on 'short sweet'nin'.' Putting away the jug, she picked up a big lump of brown sugar, bit a corner from it, and dropped it into his cup.

"I just about choked with laughter. I tried my best to conceal it by coughing, but every time I caught Clint's eye I went off again. It was only next morning when we were safely on the road and out of hearing that I could let myself go. 'Long sweetnin' or short sweetnin' was a choice I never let my partner forget."

Not all of their entertainment was of this primitive sort, but it was all very plain and sometimes poor. No one lived in comfort. The whole state was a camp of bordermen. There were but two stage roads leading out of Milwaukee and they were bad.

However, as they approached the lake, on the shore of which they expected to find the Edwards home, the country showed a somewhat higher stage of settlement. It was still mainly wilderness, but here and there a neat farmhouse of pine boards gave evidence of New England thrift, and the village which stood at the outlet of the lake took pride in several painted buildings.

The postmaster of this colony, a Yankee with a red nose and a cold blue eye, proved helpful. In response to their questions he replied, "Yes, there is a Johnny Bull by the name of Edwards livin' on the east shore of the lake about two miles up. Are you friends of his?"

"Well, no," answered Clinton, "but we came west on the same boat with his daughters."

"Well, they're all right, the girls are but their dad's a pill, a regular sardine. Won't have anything to do with us common folks. Thinks he's a little tin god on wheels. Calls his place 'New Albion.' Has the name painted on the gate-post!"

The explorers left the post-office in subdued spirits. Richard was all for turning back, and when they came in sight of the home which had so aroused the scorn of the store-keeper, Clinton also betrayed hesitation, for it was a most imposing structure. Built of lumber, two storeys in height and standing on a grassy knoll in a native grove of noble oaks, it towered in such violent contrast with the cabins of the region that Clinton was daunted.

"I wasn't expecting anything quite so splendiferous as that," he confessed. "I begin to have my doubts about calling on the girls in this rig," he added, looking down at his baggy trousers and muddy boots.

Richard grinned sourly. "This is *your* party, Clint. I never would have thought of coming round this way but for you. Go in! Don't mind me. I'll wait here in the road."

Clinton sat down and opened his bundle. "If I had any way to take the wrinkles out of my one clean shirt, I wouldn't mind," he remarked while musing on the garment in question.

It was indeed a lamentable crumple and Richard chuckled. "They'll think you've been sleepin' in the barns along the way—which you have. No, Clint! Right here I balk. I'm in no condition to call on a girl in a palace like that, and I don't see any way of bettering my looks. You ought to have thought of this situation before you started. Go ahead. Take a chance. It's none of my funeral."

"Maybe there's some mistake. Maybe this is not the Edwards estate, after all"; then he added, "I need a shave."

"Oh, no! Your face is in keeping with your shirt."

Perceiving an old man fishing from a log on the bank of

the lake, Clinton accosted him. "Uncle, can you tell me whose house that is just ahead?"

The fisherman, who was another Yankee, replied with evident gusto, "That's what folks around here call 'the Edwards Castle.' B'longs to an English nabob who bought in here some two years ago. They's a whole raft of these English lords and dukes comin' in—so I hear. They're all great on dogs and horses and none of 'em sociable with us workin' folks. Edwards' girls are clever enough, but Edwards! He's so all-fired stuck-up he can't see a Wisconsin man, 'less he's a congressman or a general. You'd orta see him ridin' out with a passel of fox-hounds fuglin' round him, and the way he goes teeterin' up and down in his saddle makes me think of a cawndemned jumpin'-jack. Can't tell him anything about nawthin'. He's one of these high-steppin' English 'ristocrats who think anything made in America's no good. He won't last long the way he's throwin' his money around."

It was evident that this eloquent democrat represented the prevailing sentiment of the neighbourhood so far as Edwards was concerned, and Richard stubbornly insisted on going back to the village. "I'd hate to have Clara see me with a pack on my back. If I had my Sunday suit and a shave, I wouldn't mind, but to be presented to her dad in the clothes I've been walking in would put me at a disadvantage."

"At the same time," said Clinton, "I don't believe in letting 'his high and mightiness' scare us out. I'll chance a call if you will."

Richard was embittered. He resented Edwards' implied superiority. He had been educated to believe that a Graham was as good as any other man, provided he behaved himself as well, but now that the test was about to be made, he realized that as a man on foot tramping through the land like a gipsy, he stood in a far different position to that which he had occupied on the boat. Edwards would not meet him in the spirit of the New World as his daughter had done. He presented something hard and cold, a barrier which could not be overleaped or overlooked. In him the caste of the Old World persisted.

As the boys neared the arched gateway which bore in ornamental letters the words "New Albion Hall," Clinton definitely capitulated. "I guess I've miscalculated," he said with bitter humour. "The portcullis is down and the moat is full of water."

"Let's hurry by," urged Richard. "I don't want them to even *see* us."

Clinton agreed. "It seems cowardly, and yet to put ourselves in a position to be kicked would be foolish."

Had they been more deeply concerned they might have risked a meeting, but as it stood, neither of them cared enough about the girls to warrant an entrance. Richard never mentioned the episode again and Clinton only referred to it humorously now and then.

At Portage they came back to the Wisconsin River, a swift and sombre stream, and between there and Stevens' Point (the "Gateway of the North") more than a hundred miles of wilderness outspread, with a few saw-mills scattered along the river, and an occasional lumbering-camp notching the fringes of the mighty forest.

New-fallen snow made walking difficult, and when (on the second day out of Portage) the driver of a freight team offered transportation, they accepted with relief. Tramping had become a tedious waste of valuable time.

The "Marshall Cooper Camp No. 3," to which Clinton was articled, was located on a branch of the Wisconsin River just above Mosinee Mountain in a noble grove of pine. It consisted of a long log cabin, with a chimney at each end like a hunter's lodge, in which the men ate and slept, and two smaller structures which harboured the teams and tools. It was quite as rude and as temporary as a road-maker's camp, but coming as it did at the end of a long journey, it offered a pleasant haven for the cold and hungry boys.

The cook was busy at one of the fire-places, and a long dining-table, built of planks, stood in the centre of the room. Supper consisted of baked beans, salt pork, hot bread, and potatoes. Butter was not served and milk was unknown. Tea was the beverage. The men slept in bunks along the walls, and all hands dressed, smoked, and played cards in the open space around the second fire-place which stood at the western end of the shanty.

The crew, which numbered about twenty men, was made up of natives of Michigan, New York, and New England, a decent, hard-working lot, cheerfully loyal to their boss. All were young and of notable hardihood. The few who were disposed to drink or gamble were held in check by the spirit of the majority, and the life of the camp, while rude, was orderly and decent. Clinton and Richard understood the men, and were accepted by them at once. Names didn't count for much. "Boston Charley," "Michigan," "Nutmegs," and other nicknames were the rule. Clinton became "Ver-mount" and Richard "Yankee Dick."

Healthy as bears, these choppers ate everything that was set before them. What skill, what endurance, what courage the smallest of them displayed! Up at break of day, eating their buckwheat cakes by candle-light, they were at work at dawn. Wallowing mid-leg deep in snow, they attacked towering trees with confident air, whistling, singing, and shouting. Their action was titanic, their cheer superb. A day's labour reached from dawn to dusk, and no man thought of shirking his duty, or if he did he was shamed into action by his fellows who took a savage pride in long hours and fatigue.

Sheltered from the savage winds by the high pines, they

toiled even while the storm-clouds whirled in furious rout above the trees, and snows fell thickly, softly through the tossing branches above their heads. There was charm in the sense of safety which the forest gave. The calm at the roots of the trees was like the quiet of deep seas.

Sunday, the day of rest, was given over to shaving, washing, mending clothes, and other brave attempts at restoring the decencies of civilized life, while the cook, in the effort to make the mid-day meal a Sabbath feast, baked a "plum-duff" or a huge dried-apple pie. Some of the men occasionally drove away to the nearest saloon, but most of them remained in camp.

It was precisely the sort of life to appeal to Richard. His three years in Boston had not robbed him of his skill in the use of the axe, and his work on Robey's farm had hardened him, so that he was able, even on his first day in the woods, to play an honourable part in the swamper's heroic game, but Clinton, not an expert with the axe, was at a disadvantage. He became a teamster, and "by main strength and awkwardness" assisted in loading and hauling the logs to the river-bank. His intelligence and humour made him popular with the crew, even if he was unable to "strike twice in the same place" with an axe. "I am a town-bred loafer. I admit it," he remarked vith a laugh.

The fact that neither he nor Richard chewed tobacco or drank whisky was rather against them at first, but their strength and skill entitled them both to be as singular as they pleased. Their sobrieties soon ceased to be counted against them.

Richard was not humorous. He contributed little to the amusement of the crew, but he was a lucky hunter and often spent his Sundays in providing venison for the camp. It was not his skill with a rifle but his sense of direction which made him valuable. Unerring as a wolf or bee, he was able, no matter how grey the sky or how thick the swamp, to find his way back to the clearing. He appre-hended the points of the compass by some subtle valuation of temperature or wind-pressure and his services as a guide were in demand.

Stories of being lost were common and some of the best riflemen in camp admitted to being "turned round" in the swamp on a cloudy day. For these reasons, Richard, while an indifferent shot, was called upon to safe-guard those who were his superiors as marksmen. He plunged into the endless forest or circled a tamarack swamp with a con-fidence which seemed miraculous to his fellows.

Both of the boys came to love the camp and its sounds. The click-clock of the axes, the ringing chant of the cross-cut saw, the crash of falling trees, the jingle of sleigh-bells, the shouts of teamsters, and the snap of long whips, united to form a cheerful, day-long chorus, while on all sides, and diminishing these sounds till they seemed the voices of insects, the roar of the forest was like the sound of ocean's majestic anthem. Sometimes at night, the stillness of the snowy outside world was a stern menace to which the hearty comradeship around the fire presented a joyous contrast.

A curious commentary on the psychology of these young animals lies in the fact that on Sundays, or during the long evenings, they joined in contests of strength or skill. You would think they would require rest, but no! They wres-tled, jumped, chinned a bar, pulled sticks, tried out each other's grip, and in every conceivable way established ath-letic rank. Richard was a good catch-as-catch-can wrestler, Clinton could pull up any man (while seated on the floor feet to feet) because of his superior length of arm, but the champion bear-hug wrestler was Cooper, the boss. He was the heaviest man in camp, a brute of a man, admirable in many ways, but profane as a sea-cook. Famous for his skill as a fist-fighter, he was accustomed to say to each new crew, "If there is any man in my camp who considers himself a better man than I am, I want to know it."

As he said this one Sunday morning, Clinton spoke up. "I have me doots, Mr. Cooper," and while the boss stared in surprise, the youth walked slowly round him, saying reflectively, "No, I don't see it. I hate to do harm to an older man and my boss, but——"

At this point Cooper broke into a roar of amazement, and made for the audacious boy like an angry lion. Clinton slipped aside and called out, "Hold on a moment. What is it to be?"

"Anything at all," growled Cooper.

This relieved Richard's mind, for he knew Clinton's skill at rough-and-tumble, whereas Cooper's weight and strength made him formidable in a bear-hug.

The blood of the camp rose to fever-heat. All hands including the cook and the cookee were in the dense circle of onlookers. For several minutes Cooper manoeuvred, unable to get a secure hold upon his nimble young antagonist. He clutched, he rushed, he clawed, but in some way Clinton always got free from his hairy paws and went dancing away. Suddenly he changed his tactics. With a darting leap he caught the big man low about the waist, and threw him under the table.

For a moment the men were stunned with surprise—the downfall of their chief was awesome—then the humour of it overcame them and they howled and stamped in joy of his sheepish look as he rose from the floor clutching one shoulder as if in pain.

Clinton stood to meet him. "Want to try again?"

Cooper grinned. "Not today, young feller. I've had enough for today. When I tackle you again it will be in some other fashion."

Such a camp is a school of hardihood, and its duties a test of manhood, but to Richard and Clinton it was more then this. It transformed them, made them Western. Richard, though at once nicknamed "Yankee Dick," lost most of his "State of Maine lingo." Boston receded into ever more remote distance, and he seldom mentioned his experiences there except when the cook, who came from Medford, called upon him for confirmation. He had no doubts of the future, no regrets for the past. His hopes united with the State. He was a Wisconsin man.

During the early part of the winter the talk among the men was all of the forest and its lore, but as the days lengthened and the snow softened discussion shifted to the problem of getting logs to the mill and lumber to the market. "Log-driving" was the next job. Some of the men who owned farms were pledged to go out in April to sow their seed, but Richard and Clinton engaged themselves to drive logs, much to the relief of the boss who was in sore need of their assistance.

The logs, piled along the banks of the creek, were worthless unless they could be floated to the mill, and this job was but the prelude to rafting the sawed lumber to the market which was far below, in towns along the lower Wisconsin and upper Mississippi. From Big Bull Falls to Sauk Prairie, the river ran through an almost unbroken wilderness, presenting a succession of rapids, sand-bars, sharp bends, and canyons. To pilot a raft down this stream during the spring flood demanded definite knowledge, instant decision of action, and the hardihood of a Viking.

Cooper, the boss of Richard's camp, who was one of the best-known pilots of the region, offered to teach Richard the business. "As soon as the logs are all in the 'boom,' you and I will go down to the mill and start building 'cribs.' The chopping, driving, and milling are only the beginning. Your lumber isn't worth a damn till it reaches settlements where people are building."

The Logging-Camp

He described the crib-raft, which was a device for binding lumber together in order that it should withstand the buffeting of the water of the rapids. "Sometimes after a crib shoots the falls, it wallers along under water, and sometimes it turns bottom-side up. They must be built to stand grief. Jinny Bull Falls, Grand-daddy Bull Falls, and the Notched Rock in the Dells are the worst points, but it's work all the way. Jinny Bull Rapids is three miles long."

"Where did those names come from?" asked Richard.

"I don't know for sure, but I'm told they came from old Bullieu, one of the French trappers who lived there. He must have had a daughter Jennie, and those falls are named after her. All I know is the upper falls are put down on the map as Bullieu's Falls, and they are a terror. It's no job for a softy! Don't go into my crew thinkin' you're goin' to float down to St. Louis on a kind of picnic journey. You'll be under water half your time on the upper river, and you'll be hungry and cold the other half. It takes a *man* to run a raft on the Wisconsin, a man who is a mixture of wildcat and alligator."

All this, so far from daunting the boy, roused his pride, his determination. "Can you do all that?" he asked with truculent inflection.

"I've done it for two years and I intend to do it again."

Something set and hard came into Richard's face. His grey eyes took on the round stare which expressed the reckless will of the eagle. "Then I can do it."

"That's the talk," Cooper replied with a smile. "You'll do." Not yet twenty-one years of age, Richard was a dangerous adversary. His winter as a chopper had hardened his muscles and strengthened his self-reliance. He weighed one hundred and seventy pounds and was firm as oak. Enoch Lawrence would not have recognized in this sinewy red-shirted, unshaven lumber-jack, the fair-skinned shipping-clerk he had lost, and whom he was still expecting to welcome back to Boston.

Although not as strong as Clinton, Richard was as swift of foot, and even more instant in action. In all contests involving agile grace and dexterity, he was almost invariably victor. Several could outlift him, and one or two could jump higher then he, but none of them could best him in catch-as-catch-can wrestling and he could hew to a line with the precision of the oldest man in the crew.

Hating books, he went to school in the pines with zest. His judgment on the value of a tree was almost unerring. How was it that in a few months he had acquired such ability in woodcraft. Was it an inheritance from his New England pioneer ancestors? Perhaps. Anyhow, he had reached a high place in Cooper's estimate. "You're a good logger, now I'll make a master pilot of you."

From that moment Richard's ambition shifted. He forgot his dream of free land and a beautiful farm and fixed his mind on his approaching contest with the rocks and rapids of the river. He was always like that. He loved danger for danger's sake. It was a vanity in him, of course, but a vanity which had redeeming features.

Clinton showed more of the business man's insight. He asked many questions concerning the lumber business and finally said to Richard, "What we want to do is to get into this timber game. This is a new state. It's got to have enormous amounts of building material. Think of the towns to be built, barns, factories, sidewalks! I can't afford to work for wages. I'm going to have lumber-camps and a saw-mill of my own."

Richard paid little heed to such talk. He was too young, too adventurous. The river and its dangers now filled his mind to the exclusion of all else.

CHAPTER XII

Running the River

THE physical changes which the warm airs and suns of April brought to this ice-bound northern forest were prodigiously, incredibly swift. A few clear days with a cutting southern wind, and half the valley was under water. Creeks became rivers and rivers rose in foaming torrents. All teaming was at an end for the tote roads, pikes of trodden snow based on frozen muck were treacherously softened, roots and stumps and dangerous mud-holes developed. Only a man on foot, in water-tight boots, had any warrant to travel. Chopping ceased, and all hands turned in to break the roll-ways on the banks and start the logs on their way down the rising waters of the creek toward the mills which stood on the main river just above the falls.

"The Drive" appealed strongly to both Richard and Clinton, for it offered contests with log and sand-bar, eddy and rapid. They delighted in its danger, as well as in its daily change of scene. The occasional jam in the bends, and the boiling eddies into which the logs drifted, presented joyous opportunities for skill and courage. They admired the men who could leap upon a floating log and tread it and direct it as if it were a canoe. The grace and precision of these drivers were in keeping with the wilderness and its torrents.

Many were the duckings Richard suffered before he could tread and master a rolling log. His vanity would not permit him to take second place. He accepted every "dare" and obeyed every command, no matter how many times it drove him into peril. His devotion and his desire to succeed were so intense that in a few days he won the respect of his most experienced companions. Cooper watched the crew with a grin of approval. From a nest of ants gnawing at the roots of the forest his crew had become a group of water-bugs.

The stream on which the winter's camp had been situated was small, and the boss, fearing that freshet might pass and leave his logs stranded along the shallows, drove his gang with desperate energy. Something stirring, something adventurous was in every hour of day-light, and when night came and the crew gathered round a camp-fire under the firs, to dry out their clothes and to eat their well-earned supper, Clinton said, "Well, Dick, we're seeing the 'Golden West!' It isn't exactly what I thought it would be, but it's not like Boston, is it?"

In this spirit they accepted the river. It was a part of their great exploration. Their immediate ambition was to drive logs as well as the boss. Beyond that lay the battle with the falls which had claimed so many victims that one piece of its water was called "Bone-Yard Eddy."

The closer the boys got to Mosinee the more grisly became the tales of running the rapids, and when, one Sunday morning at the end of his drive Richard reached the mill, which stood on the west side of the quiet water just above the rapid, and looked out upon the Wisconse (swollen beyond record) as it came sweeping out of the northern wilderness, grey with wrath and filled with ravage, he began to understand a little more clearly what it meant to enter that tumultuous torrent with a clumsy raft.

"It don't seem humanly possible to live through it," said Clinton, "and yet it has been done, it *must* be done. Our lumber is worth nothing till it reaches the lower river. I'd like to meet the man who first grappled with that problem and solved it."

The spirit of the West was in this commerce, and Richard rose to the challenge. A desire to prove himself, to acquire a mastery of this last and final stage of lumbering, entered his heart. It was a kind of service which money could not buy. It called for men who welcome hazard and feared neither suffering nor death.

While the other hands one after another said, "Excuse me, this ain't the time of year fer me to swim," Richard, the more firmly set upon becoming a pilot, answered, "Where others go, I can go." Clinton was less the heroic fool. "I'm not hankering for a coffin," he confessed with a laugh. "You are taking a whole lot of chance when you start out into that current. All the men who've been through it admit it's a savage job."

"That's the job I like," responded Richard.

Early the next day he joined the crew at work building the "cribs" which were to be driven through the falls to market down the river. His director in this work was Freeman Cooper, an older brother to his logging boss, a man of irascible temper, but altogether admirable in his strength and skill. Fearing neither man, beast, nor flood, his fame was already established, for he had been one of the first men to put a raft through this rapid. He was a great, shaggy man with a roaring voice, and all his men held him in fear touched with admiration.

During the afternoon while Richard was at work with a dull auger, boring holes in a plank, old Freeman Cooper came along. After watching him for a moment, he said, "You seem to be having a hard time."

"I am. This cussed auger won't cut."

"Throw it in the river," commanded Cooper.

Without a moment's hesitation, Richard flung the tool far out into the current.

Cooper uttered an oath of surprise and roared, "What did you do that for?"

Richard straightened up, looked him in the eyes, and replied, "Because you told me to. I'll throw you in if you say so."

Cooper returned the boy's glare for a moment in silence, then his mood changed. "I don't always mean just what I say—at the time."

"Then don't say it," retorted Richard. "Explanations *after* an order don't go with me. Better make 'em first."

This was so obviously just that Cooper's scowling face broke into a smile. "You're quick on the trigger, aren't you?" he remarked as he turned away, and a little later Richard heard him chuckling to himself.

When some thirty or more cribs of tightly bound lumber were ready to be launched, four of them were tied together, and from end to end Cooper stretched a rope, fastening it firmly at bow and stern. This was the "sucker line" of which Richard had heard so much during the winter.

"Now, boys," said the boss, "you and I, with some help, are to take this string of cribs through the falls. I will man the bow-oar while you and Clint grip the stern-oar. Keep your eyes open and remember everything you see. The water is high, and on some accounts that is an advantage, but it increases the danger at other points."

"Where you go, we can go," retorted Dick.

Notwithstanding this boast he approached the time of

casting off with an uncomfortable sense of his youth and inexperience. The water was still rising. The central river, a swirling, tossing mass of conflicting currents, was filled with logs, bark, and saw-dust, and as Cooper took his place in the bow he addressed his crew. "You see this rope? When I yell 'Grab a root!' every man-jack of you fall on that line and freeze to it. Hang on like death to a nigger. We'll go under, but stick to it as long as you can breathe. We usually come up, but you never can tell when. Generally speaking, your job is to stay with it as long as you can keep the water out of your lungs."

Richard thought Cooper was exaggerating in order to impress his men, but as the craft on which he stood swung into mid-stream, and began to move toward the first smoking fall, he perceived his danger; it could not be overstated. Boiling with fury, the torrent swept to its plunge with ever increasing speed, and the great steering-oar, which he and Clint wielded, seemed powerless to affect the cumbrous vessel's erratic course. They felt like insects on a chip as they whirled along.

"Grab a root!" yelled the pilot, and every man fell upon the sucker rope with instant obedience. Dick, with both hands clenched upon the line, saw Cooper crouched on the head-crib as it dropped into the abyss. An instant later he felt himself falling. Deep under the icy flood the raft plunged and there wallowed helplessly like some awkward animal, bewildered and lost. With mouth shut, the boy held his breath, waiting for the creature to rise, whilst his body, whipped to and fro by the savage flood, went limp as a rag in a wind.

Just as he seemed on the point of suffocating, he felt the wind upon his face and the sunshine upon his head. His lungs filled with air; his eyes cleared. He saw Clinton spitting water, and perceived that the cribs were still linked together with Cooper on his feet and in command. With one glance to make count of his men the grim pilot shouted, "*Man that oar!* To the *left!* Swing her to the left! Keep to that streak of clear water. If you don't, we're mashed. Everybody to the oar!"

For a few minutes the rafts enjoyed comparatively smooth sailing, but soon another swirling, ferocious stretch of water called for the coolest judgment of the pilot and the utmost skill of all hands. With rocks on either side, the cribs, tossing like bits of bark, leaped fall after fall, rapid after rapid, rocking and twisting and plunging, and when at last they made the final plunge into the upcurling waters of the eddy below the canyon and were safely moored to the bank, Richard and Clinton looked at each other with profound relief, too tired to do more than silently rejoice at their escape.

Cooper studied them with humorous eyes. "So much for so far," he observed quietly. "Now we'll go back and do it all over again."

This came as a shock to Dick as to all of the men. One of them said, "Not for me! Once is enough. I'm not taking any more chances like that, not today."

"Once is enough for me," remarked another. "I'd hate to get the habit."

"All right," said Cooper, "but you don't get paid for this trip. How about you, Dick?"

"God forgot to make the man I couldn't follow," answered Richard with boyish self-confidence.

"You're my kind," said Cooper. "How about you, Helmstock?"

"I'm with you till hell freezes over," retorted Clinton.

"Come on!" called the pilot and set off on a trot, along a muddy path leading up the river to the mill.

They were all wet to the skin, the wind keen and the trail rough, but they covered the three miles in less than an hour, and with two new men again swung into the flood

144

to take the same chances and win the same victory as before.

All that day they worked at this desperate task, taking their lives in their hands not ten times, but a hundred times. In addition to the risks involved, they covered thirty-three miles of trail in the teeth of a biting wind. It was a savage test of manhood, and Richard could hardly walk as he started back on the eleventh return from the eddy below the falls. Nevertheless he permitted no word of complaint to escape him, and, when on arrival at the mill, Cooper said, "Well, boys, shall we make another trip?" Richard retorted, "You're the doctor," and Clinton said, "We'll go as many times as you do." As Eastern men they felt it necessary to make a record.

These replies pleased Cooper, but he said, "I guess we'll wait till morning;" then with a jocular, yet warning note, he added, "but the breakfast-bell rings at five."

As they were about to turn into their beds that night, Clinton remarked, "We're in for it, my boy! But there's nothing to do but go on. However, I don't think I shall take up rafting as a steady job."

"I like it!" retorted Richard. "By the time I run this river two seasons I'll be able to map it. I'm going to qualify as a pilot."

The rising bell rang at five as Cooper had predicted, and Richard, stiff and sore, but resolute, was the first man down.

Cooper called out jovially, "Hello, Boston! Are you alive? I expected to hold an inquest over you."

Richard looked at him smilelessly. "It'll take a better man than you to run me off my legs."

His boss laughed. "You're about the grittiest little Downeaster I ever met. Where's your partner? You know what I'm going to do with you? I'm going to put you in charge of this last string of cribs. You've been through eleven times and if you've kept your eyes open you ought to know every rod of the rapids."

"I do," replied Dick. "I can map it for you."

In very truth he could. His keen eyes and tenacious memory had fixed in their proper relation every rock, every fall, every whirlpool, and he took his place at the bow of the raft with confidence. Cooper was with him but it was Dick's voice which sounded the warning cry, *"Grab a root!"* Under his direction the string of cribs came safely to harbour in the eddy below the falls, and Cooper's word of commendation was more important for the moment than his wages. The old pilot, who had no son, was sincerely disposed to promote him.

Here now the cribs, linked together into a big "fleet," started on down the broad current toward the next piece of mad water. At each fall or rapid, the raft was again separated into cribs and sent through the rough water, three or four sections at a time. This brought repeated observation of every dangerous spot and Richard attained in a single season an amazingly detailed and accurate picture of the stream.

For more than three weeks, he served apprentice to a boss whose herculean strength and stern power of endurance he adored. Wet all the time, watchful, tense, and for the most part silent, he stood at the pilot's side or toiled under his direction. Sometimes they ate a snack at mid-day, but more often they didn't, for Cooper had acquired the redman's indifference to hunger and cold. One night six inches of snow fell upon the raft, and they woke at dawn in a white storm. A few days later they passed under a cloud of passenger pigeons on their way to the north. Each night as they tied up they heard timber-wolves howling dolorously. For over a hundred miles the river was without settlement, and they lived like hunters, cooking their meals at a camp-fire on the raft or under the trees.

Running the River

After passing Whitney Rapids, Cooper's talk was all of "The Dells," which was the name of a canyon five miles long, through which the river rushed with sullen speed, confined in places by high walls fifty feet apart. At a certain turn, called "The Notched Rock," the current striking the perpendicular wall rebounded in swirling masses of foam.

"Just below The Notched Rock," Cooper explained, "is a sharp bend which forms a whirlpool. I've seen the swirls ten feet deep in that eddy. Last time I went through there my oars were all unshipped, and the raft covered waist-deep with water and fish. However, just below the Dells is a tavern where we can all get a square meal, and a drink. Set your minds on that and forget the whirlpool."

Neither of the boys cared much about the drink, but the thought of a well-cooked meal eaten at a table was especially alluring. They felt like soiled and ragged vagabonds which they were. Richard was eager to acquire a clean shirt and a new pair of boots.

Cooper admitted that the Dells intimidated him. "I don't mind rough water in the open, but this being shut in by walls three hundred feet high is another story. However, it's all a part of the excursion."

The beauty of the gorge caused the boys to forget their fear of it. The sculptured walls wrought into their sweeping curves and deep-red and green coloring, were most impressive.

For a part of the way the raft swept along smoothly, swiftly, silently. At times Cooper's warning voice was the only sound, the only light a narrow strip of sky above. The river, closed in by frowning cliffs, hurled itself from side to side as if enraged by its barriers. At such turns the pilot's utmost skill was tested. Every ounce of his weight was put upon the steering-oar. Again and again they were deluged by the spray flung back from the sheer cliffs, and after each of these inundations scores of fish went flopping about the decks. Half the way the men stood in water to their knees.

At last they came in sight of the dreaded Notched Rock and Cooper's voice rang out, "Peel your eyes, boys! Swing her to the left! Scrape that point of pines! Keep her to the left! *Left!* LEFT!"

In spite of every effort, the head-crib came so near to the rock that the rebounding waters up-ended it and flooded it. The men saw Cooper drop to his knees and seize the rope. They did the same, feeling the raft leap and tremble as if with fear, and so, just grazing the rock, half smothered and helpless, they swept on into quieter, safer waters below.

Cooper rose and studied his dripping crew. "Well done, lads! Now for the Whirlpool and after that dinner at the Dells House."

Thirty minutes later, numb to the knees, ragged, unshaven, and hungry as wolves, they walked up the path to the tavern, happy in the prospect of a square meal. The food was much the same as that of the camp, but it was served at a table with a cloth, and on porcelain plates. The cups and saucers were reminders of the civilized life which the boys had almost forgotten. Mrs. Dunham, who was a good housekeeper, made a brave show of the dishes she possessed, and her guests were grateful to her for the home quality she put into her cooking.

It was hard to go back to putting the other cribs through the canyon, but they did it, and the end of the second day saw them all safely moored, ready for passage to the quiet waters of the lower river.

Running the raft below the Dells was easier and from Grand Rapids down, occasional towns offered diversion, for Cooper made a point of tying up each night near one of these villages.

All of these settlements roared at times with rival rivermen clad in red flannel shirts, tall boots, and rough wool hats, moving from one saloon to another. Each crew kept together, fighting in loyalty to their band with the courage of Berserkers. Every night was battle night with them and there were no rules to check their Homeric contests. They fought with foot or fist, only the use of weapons was debarred.

Leaders like Cooper delighted in repulsing with their naked hands the attack of a throng of assailants. In these tournaments each man shouted the slogan of his camp, as knights of old announced allegiance to York or to Lancaster, and their hardened muscles, calloused knuckles, combined with a kind of blind fury of attack, made them more formidable than any savage.

It is probable that no more effective rough-and-tumble fighters ever lived. Twice their number of weaponless Sioux, Soudanese, or Pathans could not have withstood them, and when "Roaring Ralph," Sim Butler, or Freeborn Welsh, fearless as leopards and strong as bears, led their partisans ashore seeking those who boasted themselves "the best men on the river," timid folk did well to house. From bar to bar they marched, challenging crews or individual fighters who considered themselves invincible. "Here we are, Wildcats of Mosinee! Half panther and half wolf. Come on, you whelps!"

Richard and Clinton would gladly have remained spectators of these forays if they could have done so without losing caste, for to them such fighting was foolish. Nevertheless, their boss, who fought with the skill of a gladiator, aroused their admiration. He was one of the few rivermen who knew how to stand and strike, and when he discovered that Dick and Clinton had some knowledge of the pugilistic art, he insisted on their walking at his side. Twice they three met and defeated a crew of nearly a dozen men with only their hands as weapons. The calm unconcern of Cooper's face, the grace of his body, and his skill in defence so aroused Richard's fighting blood that he took an unexpected joy in these contests. That he was an able supporter of his chief was evident, for "Yankee Dick" left his mark in several of the towns.

All this was not exactly the training for a merchant or statesman, but it developed in this New England lad a resolute manhood. Improbable as it may seem, he refused to drink, and aside from an occasional bout in Cooper's company, he never fought. He was guilty of little that his mother would disapprove. She was never entirely out of his mind, and the memory of her dignity, her serenity, continued to be a restraining influence even in the most brutalizing of his experiences. Not even the worst of the river life could destroy or overlay the effects of her teaching. Momentarily forgetful of her admonitions as he sometimes was, he came back to them the instant the bloody mists of combat faded. In general he tried to keep clear of trouble, but once involved he felt it his duty to give such account of himself that in the future his adversaries would beware of him. In all his attempts at decency and sobriety he had Clinton's support.

As the fleet dropped below Sauk Prairie, the going became easier, but in order to avoid the many sand-bars and sharp bends, constant care was required. Cooper cheered them by saying, "Once we reach the Mississippi, all will be easy. We'll bring our rafts all into one big float, with our camp in the middle and drift along with nothing to do," he added with a grin.

It amused him (he was of that temperament) to announce as they issued from the Wisconsin into the Mississippi, that a tremendous thunder-storm was coming. The sky to the west was black as ink. Richard was appalled by the mystery of the mighty torrent into which they were sweeping, helpless and blind as puppies. For hours nothing could be seen save when the lightning lit the river with blinding light and even then he perceived only a waste of waters on the right hand and low, mysterious, wooded shores on the left. Huddled together in the centre of the raft the crew waited for orders which did not come.

Cooper acknowledged that nothing could be done but wait. "We must trust to luck," he said lightly. "If we keep in the current and don't meet a steamboat, we're all right. If we run aground, we're dished. However, its all in the game! No use cussin'."

Luck was on their side. They kept going, steadily, smoothly, and when the sky cleared they found themselves so near the Iowa bank that Richard volunteered to take a line ashore. By "snubbing" to a tree they brought the raft to a stand in quiet water and the men went to sleep with a sense of victory and relief. Their long three weeks' struggle with the Wisconsin river was at an end.

The warm sun next morning cured most of their miseries, and they set off down the Mississippi, whooping like sand-hill cranes. Thereafter the work was easy. "Care must be taken to keep the main channel and to clear the ripples and mud-banks," said Cooper. "Once we slip into a bayou there's no getting out. Watch for steamboats, their 'wash' throws the float into confusion."

To Richard this was an almost perfectly satisfying life. He was not only exploring a new world but doing it with ease and comparative safety. "This is what I came out West to see!" he exulted.

At Dubuque, Cooper sold his raft, but Richard, filled with a desire to know more of the lower river, hired himself to another man who was taking a raft of lath and shingles to St. Louis.

Clinton refused to go with him. "I've had enough of it for one season. I'm going home to get the water out of my bones."

Cooper, in taking leave of Richard, said, "Now, see here,

Dick, Ben and I want you next winter. In fact we want you this fall. We want you to take a man or two in August and go up beyond our last winter's camp and pick out a site for a new cutting. You come to Portage in late August and you'll find an outfit waiting for you."

Richard readily promised to do this, and entered upon his trip down the Mississippi with a joy which was beyond his power to express. The wide, untroubled stream, the glorious vistas opening at every turn, the long rafts, the occasional roaring steamboats, the mill towns with their howling saws, the fishermen in their canoes, all these sights and sounds made every mile a revelation of mystery and charm.

The owner of the raft, a citizen of Stevens' Point, named Plummer, was a Massachusetts man, and when he learned that Richard had lived in Boston, his manner changed from indifference to liking. He was a short man with a queer habit of sniffing while he talked, which made even his most positive statements seem hesitant. He was, however, both shrewd and fearless. He confessed that he had put every dollar he owned into this raft of lumber, and that unless he found a good market in St. Louis, he would be "busted."

He treated Richard like a son during the voyage, and on arrival took him to his own hotel, an honour and pleasure which puzzled the youth a little. To be sure it was not an expensive hotel, and he had not yet received his wages. "I wonder what his game is," the boy asked himself. He was soon to learn.

On the afternoon of the second day, as he was sitting in the barroom waiting for the supper bell, Plummer came along with a worn leather bag in his hand. Putting this on the floor, he took a seat near Dick and said, in a low voice, "Dick, I've sold my lumber, and I'm going to trust you as I would a brother. All my money is in that valise. It's in gold and it's going to be a care. I can't carry that bag around and watch it all the time. I must eat and I must sleep. I'll pay your fare back to Dubuque and regular wages besides if you'll help me guard that bag. I need help. Now, I like you and I'm willing to trust you."

Richard was flattered and being keen to earn money accepted this offer without a moment's hesitation.

Plummer then added, "It ain't wise to risk it all in one place. I've bought two belts and we'll each carry part of the money that way. It's mostly in twenty-dollar gold pieces."

Without realizing the seriousness of the obligation, Richard consented to share the burden, and in their room that night they each filled a belt with coin. At Plummer's suggestion Richard buckled his belt around his waist under his riverman's shirt.

"Now," warned Plummer, "we must wear these belts day and night. We can't take any chances, and we mustn't appear anxious about this old bag. I'll leave it around in a kind of careless way, but one of us must always have an eye on it. These Mississippi steamboats swarm with gamblers and thieves, and our lives wouldn't be worth a hoot if they knew what we had with us."

Richard wore the belt two days before the boat left St. Louis and for three days afterward. The boat got on a sand-bar and was delayed and the pain caused by the chafing of the belt made sleep almost impossible. Once when the boat was racing with another steamer, he said to Plummer, "What would happen to us if we had to take to the water with all this metal around our middles?"

His employer laughed. "The steamboat *mustn't* blow up. You and I can't afford it. We'd go down like a sack o' shot. However, if you're afraid——"

Again that stark trait which Cooper had discerned in the boy came to the surface. Being given a task, his vanity or pride or whatever you may call it held him to the end.

The fact that an obligation turned out to be unexpectedly painful or actually dangerous only put a keener light into his grey eyes and a sterner line into his lips. "I can stand it if you can," he replied.

His grit pleased Plummer. "I like you," he said. "You're a lad after my own heart. I want you in my crew next year."

They reached Dubuque safely, and Plummer as he paid the boy added an extra gold piece. "I'd like to have you go home with me. I'll find a job for you in one of the mills."

Richard shook his head. "I must get back to my folks," he said. "I want to help in the planting."

Thus ended his first year in the new land. In some ways it had been a disappointment. He had no claim to wide acres, no deed to a mine, but he had proven himself as hardy a woodman, as daring a pilot as any other youth of the region, and with a few gold pieces of his own in his belt, he set out on his way back toward his mother's cabin in the edge of the forest at Brownsville.

CHAPTER XIII

The Stir of Settlement

IT was a lovely summer day when Richard re-entered Brownsville, an afternoon very like the one in which he first saw the village, and in the sweetness of his return lay a drop of reminiscent bitterness. What a dolorous time that first month had been! However, he found his mother in better health than when he had last seen her, and the presence of his brother Addison added a further glow of unexpected pleasure. The Grahams were now united in the West as they had originally planned. For good or ill they had burned their bridges behind them.

The cabin, enlarged and comfortably furnished, partly by his father's skill and partly with money contributed by Addison, had taken on something of the homely charm which his mother had the faculty of creating wherever she was. As dwellings on the border went it was as good as the average.

That evening was a joyous one for Harriet, although the

conference between her sons was not entirely harmonious. Much as they liked being together, their ways of life were directly opposed. Addison was set on merchandising. "I'm going to settle in Galena, and if you'll come along I'll make you a partner in the store I expect to establish," he said.

"Not for Joe!" replied Dick bluntly. "I'm no trader, and besides I've promised to go back into the woods in August. I am to boss a camp this winter, and next spring I intend to run the Wisconsin River again as a pilot."

Addison smiled with quiet amusement. "Suit yourself, son. I believe in every man doing as he pleases so long as he doesn't interfere with the other fellow. One day of the kind of life you've been living on the river would finish my earthly career. However, if you like it, go back to it."

Although Mrs. Graham did not put her feelings into words, she was prouder of Richard's boyish red-shirt swagger than she was of Addison's quiet, capable dignity. She, too, declined moving to Galena. "We feel at home here now, and your father is busy and happy. I guess we'd better stay here for the present, and besides I want to remain near the McLanes."

Addison was a noticeable figure as he went about the village. Tall, black-bearded, and slender, he stood away in sharp contrast to Richard, whose rowdy shirt and sonorous voice proclaimed his experience on the river. Addison seemed almost elderly by contrast, but there was nothing elderly in his perception. His mind was quick and precise, and while he seemed a bit out of place in the West, he was readily adaptable and professed a liking for the region. "After all, Galena is only a short distance away. I'll be able to drive over and visit you now and again," he said to his mother.

Richard went at once to visit the McLanes, for next to his mother, old Hugh was the most venerated individual in his world, and David was, in a sense dearer than Addison.

The Stir of Settlement

He found Luke and David in the yard splitting logs, and he was able to appreciate more fully their display of skill and strength, after his winter in the woods.

They greeted him cordially and soon had him telling his experiences. He was an admirable story-teller and became especially dramatic as he recounted his first run of the falls. That was a "trick" they had seen but had never shared. Accustomed to taking chances in other ways, David agreed that to pilot a raft through such waters for a daily wage was more than humanly foolish. "Money don't mean as much to me as that," he added.

"Oh, it's not a matter of pay; it's fun," Richard protested.

"Your idea of fun isn't like mine," David retorted.

In truth there was in Richard a recklessness which these hardy woodsmen utterly lacked. He enjoyed the dangerous deed, whereas David was never foolhardy. At need he could and did do daring deeds, but he never sought danger.

Richard's regard for David had been deepened by absence. There was something unaccountably fine in this musician and hunter. His sobriety, his native dignity, and a singular sweetness of temper made him wholly admirable. By contrast with the men of the river and the camp he appeared gentle, notwithstanding his great form and his skill with the rifle. He never drank; he did not even use tobacco. He possessed a natural grace which his rough clothing could not conceal. All the McLanes loved games and hunting, but the life of the tavern had no charm for them.

David and William had spent part of the winter teaming to Milwaukee and part of it in hunting. Their spring's work was done and they were now getting out rails for fencing the new ground which they had planned to sow with winter wheat in the fall.

At their earnest invitation Richard stayed to supper and

was welcomed by Mrs. McLane and her husband with quiet but sincere regard, and by Deborah with a shower of questions.

Richard found Isabel greatly changed. She had put up her hair, as was the custom for girls of her age on the border, and the difference which it had made in her was surprising. She had taken on the ways of a woman, although her older sisters were still disposed to keep her in the background. Reticent, modest, feeling herself the Cinderella of the household, she took her rightful place only when she sang.

"Belle is singing in the choir this summer," Deborah informed Richard at once, for with all her domineering qualities she was proud of her sister's voice. "I think she's too young to sing in public, but it don't seem to do her voice any harm, so I suppose she'll go on with it. The new minister is to blame if anybody is; he got her into it."

In all the talk of the winter's happenings, the growth of the state, the new houses in the village, and the like gossip, there was almost no mention of politics. Entirely anti-slavery in sentiment, they manifested only a mild interest in the political controversy which was raging in Congress. Washington was very remote from the world of the McLanes. They remained unperturbed by elections and debates, and Robert Graham, who could deliver an oration at any moment on the necessity of abolishing slavery, was sorely irritated by this indifference. This tolerance of wrong by Hugh and his sons was akin to certain shiftless methods of farming which offended him. "If they spent less time fiddling and singing and hunting, they might find time to read the newspapers," he said to Richard.

Richard, while he did not share his father's mood, admitted that the McLanes were a queer lot, a law unto themselves. "It's no use arguing with them."

Mrs. Graham also defended them. "I like their easy-going ways. Their kindly humour and their music are blessings to the community."

This was a good deal for her to grant, for she had not only been brought up in a school of neatness and regularity, but her people, the Shaws, Roberts, and Hamlins, had been austere in life and keenly interested in government. Nevertheless she, a New England Puritan, understood this Celtic family better than most of their Western neighbours.

Of Hugh she said, "He is a poet. He likes Mr. Whittier's verses on slavery better than Daniel Webster's orations."

David was quite as much the poet as his father, though in a different way. Curiously fastidious in his tastes, he held the roisterers of the county at arm's length. Neither he nor William sympathized with coarse jesters, and yet few accused them of weakness. "I don't want another war with Dave McLane," one man said. "A blow from his fist is like a mule a-kicking," and as for William, no one ever ventured to arouse his anger.

David's violin was his dearest possession, and Luke "let the cat out of the bag" when he said, "The reason why Dave won't go into the woods or run the river is because he's afraid his precious fiddle would get wet and catch cold."

David only smiled at this. The tender care which he lavished on his violin would have been comical to his fellows had it not been for his skill in its use. They forgave him all his solicitude after they had heard the angel voices which his hand was able to evoke from that small and fragile instrument.

Every village of that day had its "fiddlers," even in the lumber-camps such performers were plentiful, but the most skilful of them were no more like David McLane than a blackbird is like a thrush. They mostly performed with a mad scramble of fingers and a fantastic jerking of elbows, whereas David, with long, graceful strokes, drew from his instrument tones of such sweetness that his hearers marvelled. How had he learned this method? Richard never knew, but he recognized the difference. None of the mechanical, scraping noises which accompanied the playing of other fiddlers could be heard when David's bow was in action, and although he good-naturedly played jigs and reels for dances, his best beloved "tunes" were strange and beautiful melodies. His adoration was Ole Bull. "Some day I'm going to hear him play," he vowed, and treasured every word which came to him descriptive of the great Norwegian's art. Some of the tunes he played were those Ole Bull was reported to use.

In spite of his wondrous gift, David took a hand in all the forms of work, now swinging a scythe against the grass, now the cradle against the wheat, and in these tasks Richard loved to have him for a leader. To rake and bind after him was considered a test of any man's quality. How he could play the violin after such labour was a mystery, but he often did it.

Richard had been lured into the West by vague dreams of sudden wealth, but every dollar thus far had been won by his strength, his skill, and his daring. He had no thought of earning money in any other way than with his hands. Face to face with reality, he planned to return to the woods in August and to apply his earnings as lumberman and pilot to the purchase of a plot of land—a natural and logical design for him. Others might trade or practise law, but his way of life was in the open air. Meanwhile he hired out to Arnold Robey whose farm was larger than before.

Day by day he witnessed the stir of settlement. Covered wagons came by in procession. Farms were being cleared. Villages were developing into towns. The tap of the hammer, the ring of the saw, the clack of the axe could

The Stir of Settlement

be heard at every turning of the road, and to the grey-eyed
boy these sounds were music. He rejoiced in the buoyant
Western atmosphere. He had no regrets, not even when
he recalled the Howard Athenæum and the voices of Booth
and Forrest. He was glad of his Boston experience, but no
thought of going back ever entered his mind. His eyes
were fixed on the new, the undiscovered. He listened with
joy to every tale of the "West" which he was so eager to
explore.

As autumn came on, he urged David to accompany him
into the woods. "Cooper has asked me to take a man or
two and go up the creek a few miles above last year's
camp and locate a new one. He wants me to go in early
enough to cut hay for the teams and to cruise for pine.
Clint has another job and can't go in so early. I want you.
Come along."

David was sorely tempted to do this, for he loved the
wilderness. His rifle was almost as dear to him as his
violin, and this enterprise appealed to him. At last he
agreed to go.

In putting this important task into the hands of a boy,
Freeman Cooper had shown a confidence in Richard which
was not entirely due to friendship. He had fully tested
the boy's resolute spirit.

Acquiring pine land in the fifties was a very simple business. It often consisted in buying a few acres in the midst
of a noble government forest and thereafter ignoring boun-
daries. "Uncle Sam is rich enough to give us all a farm"
was taken to mean a tract of pine land. The supply of
pine trees seemed inexhaustible. Clearing the land was a
virtue. Some operators did indeed take the trouble to
acquire a temporary title to coveted sites, but others went
calmly in on the unsurveyed land and helped themselves.
Legal and illegal, they all left the ground a tangled mass
of tree-tops which, in later years, became fuel for vast and

destructive forest fires. Economy was an unknown virtue among these devastators.

Too young to question "Cooper & Cooper's" rights to the land or their methods of cutting, Richard, accompanied by David, took his way back to Mosinee.

CHAPTER XIV

As Forest Vedettes

R ICHARD returned to the village of Mosinee with a fine sense of familiarity with the scenery and the life of the mills. Outfitting at the store, he bought a handsome Chippewa canoe and filled it with his supplies. It was not far from his twenty-first birthday when he started, with David for companion, gay with the spirit of adventure, to explore the forest. David as the more experienced hunter carried the rifle while Richard plied the paddle.

David, who had never before stepped into a canoe, came near to overturning it at the outset, but his awkwardness soon wore away and before long he was able to lend a hand as they pushed against the current, stopping now and again to explore a creek or overlook a meadow. Richard kept moving until, late in the afternoon, a rain set in. He then went into camp on a bank under a high balsam fir whose broad, drooping branches gave almost perfect protection from the rain. Not a drop of water or a flake of snow had ever fallen there. The ground was as dry as ashes.

The storm added charm to their fire-lit retreat and deepened their sense of obligation to the great green tent above them, and the fact that they were now actual pathfinders in advance of the northernmost line of pioneers, and that only redmen and occasional trappers had ever visited this ground, filled their hearts with boyish satisfaction.

David, strange combination of rifleman and minstrel, poet and trailer, loved the smells, the lights, the sounds of the forest even more keenly than Richard. As darkness fell he sat before the fire with musing face, his dark eyes glowing with inarticulate emotion. "I never got so deep into the wild country before," he admitted. "I like it. I'd like to go on and on to the north."

They slept uneasily that first night and were up and astir at dawn. After a leisurely breakfast, they entered upon another long delicious day of paddling and exploring, inspecting and estimating. At last, after several days of inspection, Richard decided on a permanent camp. It was a level bank in the heart of a noble forest of pine, and on the bank of a river not far from a small, round meadow in which the rank grass was standing breast-high and still green enough for fodder.

"We can't build a cabin till the hay is cut," he explained to David, and so they sharpened their scythes and set to work cutting the rank, wiry grass. Day after day they toiled, their blades snarling against the stiff stems, and the cheerful clink of their whetstones resounding in the silent halls of the forest. At night as they lay in their blankets, they talked of the wilderness, and Richard developed his plan for exploring the land beyond the Mississippi. "I shall never be satisfied till I have seen what the prairies are like," he declared.

David readily agreed to go with him on this great adventure. "June would be the best for me," he said.

As Forest Vedettes

When the hay was all in rain-proof piles, they started work on a cabin, and the click-clock of their axes was like the ticking of a giant timepiece, warning of winter. What endurance, what skill they had! To see David approach a tree, glance at its top, measure its trunk, and swing his keen blade against it was to witness the graceful, powerful action of a master woodsman. Although Richard had neither David's reach of arm nor breadth of shoulder, he could notch a corner of a rising cabin, or hew to a line on a beam as well or better, and his endurance was greater, for he would not suffer defeat.

They both felt the need of a roof, not merely because of the increasing chill of the nights, but because the voices of wolves, panthers, and bears broke in upon their sleep, and Richard, with no great fear of them, was excited by them. They kept him awake. The thought of sleeping within doors was agreeable to them both, and even before completing the roof they moved inside the sheltering walls with a sense of relief. The next day they contrived a door and laid part of the roof.

"Our next duty," Richard said, "is to blaze a trail out to the old camp and bring in a yoke of oxen to haul our hay."

The trail, as they worked it out, was only twenty miles in length, but quite impassable for wagons by reason of its muddy spots and felled timber. "Supplies must wait till the ground freezes," said Richard.

No one was at the old camp but a caretaker who told them that Mosinee, fifteen miles farther south, had only just begun to feel the returning life of the loggers. "Everybody is waiting for snow," he explained.

In all these weeks Richard and David had seen no other white man, and they enjoyed this evening at the old camp, and were rather glad to get a change of cooking.

One evening, shortly after their return to their cabin,

and while they were eating their supper, Richard, who was facing the window, suddenly called out, "Look there!"

David turned and saw in the window, like a picture in a frame, the furry head, alert ears, and pointed muzzle of a bear looking in upon them.

As David raised his hand toward his rifle on the wall behind him, the animal vanished so silently and swiftly that it was difficult to imagine that he had ever been there.

While David seized his rifle, Richard pulled the door open. A path of light ran toward the forest, and at the end of it a huge, rounded shadow could be seen shambling swiftly into cover.

David fired, and like an echo of his shot came the report from another gun, and a moment later the shout of a man in the darkness.

"Y'gorry, we've got 'im! Bring a lantern."

Dick took the lantern and they went to meet the hunter whose words kept pouring forth as he approached. "We hit him but he vamoosed. I wish we had ol' Zip here. He'd have that feller by the heels in no time. I'm afraid he ain't crippled as much as I thought he was, but we may overtake him."

In the light of the lantern the stranger developed into a middle-aged man with a long beard, a tall, uncouth figure of serious mien.

"I didn't dast to fire while he was lookin' in your winder, and when he got down I couldn't see 'im till you opened the door," he explained. "All the same, I teched him."

With Richard carrying the lantern, they all went to the spot where the bear was last seen, but he was gone and to trail him without a dog was impossible.

"If I had my dog we'd tree him in fifteen minutes," said the stranger. "As it is we might as well give him up for tonight. He'll keep till morning."

"We were just eating supper. Better come in and take a snack," suggested David.

"Don't care if I do," the hunter replied in the same unemotional drone. "I'm kindo sick of my own cooking. I didn't know you men were here until today. I just happened to make camp up the crick a couple of miles—I'm on my way to Mosinee—and seein' your smoke I thought I'd come down and make you a neighbourly call. I'm kind o' hungry for news."

"By the way," Richard began as he set a couple of buckwheat cakes before him, "what's your name when you're at home?"

"Tom Walsh. Otherwise Mosinee Tom."

"I heard of you last year. You're a trapper."

"That's me. As I was saying', I saw yer smoke and, thinks I, I'll just drop down and see whose camp that is. So I laid a few logs on my fire and I says to my dog, 'Now, Zip, ol' boy,' I says, 'you better hug this blaze pretty close or the wolves'll pinch ye, an' so I left him in charge of things an' come down."

"I'm glad you did," replied David. "I've been feeling kindo lonesome myself these last few days."

"Lonesome!" The old fellow laughed. "W'y, young man, I don't know what lonesome means. I tramp from here to Lake Superior, an' never see a human bein' from one month's end to another. Oh, of course, I like to drop in on a white man, an' have a little confab once in a while— but that ain't gettin' lonesome."

"Oh, isn't it?" retorted Richard ironically. "Well, that's the way I feel when I'm lonesome. How's that for a mouthful?" he said as he slid another ten-inch cake into the stranger's plate.

"Jest my size," declared the trapper. Cutting it into quarters, he rolled each piece up like a quilt and poked it into his mouth as if it were a mere crumb.

"Look here," exclaimed Dick, "you must be holler clean to your boot-heels."

"I am," he replied, "or rather I was. I'm fillin' up a little."

When he was "chock-a-block," as he expressed it, he lighted his pipe and began to talk in an easy, unhesitating, and deeply interesting fashion of his life in the forest. He knew the wilderness as the red man knew it, by having traced its paths. He could map all its rivers and lakes and he did so on the cabin floor. "It's all wild from here on, but the lumbermen are crawlin' up the Black and Chippewa rivers."

In reply to a remark of David's, he said, "A good many yarns about bears and wolves are all bosh. Bears an' painters are mostly jest as glad to git out of your way as you are glad to git out o' their way. A sow will turn on a man when her young are hurt, an' so will a bear. A wild-cat will fight when you corner 'im. Most any crittur will fight in a trap, but with space to run away in, it's nachural for all wild critturs to scatter the minute they see a man. They jest nachurally *puck-achee* when they smell a gun, but there's always a bad one amongst 'em jest like some men—individuals achin' for a fight. Most people think a bear is a bear or a wolf is a wolf, but they differ individually jest like dogs. Some are timid. some are shy, and some just nachurally vicious."

"Ever had a tussle with a bear?"

"Oh, yes, lots of times. They sometimes turn on me when I hurt 'em. Back him into a corner and a painter'll fight fer dear life jest like a man will."

"How about wolves?" asked Dick, who had grown up on wolf stories of the Maine forests.

The old man drew several whiffs of his pipe before he answered. "Wolves up here are different from them that range near settlements. They're jest nachurally vicious—

168

there ain't no two ways about that. You see they ain't afraid of a man and they've got a lot of judgment. They don't tackle anything they can't whip and they don't walk into traps. They'll eat a man up when they git him down, but they don't take poor chances. They don't bluster, but they git their meal, you bet."

As he talked on steadily, his pipe in his mouth and his hands on his knees, his voice took on a tone which was akin to the hum of the winds in the pines, and David, sensing its unconscious melancholy, stirred up the fire to lighten the gloom. To him the trapper was the spirit of the sad, solitary spaces.

At last the old man rose, and knocked the ashes out of his pipe.

"Yes, I've been chawed by bears an' clawed by cata-mounts, an' I've had a buck deer tramplin' me into the snow, but I've never had a wolf's tooth into me—yet. When I do, I'm gone. They don't lay hold till they know their advantage. A bear'll git blind, crazy mad, an' go in where he's plumb sure to suffer, but your wolf, he knows better than to go into a losing business. If he miscalculates, he jest limps off into the woods an' swears vengeance."

David related a story of how his father was once treed in Oxford County by wolves, and Long Tom listened with an occasional corroborative nod.

"That's jest it! They're sharks. Seems as if they can smell a sick or a wounded man ten miles. A shark is a wolf in the water. A wolf is a shark in the woods. If they ever set foot on me I'll know my time has come to die."

"I should think you'd keep out of their way if you're afraid of them," said Richard.

The old man's face darkened. "See here, boy, do you mean that?" He turned. "I guess it's time for me to go."

Richard apologized. "Sit down, sit down! I didn't mean to stir you up. You spoke as if you did kind of dread 'em and so I——"

"I do dread 'em sometimes," the hunter confessed, "but I ain't afeard of 'em. I know their ways. They won't come into a camp so long as it has a fire. I build a fire in front of my little shed, lay my rifle handy at my feet, and with Zip beside me I sleep sound's a baby in a cradle. If the fire gits low, Zip growls and I git up and throw more wood on the embers an' go to sleep again. But they're after me, I know that, I've killed so many of 'em. Some day I'll make a mistake, an' they'll pile in on top o' me, an' that'll be the end of ol' Tom Walsh—jest a little pile of clean-picked bones. I've passed such piles on my travels. Waal, I guess I'll pull out."

"Better stay all night."

"Oh, no, I mustn't think o' that. The wolves would clean out Zip an' my whole camp afore daylight. Hark!" He lifted his hand. "They're on the rampage tonight. They always are before a storm." Afar off, blent with the rising snarl of the wind in the pines, the boys could hear the distant clamour of a pack on the heels of a flying deer. The old man grasped his rifle. "Good night, boys. I must git back to camp. I've stayed too long."

"Hadn't one of us better go with you?" asked David.

"Oh, no, I'm all right. I'm not worryin' about myself—it's my dog."

"Come and see us again. Our door is always open. Good luck."

"Same to you," answered the old man with absent-minded politeness, and a moment later his form was lost in the dense shadow of the pines.

Richard turned his face toward the grey skies. Fine flakes of snow were beginning to fall, sifting down through the tops of the tall trees. Wolves were astir in the swamps and a wildcat across the river was growling as he scrambled along the cliff.

From the door of the shanty, David said, "I don't want old Tom's quarters tonight."

"Neither do I!" Richard replied, "but I wish I knew the country as he does."

He apprehended vaguely that in this uncouth, illiterate wanderer he was in touch with the true trail-maker, the advance surveyor of the new lands, the vedette of civilization's army.

He was in the midst of a dream in which a man sinking in the snow was crying "Help! Help!" when he awoke to realities. For a few moments he could not tell whether he was still dreaming or not. As he sat up in his bunk and looked about him to convince himself of his dream, he heard again, faint and far-off, a definite appeal for help.

"For God's sake open the door!"

Springing to the door he opened it, just as the hunter reached the little clearing. He was running heavily, carrying his dog in his arms, while a few yards behind him, their red tongues lolling, their eyes shining with phosphorescent fury, came a dozen wolves, so savage, so determined, that as the fugitive crossed the threshold Richard shut the door almost in their faces.

Wild with wrath and remorse, the old trapper laid his wounded dog upon the floor and shouted, "Gi' me your gun! I'll kill 'em all!"

Richard opened the door and the trapper fired. One of the beasts fell and the others fled. "Load it for me," he said to David. "I can't do it, I'm all broken up. I stayed away too long. The fire burned down. They sprung in on my dog. I got there just in time. I killed one and they scattered, but only for a minute. They didn't give me time to load. They turned on me. I had to club 'em with my rifle. The dog couldn't walk and I carried him all the way down the river. When I got near your cabin I dropped my gun and streaked it for your door."

He wept as he examined his dog's wounds. "To think I'd play him such a trick as that! And him trustin' in me all the time. 'Ol' Tom'll be back soon, an' then you'll git out of here,' he says. And all the time I was sittin' here smokin' an' havin' a good time. It's uncivilized to treat a dog the way I treated him. Why, that dog has travelled with me more'n six years! He's been my only company. I don't know how I'd git along without him."

David brought water and washed the dog's wounds. "He ain't dead yet by a long shot," he said to the old man. "His legs are badly chewed up, but he don't seem to be much injured around the throat. He'll be all right in a week or two."

"If he does git well, I swear to you right now I'll never take him into the woods again. I'm gittin' too fergetful. I don't mind about myself, but I don't think it's fair to take a dog into a tight corner and then go off and leave him."

The dog was alive the next morning, and David went with old Tom to find his rifle and to recover what the wolves had left of his camp.

In two days' time the dog was able to travel on three legs, and the hermit set out for the nearest doctor. The boys never saw him again, but he remained ineffaceably in their minds as a typical, elemental spirit of the solitudes into which they had been thrust.

CHAPTER XV

Wolves on the Trail

IN the days which followed this dramatic event, David often discussed the tales in which Long Tom had given such vivid conception of the illimitable Northern wilderness, a wilderness which even Richard admitted could never be cleared of its pines and planted.

"What does it matter whether Cooper logs on government land or his own?" David bantered. "There's enough timber here to house the world for a hundred years."

"It matters a lot," Richard retorted. "If this timber belongs to Uncle Sam it don't belong to Cooper. Unless he buys his lumber he's stealing it. How can Uncle Sam give us all a farm if a few men grab all the land in sight?"

The close association of these weeks had increased Richard's love for David. He was constantly disclosing new moods and strange fancies. He also had his hours of sober musing in which he manifested a reticence so deep, so stubborn that he could hardly be led to answer a question. At such time he went about his work with mechanical action, with dreaming, introspective eyes.

"What are you mooning about?" Richard asked one day, and David said, "I was thinking of Isabel. She should be schooled. I wish I could send her East to study music. She has the making of a great singer."

In other moods he questioned Richard about the players, the singers he had heard in Boston. "I don't see what brought you out here. If I'd had your chance to live in Boston, I'd have stuck there till I'd made something of myself. What chance is there for me out here? A chance to grub and hoe, that's all. And there's Belle. That girl has a voice that would make her famous in a city, but what's the good of it in Brownsville? She can sing in the choir, and in a year or two she'll marry some farmer or clerk and that'll be the end of her. Or take my case. I've never heard a real violinist in my life. I didn't know how to draw my bow till the town drunkard, Jens Peterson, showed me how Ole Bull does it. I got some of my best tunes from him, but that's all the instruction I've ever had. What's the good of trying to be a violinist out here where jig fiddling is all the people want—or will pay for?"

This depression was only a passing cloud, for David was hunter as well as musician. Richard felt obscurely in his case a waste of genius, but what was to be done? "I don't know a thing about music, Dave, but so far as I can tell, you play as well as any of the men I heard in Boston. However, what's the use of dwelling on that now? We're out in the pine woods with a lot of hard work to be done. That hay has got to be hauled in and the stable made ready for the teams. We've no time to be dreaming of music in Boston or anywhere else."

David admitted the truth of this but claimed the right to dream. "Some day I'm going to hear Ole Bull if I have to walk to Milwaukee."

Wolves on the Trail

Hardly had they finished chinking the walls of their cabin when David fell ill; mysteriously, violently ill. "Ptomaine poisoning" it would now be called. All that night and the following day he suffered so acutely that Richard was in an agony of fear as well as of pity. Nothing that he could do gave relief. The young giant's strength melted away swiftly. In a few hours he was delirious with pain.

He was like an animal in its death struggle, the sweat of his agony standing out upon his face, and Richard, torn between an impulse to run for help and a terror lest the sick man should die in his absence, was in dismay. The wilderness which they had both loved had suddenly become a pitiless foe.

All the afternoon he debated his problem, his perplexities sharpened by the voices of the wolves. Their signals, which had hitherto been merely interesting, now took on a menace which made his blood run cold. He recalled old Tom's assertion of their uncanny power of scent. Were they already possessed of a knowledge of the sick man's weakness, and assembling for a siege? It appeared so to Richard.

Accustomed to them as he now was, their approach at this time filled him with a sense of his own weakness such as he had never acknowledged before. "I can't leave David alone, and yet—it must be done. I can't stand here and see him die."

That David was growing weaker mentally as well as physically was evident. He had ceased to reply to questions and Richard's fear became a panic. At last, leaning over him, he said, "Dave, I'm going for help. I must leave you for a while. Do you understand? I'm going for a doctor. I won't be gone long. I'll put food and water here beside your bunk and I'll fix a prop against the door so that no animal can get in. I'll bring help as quick as God'll let me. I hate to go, but there's no other way. You see that, don't you, Dave?"

David looked up with a pitiful, slow stare, and the contrast between that look, the expression of a bewildered, suffering animal, and the alert, joyous companion he had been, very nearly broke Richard's heart. For just a moment it seemed that all was over. "He's past help. He'll die before I can reach the camp," but David roused himself to whisper weakly, "Go on. I know; I'll be here, waiting."

Richard's resolute soul awoke to action. Cutting a pole of just the right length to act as a brace against the door which opened inward, he set a pail of water within David's reach, placed the prop in position, and went out, closing the door behind him. As the pole fell into position against the lower cleat, he tried the door sharply, to make sure that it could not be opened by any outside pressure, then turned and set off down the trail, every faculty alert, every muscle tense for the race with death, which he knew this desperate errand to be.

His heart contracted and an ache came into his throat as he thought of that glorious young form, lying there, helpless and alone with a remorseless enemy assembling around his shelter. "There is only one thing to be done— to go on!"

The trail was rough and not easy to follow, even in daylight, but he ran steadily on, rising and falling with banks and bogs, now wading the water of the streams, now stumbling over roots, rejoicing when, beneath the balsam branches, his path was dry and firm. For the most part he trotted, too wise to wear himself out with undue speed. "Four miles an hour will bring me to last year's tote road before the moon sets. From there it is only three miles to camp. I ought to get in by midnight."

His only weapon was a bowie-knife (he could not burden himself with a rifle), and his clothing consisted of a blue woollen shirt, thick grey trousers, and a pair of moose-hide moccasins, admirable outfit for a runner.

At times he stumbled over boulders and leaped fallen tree-trunks, with nothing to guide him but the general lay of the land. He blamed himself for not having left more "blazes" on the trees, but he lost no time in seeking for signs. If he lost the trail, he kept going, trusting to that sense of direction which he had hitherto found so dependable, a sense which he could not question now. "It must not fail me now."

As the night deepened he had a sense of pursuit, of being followed, and at last caught sight of his pursuer, a great grey wolf, whose alert ears and waving tail so resembled those of an amiable dog that he spoke to it without fear, but later as he rose from drinking at a little stream and found the silent beast almost within springing distance, he changed his estimate. Thereafter he took a more serious view of the character of his pursuer.

He had not been afraid of wolves so long as he could see, but at this moment, on the edge of a dark and tangled swamp, he felt less confident. A long-drawn, mournful howl arose, a sound he knew. It was the gathering-call of the pack. This signal was answered by a slightly different, modulated yelp from the front, followed a little later by another from the right. He was no longer followed, he was beset.

I am aware that in these later days, stories of attack on the part of wolves are somewhat discredited, but the reader must remember that wolves in the upper Wisconsin valley seventy years ago knew nothing of fire-arms and owned little fear of humankind. They were not the solitary skulkers they afterward became. As rulers in a realm of their own, they were freebooters to whom man was only a desirable two-legged quarry. The band assembling to test Richard's quality was composed of warriors whose methods of attack had the arrogance of those to whom defeat was unknown.

Without pausing to make test of their temper, Richard simply accelerated his pace, recalling (he could not help recalling) the many tales he had heard or read of relentless beleaguerment by similar bands, but the conviction that they were sniffing at the walls and pawing at the door behind which poor David lay, steeled his muscles and put a desperate courage into his heart. He ran on silently, sprawling now and again over a root or rock, his long knife ready for use in case of need.

"The other camp should be near," he felt, but the night had grown very dark and he was no longer able to distinguish the blazes on the trail. He kept close to the stream, feeling his way through the low ground as best he could. "I must play safe," he said.

He was beginning to lose faith in his course and to wonder if his pursuers would force him to climb a tree and wait for dawn, when he caught the smell of freshly made pine chips. He knew his position. He had struck the end of the cutting. Ten minutes later he was battering upon the door of the bunk-house of last year's camp.

There is always one man in a crew who prides himself on knowing something of medicine, and the man who opened the door for Richard was of this type. He was a small, alert, brown-bearded man whom Richard knew as "Mechanic Falls," for the reason that he was always talking of his native town, but his real name was Bailey. Quick to perceive distress, he drew the exhausted youth in and put him in a chair before the fire.

"What's the matter?" he demanded. "What has happened?"

Almost unable to speak, Richard explained: "My partner is sick. Send some one for a doctor. Dave must have help. You must go back with me at once."

"Why, man, you can't go back tonight. It means another twenty-mile run," exclaimed Bailey.

"It's got to be done. He mustn't die up there alone."

Rousing one of his crew, Bailey ordered him to go for the doctor, and while he collected his medicines he drew from Richard a detailed story of the case. In less than half an hour they started on the return journey, Richard leading the way.

They made but slow progress at first, for Bailey was not a rapid walker, but as the dawn came on they made better speed and three hours later they came in sight of the cabin.

"They haven't got in!" exulted Richard, indicating three of the sinister brutes sitting like sentinels at the edge of the clearing. At his shout, feeble as it was, they disappeared.

On nearing the door he called out, "Here I am, Dave! I've brought help," but no sound came from within.

He tried the door, but the bar which he had so carefully adjusted refused to budge, and the heavy slabs could not be broken down. He was forced to mount to the roof and tear a hole in the bark before he could even catch a glimpse of the sick man. As he dropped to the floor, David turned a wan face and whispered, "I'm not dead yet. I think— I'm better."

He was indeed a long way from being dead, for when Bailey stooped over him and asked, "How are you?" he answered, "Out of pain, but weak."

With a boyish faith in the older man's skill, Richard rolled into his blankets and went to sleep, a sleep of exhaustion so deep that it lasted till late in the afternoon.

When he awoke he found David lying quietly on his bunk, with Bailey sitting beside him.

"Hello, Dave," called Dick. "How are you?"

With cheerful inflection, David replied, "Helpless as a kitten but on the way back."

The doctor from Mosinee did not arrive till two days

later. He was a quaint old sawbones, this man. When wanted, he was usually in some saloon, singing to the barkeeper, for after three drinks of whisky he fancied himself a singer, but there was something fine in him for all that. He never failed of response to a call. Undaunted by trail or storm, he went when called with uncomplaining devotion.

He complimented Bailey on his treatment. "Nothing for me to do," he said. "Feed the man sparingly and keep him warm."

He ate heartily of Richard's cakes and venison and rode away gaily.

For two weeks, while David came back to health, Richard continued to hold his outpost on the northern borderline. The snows came, and rabbits, squirrels, quail, partridge, inquisitive bears, and marauding cats played or hunted or fought according to their kind, leaving the record of their deeds on the white pages of the meadow. The sound of the axe seemed not to alarm but to attract these forest folk.

Those two final weeks were the most glorious part of his second autumn in the woods, for they brought an education in woodcraft as well as a deeper understanding of his companion. He again asked David to join him in the winter's work, but the musician replied, "No, I must go back to my team and my fiddle."

After David left for home, Richard entered upon his duties as boss of the new camp, and much of the poetry and mystery of the forest vanished. It became a field of labour, a place of accounting, a test of endurance.

This winter was a repetition in all essentials of the first one, except that Richard was a year older and in command. Young as he was, he brought his men through the winter's work without accident, and when the logs began to run, Cooper again claimed him. For three weeks he ran rafts through the falls at a salary of five dollars per day which was considered high pay.

It is incredible, but it is recorded that he put two hundred cribs of lumber through the rapids successfully. He ran the falls from ten to fifteen times each day, "gigging back" from thirty to forty-five miles. At the end of April he was so weak and benumbed that he could scarcely feel the ground with his feet, and his boss interfered. "See here! You take a raft down the river and rest up. You'll be crippled for life if you keep on."

He took command of a raft and started southward. Coming after a month of incessant danger and ferocious labour on Big Bull Rapids, the work on the lower river seemed easy, and, after passing the Dells, the weather was glorious. During long stretches he could sit in the sun and watch the wild geese pushing their flight into the north or the crane, bugling as he swung in vast circles against the clouds. The singing of birds and the blossoming meadows brought a realization of spring-time which his month in the roaring tumult of the rapids had prevented.

In every town he noted signs of the thickening flood of settlers. New buildings had arisen, others were under construction. Ploughing and seeding were going on along the bottom lands, and something in this stir of settlement, this improvement of farm and village, made him rejoice. It brought back some part of the feeling with which he had left Boston.

Like the youth in the city who from his garret hears the roar of vast enterprises and imaginatively shares them, so this young Yankee, working for wages on a raft, imagined himself a part of the upbuilding of a great state, and was happy in the belief. In all this he was typical of his generation.

CHAPTER XVI

Pastures New

CONCERNING the life of Richard Graham between the year 1852 and the year 1856 I have only scattered and rather vague report. That he continued his labours as a woodsman during the winter months and acted as pilot on the Wisconsin River during the spring and summer, I am certain, but beyond that all is conjecture. I should like to assign to him deeds profitable to himself and honourable to the state but I can not do so. That he dared and suffered and conquered in a physical sense I have no doubt, but that he continued in his boyish mood of exalted purpose I find no trace. Apparently he had forgotten or abandoned his desire for a farm, although he sent money regularly to his father to pay for the cabin in Brownsville.

All around him during these four years, towns were building, railways extending and mills rising, but he remained "Yankee Dick the Pilot." He must have visited the McLanes during this period but I find no record of it.

Pastures New

I can not say that he continued to keep Isabel and David in mind—but I like to imagine that he had asked Isabel to wait for him. I do not know this to be the fact, and I can not say why he waited for her. So far as I am aware no other woman intervened. As he neared twenty-six he must have calculated that Isabel was almost sixteen and sixteen was a marriageable age in those primitive communities. At any rate he reported to his father and mother in that year.

His life during this period is heroic according as one judges it. His endurance, his courage, his skill remain and are incredible. As foreman of a camp, he toiled with an intensity which inspired even the laggards. He was a leader (in a physical sense) and not a driver of others. He shirked nothing. Foolishly loyal to his job, he was the first of his crew to roll from his bunk in the morning, and his call to action never failed of a cheerful power. He had a tuneless chant which he usually roared all on one note, whose final words were, "ALL UP! ALL UP! DAYLIGHT DOWN THE CREEK!"

He never said, "Go, boys"; it was always, "Come, boys." He shared every hardship and led the way into every danger—but always as a hired man, an agent of some other man or firm. He had no confidence in himself as a business man apparently, for there is no record of his attempts at rafting for himself.

It was not the extra pay which kept him a pilot on the rapids; it was his love of leadership. The admiration, the applause which accompanied his victorious contests with rock and whirlpool were honey-sweet tributes to him. To be known as Yankee Dick, the man who feared nothing, who took every risk and yet eluded disaster—this was his satisfaction—and a poor satisfaction it was to his mother to whom he occasionally wrote, and to Addison whom he once visited on his way down the river.

In all this time he was never sick nor seriously disabled. Day by day, each April he ran the long falls and trotted back over the trail, often forty-five miles between sun and sun, until at the end of the season (when he took charge of a raft for the lower river) his legs were heavy as lead and his body a mass of wiry muscle.

His pay, as wages went in those days, was high, and yet I do not find that he "laid up" any considerable sum. I assume that he helped pay for the little farm, and that he spent his summers in Brownsville is certain, for Isabel's power over him grew with the years. To be with her must have been his chiefest joy, for in her he found a most inspiring listener. Her absorbed interest drew from him many a valorous and fearsome tale, for he had the faculty of making a listener share acutely his adventures. Isabel often shivered with terror as she listened to his illogical enterprises. Undoubtedly he heightened his narratives in certain spots, but no one, not even an Irish minstrel, could overstate the reckless daring of his exploits.

In the summer of 1855 he took charge of a new and wonderful saw in a Mosinee mill, a job which prevented him from visiting Brownsville for over a year. He accepted this position because it brought good pay. With the vision of a home now definitely in his mind, a home in which Isabel was a delightful figure, every dollar counted. His life, appalling in its daring and foolish in its bravado, was beginning to seem so even to him. In becoming boss of a saw, he was planning to escape from the river. He had come to see that with all his skill, his suffering, his risk, he was earning less than a carpenter. Whatever the cause of this shift of plan may have been, it kept him from seeing his mother and Isabel that year.

He was a poor correspondent. His hand, so bold, so sweeping, so capable with the cant-hook, was a ridiculously feeble and hesitant member when applied to the pen.

Pastures New

Ready of speech, dramatic of gesture, and fertile of invention when telling a tale, he became a cramped, embarrassed schoolboy when he bent his back above a sheet of paper.

I do not know that he felt to the full the piteous contrast between his bold, dramatic self and the feeble scrawl which was the best he could achieve on paper, but I think he did, and why he did not apply his stern resolution to the task of educating his hand in writing remains a mystery. He could and did read the newspapers, but as a man of action he hated the quiescence necessary to study. He wanted education to meet him on the trail, not in a cell.

Meanwhile Clinton had ceased to be the hired man. As a part owner of a saw-mill in Dubuque and of a lumber-camp on the Black River, he repeatedly urged Richard to join him. "I'll make you boss of my camp, or I'll give you a place in my mill," he wrote, but Richard stubbornly refused to accept these offers. They touched his vanity. He could not accept "favours" even from Clinton. He grimly kept to his own path.

That he thought often of Isabel, certain quaintly capitalized faded notes may testify, but they express little of his feelings save by indirection.

Without knowing anything at all about musical matters, he agreed with David that Isabel had a wonderful voice and that she might become a great singer, and yet his letters express a desire to appropriate her, thus putting an end to her hope of a musical education. To him her charm was independent of her voice, even of her words. It lay in her sunny spirit, in her smile which was entirely and wholly lovable. Although a fun-lover, she was deeply sympathetic. She took no enjoyment in the confusion or suffering of others. She was reticent, but her reticence had nothing dour or sullen in it. While possessed of many of her father's characteristics, she was less mystical in her moods.

Her skill as a housekeeper was no small part of her appeal to Richard. Her cakes and pies were especially delectable. He once said to his mother, "Belle has the knack of making any kind of dish taste good."

She was equally skilled in dressmaking. Even at sixteen she could cut and model her own gowns. True, the costumes of the border were only approximations to the elaborate creations of New York, but she followed the fashion plates in *Godey's Lady's Book*—at a distance!

Definitely working to win her he had visited her as often as he could during his summers in Brownsville. He had walked to and from church with her, and once had gone so far as to hire a horse and carriage to take her to the Fourth of July celebration at the county town. She was a good dancer, and in the local parties they had made a handsome couple as they balanced and swung in the reels and schottisches which were then in fashion.

The memory of these delightful meetings had gone with him into the snowy reaches of the northern forest, and without doubt Isabel's influence had enabled him to maintain his self-respect. In the rough life to which he was exposed, he remained of good report. His worst failing was a hasty temper. Occasionally he broke out in a rage and "ripped and tore" savagely, but this flare of unreason died as swiftly as it rose, leaving him deeply repentant. He called it "flying off the handle," and his men learned to dodge at such times.

During almost every day of these six years he had toiled with the persistence, the precision of a prodigious insect. I must return to that. Consider the chances he took! A thousand times he ran his raft through boiling floods of icy water. For weeks each April he trod rolling logs and broke huge jams in the midst of surging freshets, and after the run, he had hooked logs into the "booms" or had ridden for twelve hours per day the plunging carriers of circular saws. Often he went cold and wet and hungry while on the river. He had tramped hundreds of miles of muddy roads with a pack on his back, and through it all, despite this incessant danger, this herculean toil, he had kept his handsome body unscarred and had maintained a courage which never faltered. That he had failed of financial success was not due to lack of will-power, but to certain inhibitions over which he had no control.

He remained a wage-earner because of a lack of confidence in himself, and also for the reason that he was a conscientious citizen. He would not cheat the government, or lie to advance his interests or the interest of his employer. He wasted no money in dissipation. He dressed plainly and boarded (when in town) at cheap hotels, and yet he had, at the end of six years of killing labour, less than a thousand dollars in hand, and when, in the summer of 1857, he returned to the family home, he was stunned by the news that Hugh McLane had sold his farm and had moved away with all his clan.

He stared at his mother with wide-open, wondering eyes. "Where have they gone?" he asked at last.

"To La Crosse, a new county north of here. A colony of Swiss arrived here in April, and the money which they offered for homes upset the judgment of many of our neighbours. The McLanes and a half dozen other families immediately sold out and went away to a valley where land can be had at lower prices."

"Did Isabel leave any word for me?"

"No, but David did. He wants you to sell out and follow along."

The fact that Isabel had gone without leaving him a word of farewell hurt Richard more than he cared to confess. It appeared that his years of labour, his painful progress had led to a blank wall. For the first time in his adult life the future appeared dark.

While still in this mood of depression, a letter came to him from David in which he briefly explained how it happened that they had moved away so suddenly. "Pap thought we ought to have more land and so in May Will and I made a trip up here to see what the country looked like. We liked it and said so, and here we all are. You must come. It's a noble valley. There's worlds of game in the hills, deer, bear, and birds. The railroad is laid out along our valley and is sure to come through in a year or two. Belle says, 'Tell Dick to sell his place and bring his folks up here and buy near us.'"

This letter wrought a profound change in Richard's field of operation as well as in his spirits. "This ends Brownsville for me," he said to his mother. "I'm for taking Dave's advice. Let's sell out and move to La Crosse County. It will be nearer Clinton's camp and nearer Mosinee."

Harriet Graham, while prepared for this decision, was not entirely happy at the prospect. Poor, long-suffering woman! What joy could she find in moving? Once again she was called upon to leave a home in which, humble as it was, she had begun to take pleasure, and to enter upon another journey over tedious trails toward another "paradise" which, at its best, could offer only another log cabin on another square of primeval sod.

Nevertheless, with a courage which her frail body only falteringly sustained, she faced the task. She loved her woodsman son better than anything else in life, her duty was to him, and so, one July morning, she climbed painfully into a covered wagon drawn by two spans of oxen, and set out upon the trail to the wilder West, leaving behind her a little garden which she and Susan had planted, and a pleasant circle of friends who were sorry to have her go. Seven years of life in this village had brought to her a measure of contentment such as at one time she had not thought it possible to attain. She was comforted, however, by the thought that the McLanes were to be her neighbours in the new land.

Susan, now a slender, pale-faced girl of eighteen, sat beside her mother in similar uncomplaining endurance while the wagon jolted over the boulders of river-beds or toiled through sandy hills, with the men walking beside their cattle. Tormented by insects by day, kept awake by coons and owls at night, and cooking their food at open fires, the women suffered silently, until, at last, after a week of weariness and pain, they found themselves riding at ease along a high ridge road which overlooked the valley of their destination.

The joy, the relief which filled their hearts remained unspoken, although their faces lightened as Richard called out, "There it is! That's the La Crosse River Valley, and that clump of buildings is Neshonoc."

It was about six o'clock of a beautiful afternoon, and this wooded ridge with its cool breeze was in truth a celestial highway. On the left as well as on the right, they could look afar into lovely valleys winding westward. From certain turns of the road they were able to sight the bluffs of Minnesota, and to catch the gleam of the Mississippi River. On the floor of the vale to the north, newly-built pine cabins glittered like flakes of gold, while three ranges of hills, one behind the other, gave such dignity and depth of colour to the unknown North-West, that Richard's bosom filled with desire of continued exploration. In that direction lay the beautiful unknown.

Toward sunset the trail turned to the north and abruptly descended the ridge, so rough and steep in its decline that the reeling of the wagon filled the women with terror. Sometimes the wheels dropped to the hubs in muddy ruts, then rose above a stone, causing the vehicle to toss and roll like a boat, and this motion, coming as it did at the close of a weary day, so wrenched and jarred Harriet Graham's weakened body that her face blanched with pain.

Richard, seeing her white face and compressed lips, apprehended for the first time something of the cruelty involved in compelling her to act again the part of pioneer. Her clutching hands, her wrinkled brow, and her swaying form took away from him for the moment all the elation of the pioneer. The beauty of the landscape was clouded by the suffering from which he could not defend her.

Some part of his elation returned, however, as they reached the level of the valley and set out along a winding brook-side road. Although the valley was but a few miles in width, it was so rich, so sheltered by encircling hills, and so gay with flowers that it appeared a natural park. Its beauty brought comfort even to the tired women. It suggested the vast estate of some sylvan aristocrat, a demesne arranged and adorned for the profit and pleasure of a duke. The road followed the winding course of a small stream amid fields of wild flowers in which shapely oak trees were set as if by the design of an artist. It was the perfection of a wild, yet amiable landscape. It was the "paradise" which the Grahams had so hopefully set out from Overlook to find.

Darkness came while they were still some miles from the village, and as they neared a good-sized house on the bank of the stream, Richard halted his oxen and sang out in frontier fashion, "Halloo the house!"

A moment later the door opened and a man appeared in the lamp-light. "Halloo yourself!" he called. "Who are you and what's wanted?"

"We are new-comers with women needing food and rest. Can you keep us?"

"Drive in, stranger," was the hearty answer.

The man turned out to be Andrew McConnell, a prosperous New England settler who had come into the country two years before. When he learned that his visitors were also from the East and that they knew the McLanes and the Burnhams, he welcomed them as if they were blood-relations.

His wife made Harriet and Susan comfortable while she prepared a meal for them, and when a little later they drew up around a table covered with the plain fare of the region, Robert Graham's word of grace had a note of sincerity which touched his host.

"It *is* a good country you've got to," he said, referring back to a phrase in the deacon's prayer. "It's a hard job getting here, but once you're here, I don't know of a better place"—here he smiled—"except the place of heavenly rest."

The house was only a shell of pine boards, but to Harriet Graham it was a haven of refuge, and good Mrs. McConnell and her sympathetic daughters displayed the grace of ministering angels. They took the weary women away to bed, leaving the men in the kitchen to talk lands and conditions of settlement.

In answer to Richard's questions, McConnell said, "You'll find the McLanes across the river about two miles from Lovejoy's mill. They own over four hundred acres of fine land and are well pleased."

It was characteristic of Robert Graham that he should ask whether church service had been established in the village, and McConnell sympathetically replied, "Yes, we hold services regularly in the school building."

Richard touched the business of lumbering. "Are there any saw-mills in the neighbourhood?"

"Oh, yes, there are mills at La Crosse and a big 'boom' at the mouth of the Black River. The Black River country is the great logging district. You'll find plenty to do in that line."

Early the next morning Richard arose and went forth into the air in the conviction of having at last entered upon the land of his quest, a land in which sickness, sorrow, and age had no place. It was a radiant amphitheatre walled with smooth green hills, a sheltered paradise in which he was prepared to found a home for the girl awaiting him. What more could he ask? He felt grateful to David and William for leading the way.

The village of Neshonoc on the La Crosse River was about five miles away, and toward this point the Grahams resumed their march. Two hours later they drew up before a little tavern which stood on the level land above the bridge, a lovely spot for a village. To the east was the mill-pond. A trout-brook came in from the north, and a grist-mill rose against a conical hill around whose base the river ran in a reedy curve. On the bottom lands to the west, scattered pines were growing, and in the edges of these groves and on the banks of the stream, a group of wigwams denoted the presence of redmen. Altogether it could have been used as an illustration for a poster. It had all the elements of pastoral beauty.

From the tavern-keeper Richard inquired concerning Amos Burnham who had promised him a house and job. "He lives in Burnham Valley," answered the man. "The coulee was named after him. He was the first settler in it. Keep along the river road about three miles to the eastward and you'll come to the Burnham post-office."

Again the Grahams took up their quest, and about three o'clock turned in at a new farmstead in a narrow valley containing only two or three settlers.

Amos met the Grahams with hearty good-will. "By mighty, I'm glad to see you!" he said to Richard. "But I'd never have known ye—never in this world. Why, you're a full-sized man!"

Richard smiled at this, recalling what he had been through during the last six years. "I shouldn't wonder if I *am* getting grown up."

Pastures New

Burnham showed them the farm which he hoped they would rent or buy, and then took them up to his brother's house. Henry made them welcome as cordially as his brother had done. "The fact is I need a carpenter the worst way. I want to build a barn and Amos wants an addition to his house. This is the very place for men like you," he added to Robert. "There's a world of building to be done."

That night at supper Richard alluded to the story about Henry and the load of hay which started the emigration from Oxford County, and Henry smilingly admitted the truth of the yarn. "By gorry, you're right! That was a steep meadow! You see my steers were young and one day when I was loading hay they run the wheel of my cart over a boulder and flopped the whole blamed load on top of me. That settled things for me! When I got out from under that load I said, 'By snum! I'm done with hills and stuns. I'm going to a country where a cart can keep both wheels on the ground.' I've done it, too. Look at this farm! Two hundred acres with not a stun on it big enough to throw at a bird. Why don't you settle right here?"

In less than two days the Grahams were under a roof of their own and at work. The new country had proved more hospitable and the spirit of the settlers more cordial than they had imagined. Harriet Graham, worn as she was, took heart of hope. The landscape, larger in line and finer in colour than any she had thus far seen in the state, was charming, and the hills reminded her of those in Maine.

On the second morning following their arrival, Richard borrowed a horse of Harry Burnham and rode away to visit the McLanes. He found them living on a high, level bank overlooking the river, in a house of shining yellow pine set among hazel bushes and poplar trees. The view from the door was glorious, and old Hugh, sitting on the porch just as he used to do in Brownsville, was looking out upon the hills.

He saw Richard as he entered the gate and shouted a greeting which brought Deborah and David to the door. Isabel did not join. In the hurly-burly which followed, she stood shyly apart till Richard was able to greet her.

Mrs. McLane said, "Good even, Richard," as quietly as though they had been separated only for a day.

Hugh's devotion to "matters of the spirit" had been greatly intensified, Deborah explained to Richard, by the recent visit of a colporteur of the Adventist's faith. "A good long visit it was," she added with frank resentment. "We couldn't get rid of the old fraud. We saw through him the first day—he was just sponging his board—but Pap couldn't or wouldn't see into his game. Night after night that beggar sat around arguing and chawing his cud, getting ready for another meal. Luke and David slept on the floor so that he might have a bed."

Isabel, like her father, was too generous, too trusting to join in this criticism, but she did admit that the "stranger elder" had a good appetite. "But as he praised my cooking, I can't complain."

For an hour or more while Hugh expounded the scriptural prophecies which made clear that a certain new date for the end of the world was impending, Isabel and her mother got dinner. A wonderful meal it turned out to be; a meal which Hugh enjoyed even though the trump of judgment was about to blow, and while they ate Richard described the dismay he felt when he reached Brownsville and found them all gone. "It gave me a chill," he declared. "It spoiled Green County for me."

David spoke of their new home with enthusiasm. "William has bought a farm adjoining, but Luke and I are breaking the sod of the new homestead. It's hard to hold a breaking plough when the river swarms with pickerel, and trout are plentiful in all the brooks," he said. "Furthermore, bee trees are numerous and deer are thick in the hills. The land overflows with fatness, as pap says, but there's no cheap land which is also good land. We are all a little too late. We had to pay twice as much as we would have paid two years ago."

As he talked of seed and soil, Richard was looking into Isabel's eyes, and felt that any country where she was offered happiness, and after dinner when he asked her to show him William's house she consented.

The walk was of such beauty that Richard never forgot it. On either side of the hill-side path strange and beautiful blossoms shone. The smell of ripe strawberries rose from the warm sod. The summer sky was a crystal ocean in which prodigious clouds loitered like silver ships becalmed. Each cabin glittered like gold, and in this newness lay an appeal somewhat akin to the emotion which unites young lovers. The home-making passion was awake in Isabel and Richard, as it was in every other settler in the valley. A new world was opening for them all.

Richard made it plain to Isabel that his renewed determination to own a bit of land and to build a home was based upon his desire to have her share it. "As soon as I have a roof to shelter you, I'm going to ask your father's consent to our marriage," he said.

To this statement Isabel made no reply. She only smiled with tremulous lips, but Richard understood her silence and built upon its implication.

CHAPTER XVII

Richard Wins a Promise

THE valley of the La Crosse River appealed to Richard far more strongly than the village of Brownsville had ever done, for it possessed no unpleasant associations, and it lay more clearly in the highway of travel from east to west. "I like hills," he said, "provided I'm not obliged to cultivate them." The settlers were also much more to his taste, for they were mostly the sons and daughters of well-to-do New York or New England families.

He believed in the future of the county town, which was already a place of mills and banks, with the promise of a city in its stir. The sandy flat on which it stood had long been an Indian trading-point, and was now a place of importance to merchants by reason of its steamboat traffic. On certain days, when the air was clear, the bellowing of these river monsters could be heard at Neshonoc and beyond. Richard loved these sounds and while he agreed with the editor of the *Democrat* that "the snort of the

Richard Wins a Promise

iron horse would soon silence the steamboat," he hoped the *War Eagle* would long continue to wake the echoes of the hills.

All in all, La Crosse appeared a most favoured locality, and the Grahams set about providing a home for themselves. I do not know why the burden of these filial duties fell so largely upon Richard, but it did. If Addison helped, it was in more impersonal ways. Richard's problem involved the personal care of his invalid mother and his "notional" sire, whose vital interests continued to be religious or political. Austere as he was, authoritative as he assumed to be, Robert Graham leaned upon the shoulders of his younger, not his elder, son.

There was plenty of work to do. Harvest was coming on, and there were granaries to build and houses to finish in preparation for winter. No hands could remain idle in such a community.

The house in which the Grahams found temporary shelter was a one-storey cottage with three rooms and a "linty" (as old Hugh called it), which stood on the north valley road, close beside the blacksmith-shop and store, at Burnham Corners. To live in such a shanty was almost like camping, and Harriet needed all the sustaining power of her faith, and all the consolation which the presence of her son and the beauty of the summer landscape presented. To keep a cheerful face in the midst of so many deprivations was not easy. Beneath the glamour of this summer season in a ncrthern land, she perceived (as few of her neighbours did) its similarity to the climate of Maine. She made no complaint, but the lines of her lips were serious. She dreaded the coming of winter.

Fair as the valley appeared, she soon discovered that it harboured many pests and some dangers. Swarms of flies by day and clouds of mosquitoes at night tormented her. Skunks, coons, and wildcats abounded and rattlesnakes infested the hill-sides. Blue-racers and black-snakes haunted the edges of the meadows, and adders and garter-snakes often crossed her path in the door-yard. True, most of these creatures were harmless, but to her and to Susan they were a constant menace. Even Richard confessed, at the end of his first week in the harvest-field, "I don't enjoy picking up rattlers while binding wheat."

"Be careful where you step while you are berrying," he said. "There's a den of the brutes on the high peak back of Henry's house and his pasture is alive with them."

This hill, Burnham explained, was capped with a ledge of limestone, and its crevices furnished the winter home which the rattlesnake requires. "However, they ain't so many as they was when I came. You see, every spring they come out of their dens and lay around for a spell on the warm rocks, and so we go up there and thresh 'em with poles. We killed nearly fifty last spring. After they sun themselves for a few days, they begin to drop down toward the pastures and the meadows. I've never had any trouble, myself, but Sarah is so scared of 'em that she won't go across the road. Once in a while a critter comes in with her jaw all swelled up, but none of 'em have died so far. I'm gittin' so's I don't mind snakes. They ain't so dangerous as people think. I've never known a man to die of a bite."

Richard could not account for the plague of black-snakes and blue-racers, but the truth is they came up along the streams which emptied into the bayous of the Mississippi. While shy and non-poisonous, they were especially terrifying to women by reason of their size and their habit of lifting their heads a foot or two above the grass and presenting their open mouths and flickering tongues in sinister defiance. The blue-racers, so called because of their colour and swift motion, were also pugnacious of action. They were not venomous and were beautiful creatures, slender and shining. Richard was not afraid of any crawling thing, but he learned to walk warily in the places infested by rattlers.

In reality, insects were a worse pest than the serpents. Sometimes of an evening when a shower threatened, mosquitoes came in swarms, so intolerable that each family was forced to collect round a "smudge," a smouldering fire of wet wood whose thick flare of smoke kept the insects away but always blinded the women and children. By day black flies swarmed into the kitchen and settled over the dinner dishes like bees.

"Of course we had flies back in the state of Maine," Mrs. Burnham admitted, "but I never saw the like of 'em here. You won't get rid of 'em till they freeze. Thank goodness, the cool nights in September catches 'em. You can sweep 'em down and out of the door like so many dried currants. However, when I see Henry ploughin' this lovely level land, I says to myself, 'Sary, what do a few flies and snakes matter? They'll all pass away in a year or two, but the fine, rich land will stay."

In this remark Harriet perceived a noble philosophy. After all, the land was beautiful, beautiful and fertile.

Sarah also discussed the "Injun" question. "We ain't had any trouble since the men whipped that old Pottawatomie chief. Before that his band was a nuisance. They used to come along here every day almost, and beg for bread. Seemed like they were just crazy for a taste of wheat bread. They didn't harm us, but one troop went so far as to threaten to shoot John Mackinzie and his wife who wouldn't feed 'em, and when John reported it the hull town of Sparty rose up and went after that redskin and his tribe. They caught him and jest about whipped the hide off his back. The valley ain't had any trouble with 'em since."

Harriet Graham, while falling short of Sarah's optimism, hoped Richard would leave the river and settle down in

Burnham Valley. In imagination she saw him building a handsome house and a big red barn. "I shall not see it, Richard, but some day this valley will have a railroad and be filled with prosperous farmers living in mansions."

Up to this time Richard had never ridden a horse. His life in the West as in the East had afforded little opportunity for riding, but he now found himself in a community where the tradition of the saddle still lingered. Resolving to become as skilful on a colt as in a canoe, he acquired the use of an especially fine saddler, and before the summer was over, rode as well as any of his neighbours. I may interpolate at this point, however, that he never equalled the McLanes as a hunter. He was of no marked skill as a sportsman. He could shoot (and did shoot) deer, but he had no special love for such sport.

As he grew better acquainted with the situation in the valley he proved the truth of Burnham's statement. He had arrived too late. There were no more cheap lands. The level acres of the mid-valley were now held at a price which he could not afford to pay, and the hill-side claims were so far from his ideal that he refused to consider them. "There is but one thing for me to do," he said to his mother, "and that's to take a farm on shares for next year, and go back to lumbering for the winter. It's the work I know best and every day's work at Jinny Bull Falls will buy half an acre of land. When I buy, it will not be a ridge, be sure of that. I came West to get level land, and level land I must have. I will not plough side-hill fields. I shall never be satisfied till I have some government land."

"I hate to have you go back on the river," she wistfully replied. "It's so hard and so dangerous."

"It's the game I'm best fitted to play," he argued, "and it pays me better than farming."

In such wise his vague dreams of wealth and leisure faded. He always came back to a reliance upon his powerful hands and his unconquerable heart. He was assured only of what he could earn as a skilled workman.

At odd moments of leisure during this summer, he explored the valley whose fertility was amazing. Raspberries, blackberries, and huckleberries ripened in the meadows or on the hills. Orchards of plums, groves of nut trees, and festoons of grapes invited to holiday harvesting, and in all these joyous excursions Isabel and Susan shared. It appeared possible to make a living entirely by hunting and foraging, for in addition to these sources of fruit supplies, swarms of bees hived in hollow oaks, and after snow came venison and bear-steaks were often shared at the tables of hunters like the McLanes and Gilfillans.

One Sunday in September, as Isabel and Richard were sitting at William's table facing the open door, they were astonished to see a black bear rise and peer over the barnyard fence. With broad paws on the top log he surveyed the scene, sniffing with the comical expression of a passing neighbour, manifesting a wistful interest in the evening meal.

"Will! A bear!" Isabel whispered.

"He wants to share our bacon," laughed Richard, to whom bears were familiar objects.

William, whose back was towards the door, took this for a joke, till his wife uttered a cry of astonishment. "Good land of Goshen! It *is* a bear."

At her cry, the animal dropped on all fours and started off across the fields, while William exclaimed, "Just my luck! My rifle's over at Dave's. Come on, let's head him off and drive him over that way!"

With astonishing speed for so large a man, he set off toward the south. Richard followed, and together they succeeded in heading the bear toward the homestead, shouting to David, "Bring your gun!"

At last David appeared with his rifle, took aim, and fired.

Knowing his almost unerring skill, Richard expected the bear to fall, but nothing happened; or, rather, the bear increased his speed, whilst David stood with the rifle in his hands, looking after him in an attitude of waiting, which irritated William. As he approached his brother he asked, "What's the matter? Why didn't you try again?"

"I only had one light-weight bullet," replied David sheepishly.

I set this down as Richard told it to me, illustrating the happy-go-lucky, procrastinating character of the McLanes. David had neglected to mould a new supply of the lead pellets which served as bullets in those days. His defective charge had only stung the bear to swifter flight.

Notwithstanding his incessant toil upon the farms roundabout, these were the richest of all Richard's days thus far. The romantic charm of the landscape, his Sunday walks with Isabel, and the jovial character of the men with whom he worked united to make every hour an active pleasure. Swinging a cradle under the blazing sun on a windless hillside was almost as severe a test of manhood as running the rapids, but companionship lightened such toil.

A wonderful new invention, a horse-power threshing-machine, was just being heralded, and when William and David imported one from Milwaukee, a hazardous and splendid undertaking, Richard joined the crew, and thereafter moved from farm to farm during October. He keenly enjoyed this work. The arrival of the machine bred a delightful bustle in every farm-house and consternation in every hen-roost, for threshers were not only welcome visitors but guests of honour. Every meal was a feast. They ate fried chicken till David declared it made him queasy to hear a rooster squawk.

The wives of the farmers enjoyed the coming of the machine even though it caused a press of work, for it brought into their lonely lives a day of social stir. Neighbours' girls came in to help, and "Thrashing" was almost as joyous as a barn-raising or a husking-bee. Often the day ended in a dance, for which David good-naturedly played the fiddle.

In this machine, crude as it was, a new age of agriculture was foretold. For thousands of years, in every climate and among all peoples, wheat had been beaten or trampled out of its straw. Now, suddenly, in this new Western land, men not only began to devise machinery for reaping grain but also for separating the kernels from the chaff. For untold centuries the reaping-hook, the scythe, and the flail had persisted; now here on a Wisconsin field, a horse-drawn mower and reaper was being used. There is no explanation of these miracles.

In a dim way, Richard felt the marvel of the invention. His mind was not mechanical, but he had a nose for progress and the power of expression which David lacked. He loved to predict improvement.

As a thresher he met and made friends with all the people of the region. They were a hearty and vigorous folk, men whose "enterprise" had enabled them to pull away from their wonted hearth-fires in the East in order to establish ampler estates in the West. Physically powerful and mentally buoyant, they not only had unfaltering faith in their own future, they expressed unbounded confidence in the progress of the state, boasting with manifest contentment of their valley. "It's the finest in the West," they asserted.

In recording this complacency, I realize that I am speaking for a generation which already looks back upon its carefree youth with wistful eyes, but I contend there was more of charm in those days than is expressed by the idealization of age. It was an era of expansion, of exultant confidence. All over the border enthusiasm was aflame, and Wisconsin was among the most favoured localities. Her rich plough-lands, her mines of lead and iron, her illimitable forests of ash and pine, and her abundant lakes and rivers assured a noble future. On every woodlot the cross-cut saw was singing the song of progress, while the builder's hammers beat in rhythmic accompaniment to its strophes.

The grain on that new soil stood breast-high to the reapers. Deacon Graham declared that he had never seen such wheat, and as the improved threshing-machine, like some engine of enchantment, turned stacks of grain into streams of gold, Richard's desire for a farm of his own intensified. He put off his return to "The Woods" as long as he could, happy in his association with William and David.

Most of the gaiety of the threshing-crew was due to William, for Richard like David was not much given to joking. He was a capital story-teller, however, and made vivid and skilful presentation of his river experiences in his moments of leisure. Always welcome at the table, his tales of the woods and its denizens were a delight.

The McLanes had already won the cordial good-will of their new neighbours. Had they been merely capable mechanics or sturdy harvesters, they would have been popular, for no one who came in touch with them could forget them, but here, as in Green County, their smiling reserve, their mellow voices, their curiously concise speech, and their unusual musical skill created in the minds of their New England associates a liking which nothing, not even old Hugh's religious vagaries, could weaken.

No doubt some part of this tolerance of his faith arose from a realization of the fact that ridiculing him was not a healthy diversion, not merely because Luke and David were quick to resent any slur, but because of the demonstrated fact that old Hugh himself was still a dangerous antagonist. There were not many men in the neighbourhood who could have safely challenged him. One man who in a school-meeting gaily called him a liar, went to the floor as if struck by

Richard Wins a Promise

lightning. When he came to his senses, he found the white-haired giant on his knees beside him praying in deep contrition, "Lord Jesus, forgive me. I am thy servant, but weak and sinful of heart."

Mostly he had only remote association with the lives of his neighbours. Concerned more and more with the Apocalyptic splendours of the Scriptures he cared little for railways or the doings of legislators. To him dances and political conventions were equally vain and foolish, and yet in the midst of his musings, he could not resist the appeal of a song or the voice of the violin. Something in its tone aroused ancestral memories. Awaking from his abstraction, he smiled, drumming on the arms of his chair in time to the tunes which he himself had anciently played.

Richard, who often shared their Sunday dinner, was accepted by the young people as Isabel's recognized suitor, but he had little to bring her save a single-hearted devotion. He had no carriage in which to take her driving, and he brought no presents, trusting in an occasional word or clasp of the hand to assure her of his devotion as he came and went from week to week.

It all seems pitifully drab in contrast with present-day courtships, but Isabel expressed no resentment of her lover's poverty. She understood his reasons for economy, and when they walked to a dance or to church, her heart remained untouched of bitterness. To have him near was a joy, and when he offered to churn or pare apples, she was serenely happy. To help her bring a bucket of water from the spring was a task for which he always volunteered despite Deborah's teasing comments on his gallantry.

No doubt some of my readers will be disappointed in Richard's love-story, for I have no passionate struggles to record, no doubts to describe, no jealous fears to analyze. Isabel inclined toward him from the first time she saw him and so far as I know, had no other rival whose pretensions could be taken seriously. The lives of these young people flowed together naturally and serenely. Their courtship had nothing of modern cynicism. It was in harmony with the fair and joyous land in which they now began to plan the building of a home.

Gorgeous, golden autumn days! In after years they often spoke of them to me. Their hearts ached to recall them, to relive them. They had nothing, yet they had everything— youth, health, and confident faith. In every home they visited, the spirit of hospitality made up for scanty furniture, rough walls, and plain food. It was a friendly community, with almost no alien blood.

Harriet Graham, intellectual though she was, also expressed a deepening contentment with her surroundings. "We are beginning the world anew out here," she wrote to a friend in Maine. "Though I may not live to see it, this valley will one day be famous for its prosperity. I am sure of it."

Isabel was entirely content with her world, for she knew no other. She had never seen a city, and she listened to Richard's descriptions of Boston with its theatres and ships and palaces, as if he were telling a fairy-tale. His Yankee phrases, his courtly manners (in singular contrast with his rough dress) related him to the heroes of the stories she had read. That he was poor did not matter, for all of the young men she knew were poor. He was just making his start in life. The only disturbing factor in their companionship was the repeated declaration of his purpose to go back into the pineries in November. She sorrowed at thought of his long absence in camp, and she feared for his life on the savage river.

"I wish you could stay here," she said. "There must be work to do here."

He was touched by her words, but his purpose did not change. "Yes, but I can earn more money in the woods.

Richard Wins a Promise

I need every dollar I can make and scrape to provide a home for you."

Mother McLane openly encouraged him in his courtship. His candour and his courtesy had won her heart. He, on his part, was sincere in his respect for her. She had little of his mother's cultivation—her education had been slight—but he admired her. "I will not add one iota to your worries," he declared, once when they were alone together. "I want Belle, but I will not take her without your full consent. I will wait just as long as you think best. I'll have a home for her by this time next year. It'll be a shanty on a rented farm, but it will be a start."

Tears came into her eyes as she answered, "I won't ask you to wait longer than that, Dick, but you'd better speak to father."

Old Hugh received Richard's formal request for his daughter's hand with a silence which would have been disturbing to a lover less familiar with his moods. It was Sunday and he was sitting in his favourite chair by the window, looking out across the river as if he saw the far-shining "Hills of Moab," and on his rugged face lay the serene ecstasy of the poet.

Becoming aware of the young man's presence at last, he turned and vaguely said, "Did ye speak, Richard?"

"I did, Mr. McLane. I asked you if you had any objection to my calling you 'pap' like the rest of your children?"

"None in the world," he replied, and then as he drew closer to Richard's meaning, his smile faded. "But what lies back of all this? Ye want something of me?"

"Yes, sir. I want Isabel. I've asked her to marry me and she has consented. I hope you won't object."

The face of the old Celt took on the tender gravity of a father as he replied, "That one is very dear to me. I'll miss her sorely. Besides, she's only a lass."

"I'm willing to wait," Richard interjected.

"You've spoken to her mother?"

"Yes, I've just been talking with her, Mr. McLane. She's inclined my way and I hope to have a home of my own next year. I've taken a farm in Burnham Valley."

Fully awake now, Hugh's eyes displayed a keenness of vision which Dick had never before observed. He grew younger, more alert. "When ye have a house to put her in, I'll consider it," he said gently but decisively. "You're a fine lad; I've no fault to find in that regard, but Isabel is the apple of me eye." He smiled. "If it were Deb now, I'd say take her and welcome, but Belle—I must think of that. I shall miss her singing. Have ye money for a home?"

"Not at present, but I have enough to buy a team and some farm tools. I intend to buy a farm in another year or two and settle near here. Belle could see you often."

"Well, well! We'll cross that bridge when we come to it. Get you home and then—we'll see! We'll see," he repeated with a smile which Dick took for a provisional consent.

David was frankly pleased. "We'll all help when you get ready to build," he said. "I don't know of a man I'd rather have as a brother-in-law, but I'd like to see you give up the river. The pay don't make up for the danger."

To this Richard made no reply. His plans were laid.

Old Hugh was not ready to see his daughters married, for his belief in the coming of the last day was now complete.

Strange, incredibly strange it was, that in an age of expanding railway lines and multiplying telegraph-wires, any mind as sane as his could harbour such primitive views of nature's laws, such concept of the universe, and yet he had many fellow converts, men otherwise normal in thought and speech, who sent out over the country heralds of steady purpose to proclaim "The Second Coming of the Lord."

Richard Wins a Promise

In one of their talks Richard put the question to Isabel: "Do *you* believe in the 'second coming of Christ'?"

She hesitated, then shook her head. "I'm afraid I don't. Pap tries to *make* me believe and I try to see his way, but I can't."

David answered the same question with a jest. "Pap's prophecies won't keep me from planting corn next spring. If it comforts him and his preachers to think they are to be caught up into the heavens while the rest of us are 'swept like chaff to the burning,' I'm willing, but meanwhile Luke and I are breaking more sod to sow more wheat to buy more land. The 'New Earth' I want to see is that Minnesota prairie which is about to come into the market. There's too much to do at home this fall, but next spring, as soon as the corn is planted, you and I must make that trip we've talked about."

When the time came to return to the lumber-camps, Richard found himself singularly reluctant about leaving, and as for Belle, "Jinny Bull Falls" had become a terror. It was all very well to hear her lover tell tales of the dangers he had passed, but to think of his going back to them was appalling. "Why don't you go up into the Black River country?" she asked. "It isn't so far away and there aren't any falls to run."

Her anxiety had its effect. "I've got to go back this season," he said. "I'm under contract to Cooper, but I intend to quit the Wisconse next June. If all goes well with my farming, I'll stop lumbering altogether."

With this agreement Isabel was forced to be content, but tears were in her eyes and fear in her heart as she kissed him good-bye. "Don't be reckless," she urged.

"I'll be careful," he laughingly responded. "No more dare-devil business for me."

CHAPTER XVIII

Richard Becomes a Farmer

TRUE to his promise, Richard notified his boss that he had planned to return to Neshonoc as soon as the ice went out. It was a little hard to refuse the extra pay which Cooper again offered, but his mind was set on seeding his farm. Catching a ride in a freight wagon as far as the Dells, he set out to walk across the divide which rose between the Wisconsin River water-shed and the valley of the La Crosse.

It was the last day of March, but the wind was chill and the land sodden and bleak. Settlement was sparse even in the neighbourhood of Kilbourn City (the new town which had sprung up at the end of the gorge), and when he left his hotel at dawn it was with intent to reach the big ridge before dark. It was nearly fifty miles as the crow flies, and the way unknown to him, but he had no fear of the wilderness nor of the weather, and he was capable of doing four miles an hour even on such a trail. Seven

Richard Becomes a Farmer

years of battle with elemental nature had wrought the Boston clerk into a manly hardihood as far from the character of the slim youth he had been as the panther outweighs the house-cat or the wolf differs from the poodle. He was not concerned with lodging, but as he was carrying with him his entire winter's pay, he felt some concern for the safety of his wallet. Eager to reach home, he expected to walk all night.

For a few hours he had a road of varying sort to guide him, but as he kept on straight into the west, the land became trackless. Singular castle-shaped ledges of rock rose out of the level valley floor, which was covered for many miles with groves of dwarf-oaks alternating with marshes and thickets of willow and birch. All settlement was left behind, for the soil of this region was sandy and poor, but Richard was cheered by the melodious booming of the prairie-cocks who were just beginning their spring-time chorus (a song which he had hitherto heard only distantly as he floated down the river on a raft), and the almost continuous stream of wild fowl overhead confirmed the grouse in their seed-time prophecy.

During the forenoon the sun broke through the clouds and familiar song-birds took up the cheerful strain. Bluebirds, robins, and yellow-hammers uttered voice, while squirrels and other small animals whistled and chattered with a glee which was almost equally verbal in expression. Richard had never been a conscious student of nature, but his eyes, naturally observant, had recorded many facts, and he was interested to define the differences and count the resemblances between these signs of spring and those which he had known as a boy in Oxford County.

As he strode along, the study of his surroundings lightened in some degree the tedium of the trail.

Exteriorly he was not attractive. His heavy boots, his worn and baggy trousers, and his faded blouse or "wamus" (which he wore over a red shirt) rendered him almost as perfectly coloured to his environment as a woodchuck. His face was unshaven and a shapeless fur cap concealed the outlines of his handsome head.

He was perfectly safe! No robber would look twice at him, or if he did he would avoid him as a dangerous companion. Only a close and sympathetic observer would have detected the grace in his step and the beauty in his clear grey eyes. He was grimy exteriorly, but the skin of his body was notably white and clean. He was fastidious in this way.

The road was rough as well as lonely and obscure, and the sun had fallen low in the west as he entered the hills of the Big Divide. He had hardly paused in his long, swift march, even to eat the few slices of bread and meat which his landlady had given him, and yet he eyed the dark ridge with exultation. Once on the other side of it he would be in the home valley. From the summit he would be able to detect the bluffs which marked the site of Neshonoc. The fact that there was no trail at all across the hills at this point did not dismay him; his only care was to reach the summit before darkness fell. Accurate as his sense of direction had hitherto proved, it was possible for him to grow uncertain while winding through these wooded knobs. To pass the night there would not be pleasant, for as the sun went down, the wind regained the spirit of winter. The birds no longer sang; their confident cheer was lost.

As he plodded on he amused himself by going over and over again his plans for the spring. "First of all I must buy a wagon, a plough, and a harrow. Bingham will furnish the seed wheat. Then I'll go to La Crosse and lay in my household outfit. Susan will come over and put the house in order for me. If my wheat crop turns out well, perhaps Grandad Hugh will let Isabel marry me in June!"

So it happened that while the skies above the hills darkened into night, the weary traveller was mentally living in the midst of wild roses with the girl whom he had come to regard as unquestioningly his own.

He rose at last to the summit, but too late to get the inspiration of familiar peaks. He could not tell exactly where he stood in relation to Neshonoc, but from the touch of the cold wind in his face, he knew that he was confronting the west although the sun's light had faded from the sky. He suspected that his course had been too far toward the north, and only by keeping the wind in his eyes was he able to navigate the sea of red oaks into which he descended. On the level land, buried in the foliage, there was nothing to guide him. His eyes were necessarily lifted to the evening-star. He was tired and hungry, but these were familiar conditions with him. He accepted them as part of his expedition.

The land was solemnly silent now. No bird uttered sound, no animals moved save now and then a deer avoiding his slow progress through the thick coverts. "I guess I'll have to go into camp for the night," he finally admitted. "Like the Dutchman, I'm not lost; it's the town that's lost."

As the clouds blotted out the western star which had been his guide, he realized that this curious, sandy scrub-oak region, which was known to him only by hearsay, formed the most difficult stage of his march. It had no streams, no trees to serve as landmarks, and with nothing but the fitful breeze to guide him, he felt his way amid the weird rustling of these oaks which keep their dark red leaves all winter and only shed them when the new growth starts.

At last when it became so black that he wandered into a tangle of briars and bumped into tree-trunks, he stopped and set fire to a handful of dry leaves. By this flare he was able to discover other and more substantial fuel, but the fear of starting a forest fire led him to keep his blaze small.

Sitting on the ground in the light of his faggots, he waited for the dawn in the attitude of the patient red hunter, although his mind was very far from being quiescent.

It happened that in his crew that winter he had had two men who had made the trip into Minnesota, into the government lands which were soon to be open for settlement, and their enthusiastic descriptions of these lands had filled him with an irresistible desire to explore. In the deep of his lonely vigil he resolved to see these delectable prairies either with David or alone. "I didn't come West to live on a rented farm," he declared. "And I didn't come West to plough and sow on hill-sides."

For the first time since leaving Boston his confidence faded into doubt of himself, and small wonder! After seven years of the most wearing and unremitting toil, he was without the means of providing a home for his bride. He did not regret what he had done for his mother and Susan, but he realized to the full the burden which their care had imposed upon him. They had divided his interest. Henceforth his house and that of his father should be separate. Isabel must be sole mistress of his fireside.

The lonely figure of that woodsman is (to me) at once heroic and pitiful. With what elation, with what high hopes he had set forth from Boston seven years before! With what courage he had met every danger, every duty, every defeat. How valiantly and unhesitatingly that fine young body of his had served other men, and here now over his camp-fire, he crouched like a gipsy or red hunter, facing the problem of opening a farm with a store of gold so small that his bride must come to a scantily furnished, rented cabin.

That he had these moments of profound dejection, I

know, for he once admitted it to me, but as the dawn came, his amazing courage returned. His mental horizon lightened with the landscape.

Sunrise brought a surprising warmth with the wind turning southerly. A softness was in the air, a spring balm which forecast a noon of pouring sunlight, and the birds awoke to joyous song. As the day broadened he was able to correct his course, which he perceived was too far north of the stage road which ran from Madison to La Crosse. Stiff and weary though he was he resumed a pace which an ordinary walker, though fresh, would have found wearing.

At eight o'clock he came into a rough waggon road which led toward the new town of Sparta, and when, an hour later, he reached a small farm-house, he sought and obtained food and an hour's rest.

From this point the land was settled and fertile and all his depression passed away. Every mile brought him nearer the hills of Neshonoc—and Isabel! At noon he entered the Welsh settlement of Bangor, and an hour later was at the door of his mother's house, weary and tattered, but triumphant.

"Why, Richard, where do you come from?" she asked in her unemotional way, though her eyes were wet with tears of joy.

"From the Dells," he answered. "I left there yesterday. Don't touch me! I'm wet and dirty and as hungry as a wolf, but I can't eat till I clean up. I feel like a Pottawatomie Injun."

After a bath and a shave he ate a delicious dinner of eggs, hot biscuits, honey and milk, and tumbled into bed with the understanding that he was to be awakened at seven. "I want to see Isabel as soon as possible," he said in explanation.

When they called him the sunset chorus of the prairie-

chickens was in full volume. He was sleepier than when
he lay down, but he shook off his languor and put on his
Sunday-go-to-meeting suit while his father went to borrow
a horse for him to ride.

"Next year I'm going to have a horse of my own, a span
of them," he said, and turning to Susan, asked, "Are you
coming over to keep house for me this spring?"

"Do you want me?"

"Certainly! I need you, bad."

"Of course I'll come, if mother can spare me."

"That's so. She needs you more than I do. Well, we'll
discuss that later."

As he rode off in the deepening twilight, hearing the call
of geese in flight and watching the flocks of ducks settling
upon the pools in the marsh, he felt the magic of seed-time
as never before. The freshly harrowed fields and the bags
of grain distributed ready for the hand of the sower created
in him a feeling of regret that he had not sooner returned.
Seeding was early and he was late.

The McLanes were all sitting on the porch enjoying the
sounds and odours of the evening. They greeted him as
one of the family, quietly, cordially, and Isabel received his
kiss with such composure, aided, perhaps, by the dusk,
that no one, not even Deb, made comment upon it. All
understood his relationship and approved of it.

Luke told of the number of acres he had sown that day
and Richard said, "I'm going at my place just as soon as
I can get seed and tools."

David volunteered to help him plough and Mrs. McLane
asked, "Will your folks go on the place and keep house
for you?"

"No, I guess I'll have to bach it for the present."

All knew that he meant "till Isabel comes," but waited
for Hugh to speak. He, however, sat in silence, and to

relieve the tension David said, "If you want me or my team, just shout and I'll come over."

One by one the other members of the family went in, leaving Isabel and Richard to discuss their plans for the future.

"Belle, I hate to take you to a rented farm," he said, "but I see no help for it now. I'm going on to the Bingham place tomorrow, horse, foot, and dragoons. Part of it has got to be ploughed, and I'll have to work every daylight hour till I get it seeded. I won't have time to see you except on Sundays, but I'll be thinking of you all the time. Maybe you can come over with Dave when he is helping me, and see how you like the house. It's only a rough log shanty with a lean-to, but it has a good roof and floor and windows."

She listened to all the details of his plan with an interest which was world-old in its import. The nest-building interest was awake in her.

"I'll get Dave to drive me over tomorrow," she said. "Maybe I can help Susan put the house in order."

He laughed. "Won't be much to put in order till I go to La Crosse and buy some furniture."

It was after midnight when he mounted his horse and set out for home. As he reached the bridge over the creek his horse suddenly shied and from the darkness a stern voice called out, "Halt!"

Richard pulled his steed to a stand. "What's wanted?" he demanded, bracing himself for trouble.

A horseman rode out of the shadow and silently approached. Something sinister in his action stirred Richard's fighting-blood. "What do you want of me?" he demanded truculently.

The stranger drew alongside. "I want an explanation. What are you doing, racing along here at this time of night?"

"What business is that of yours?" returned Richard curtly. "I'm on a public highway."

"I know you are. Where have you been?"

"None of your business."

"Well, I take a different view of that, and as I'm deputy-sheriff of this county, I guess you'll have to give an account of yourself."

Richard's tone changed. "I don't see why my doings should interest you, even if you are deputy-sheriff; but if you must know, I've been to see my girl."

"Who are you and who is your girl?"

"Is it necessary for you to know that?"

"Yes, you're a stranger to me. You need an alibi."

"Very well, I'm Richard Graham and I've been to Grandad McLane's to see Isabel, one of his daughters."

The sheriff began to chuckle. "You darned fool, why didn't you say so in the beginning? Now I understand. I've spent many an evening at the McLanes'. That's a hard place to get away from. Dave played the fiddle, I'll be bound, and they had some singing."

"No," Richard replied, "but Isabel and I are to be married this spring and we were busy going over our plans. You see I've been up in the woods all winter and this is the first time I've seen her since last November. Now you tell me something. Why did you stop me?"

The sheriff's tone became grave. "There's been a man killed and robbed on the road to La Crosse and I'm one of the posse out after the murderer. When I heard you tearing along in the dark I naturally felt it my duty to find out what your hurry was. I know now. You can ride on." His chuckle came back. "I'm satisfied you're on peaceful business."

Richard also laughed. "Thank you kindly. I've been in all kinds of tight corners, but this is the first time I was ever held up as a robber by an officer of the law."

Richard Becomes a Farmer

"Good luck," responded the deputy as he rode away.

Early next morning Richard yoked up an ox-team and drove over to his farm. It was only a small, rented place, but he acknowledged a glow of delight as he reached the shanty which was to be his first independent home in the West.

The sunlight fell with full, almost summer heat upon the misty earth which palpitated with responding energy. The cabin stood in the centre of a level expanse of black soil, just the kind of a homestead he had hoped to own, but which was held at a price quite out of his power to pay.

Neshonoc was only a mile away, and before nightfall he had assembled a camper's outfit in the house, also a plough and harrow and a sufficient amount of seed-grain to plant the tillable acres.

During the second forenoon David drove in with a plough in his wagon-box, and Isabel, sitting beside him. Nothing in Richard's life, up to that moment, approached the charm, the mystery, the delight of this experience. To be tilling the soil on a glorious April day while his bride-to-be was at work in the cabin which was shortly to be her home, filled him with an emotion too deep, too subtle in its compound of pioneering, spring-time, and devotion to be put into any words at his command, and when, at noon, they ate at a bare pine table like campers, with the cackle of robins and the shrill call of yellow-hammers sounding through the open door, not one of them gave a thought to the great world of cities which lay to the east, but into the almost perfect hour—peaceful, confident, prophetic—the Farther West made way. Richard said, "I've been hearing a lot this winter about that Minnesota prairie and I'm crazy to explore."

The light went out of Isabel's face. "What do you want to go there for? You don't think of settling over there, do you?"

"I might. You see this is only a rented farm. Dave and I want homes of our own, and we can't afford to buy these high-priced farms. Over there the land is free—and level."

David, who shared Richard's notion that it was the bounden duty of a wife to leave her own people and fare forth into strange countries with her husband, put in a word. "There's no land for sale here, sis, except up these coulees where a farm would be mostly side-hills. The Minnesota land is 'perara.'"

Isabel said no more, but for her the beautiful day had suddenly acquired a cloud. This cloud expanded as the two men went on to arrange the date and details of the expedition.

At last David perceived the shadow on her face. "Don't you want Dick to have a fine, level farm of his own?" he asked.

"Yes, but not away off in Minnesota. I like it here."

They smiled at her pouting, and Richard, as he was about to go back to his work, put his arm about her and said, "Don't worry, Belle. We may not go, after all."

CHAPTER XIX

The Minnesota Prairies

FOR centuries the upper Mississippi had been the dividing line between the Sioux tribes of the West bank and the Chippewas, Sacs and Foxes—wood people of the East bank. The small streams which entered the river from the West came down from high prairie lands whose beauty was already a legend among the settlers of La Crosse County. "There's no end to the level land over there," said all those who had explored the region, but many were deterred by the menace of the red hunters and by the government's express warning that these lands were not yet subject to entry.

Notwithstanding all this, Richard continued to plan for the trip. Never a Sunday passed without a conference concerning it, and at last, on the fifth of June, he and David in a covered wagon ferried the Mississippi at La Crosse and entered upon the rough, winding road which climbed nearly a thousand feet until the level of mighty north-west plains was attained. With spades and axes in the waggon and a plough slung beneath the axle, they were fully resolved to stake a claim somewhere in the new and uninhabited paradise.

From the moment when they reached the summit of the bluffs, they were drunk with the wine of exploration, and who can blame them? Illimitably rolling to the west and north-west, the grassy ocean outspread, radiantly green, brilliant with flowers, laced with streams, and islanded with groves of trees, with only an occasional settler's cabin lying like a lonely sail against a green wave. Here were the ideal homesteads of their dreams. Here were farms without a hill or stone, the sunset region which Richard had been seeking, and yet they did not halt. He insisted on pushing deeper, ever deeper, into the loneliness, eager to reach the perfect valleys where no wheel or plough had left a mark. "This is what I came out for to see!" he exulted. "This is the kind of country I've been reading about and talking about."

David, though less expressive by way of words, was equally enraptured. "I wish Pap could see this; it's 'the other side of Jordan' he sings about."

By noon of the second day all signs of settlement were left behind. Through grassy meadows radiant with flowers, over smooth ridges of perfect plough-land they slowly moved, surrounded by the swarming life of the ageless world. Prairie-hens in myriads rose before their horses' feet. Wolves and foxes regarded them from the swells. Water-fowl covered each lake with clamour, and when they rose they were like clouds. Deer, elk, and bear roamed the green savannahs which lay between groves of unscarred oaks and thick-leaved maples. All the native creatures of the plain they saw except the buffalo. These giant cattle had all been driven into distant pastures by the arrows of the Sioux.

Never again on this continent can any youthful explorer experience the same exaltation, the same ecstasy of discovery which these young adventurers experienced on their solitary march. With the pain of unaccountable, insatiate longing in their throats, with vague dreams of some ennobling conquest in their eyes, they rode on and on, marching in a kind of delirium into ever-remoter wildernesses. Consider the marvel of it! Here lay an unappropriated world, vaster, more alluring than any poet had imagined it to be, and yet these dreamers were unable to call a halt, unable to settle upon a definite acre. With a world to chose from, they chose nothing, the urge of exploration still too strong to permit of settlement.

Sometimes they followed the shores of lovely lakes where herons and cranes stalked and loons clamoured, mocking their voices. Sometimes they forded a clear river filled with darting fish and over-hung with sweet-scented, blossoming trees. Oh, to see it all! To win it all!

Slowly they moved, amusing themselves by selecting lovely sites for homesteads, camping when night fell beside a brook or stream, feasting upon the fish and game which David's skill provided. Richard was the cook and his dexterity with the frying-pan was notable. Sometimes these camping-places were made intolerable by insects, and occasionally they were obliged to abandon an ideal site on the banks of a lake, and to make their fire on a waterless ridge. Young as they were, ecstatic as they were, they could not ignore the clouds of insects which certain localities sent against them, and yet it is evident that these attacks were not serious enough to end their advance. No mosquito or smoke could rob the landscape of its mystic, virgin charm.

Unable to make an end, unable to decide on a claim, they came at last upon a level bench of land in the valley of a placid river whose name and course they did not know, a spot which in some unaccountable way imperiously called, *"Halt! Here is the place! Set your stakes!"*

In later years I tried to draw from Richard a statement of the reason why, out of all the lands he had crossed, this remote site captured his fancy, but I never succeeded in clearing away the mystery. He was never quite able to explain its peculiar charm. It was fifty miles from the nearest settler, and the soil not so good as that which they had tested in a dozen other valleys. The grass was no sweeter, the river no brighter, the woodlands no more attractive than in many other localities they had surveyed, and yet they halted, satiated, I suspect, with surveying.

Whatever the cause of their halting, Richard unslung the plough, and David, hitching his horses to its beam, drew a long furrow around their chosen plot, thus indicating that they made claim to it as a permanent abiding-place. It was a kind of madness—a youthful, glorious madness! The fact that they were without a market for their crops, or a neighbour, made no difference to them. In imagination Richard saw their cabins built, with Isabel in the doorway watching him as he tilled the soil. That he was re-enacting the typical drama of the settler, as he saw it depicted on the posters and on the seals of prairie states, was his pride. He was the trail-maker here as he had been in the forest.

Three days later, while David was ploughing and Richard's flying axe was shaping logs to build a cabin, a squadron of horsemen suddenly appeared riding down the valley from the east.

"Soldiers!" shouted Richard, and with axe poised in his hand and a foot on the log he had been hewing, he calmly waited their approach, interested but not concerned.

The troop, which contained about twenty men, was led by a bronzed and powerful man of middle age who rode with a grace which Dick had never seen equalled. As the officer drew near, the keen glance of his steel-blue eyes was intensified by the ruddy colour of his sun-burned skin. Reining his horse to a halt, he brusquely asked, "What are you men doing here?"

"Establishing a homestead," replied Richard, a little nettled by the soldier's manner.

"Well, you disestablish yourselves out of here. I'm under orders to round up all you fool squatters. The Sioux are on the war-path and you'll be scalped in less than three days. I give you just an hour to get ready to march."

Richard recognized such authority in this order that he signalled David to come in and set about packing. Within an hour they were harnessed and moving eastward under military escort. Their brief period of exultant homesteading was at an end!

As they topped the ridge and looked back upon the confident lines they had drawn on the green page of the valley floor, David, with a sigh of keen regret, softly remarked, "Well, it was a good beginning, anyway."

Neither of them ever saw the claim again, and neither of them in later life could precisely identify the spot, but they always insisted that it was "the choicest location in the state."

As the captain with his command proceeded eastward, he gathered up other settlers who were now awake to their folly.

Here was a typical, century-old American situation. Into the hunting-grounds of the Sioux certain adventurous land-hungry settlers had thrust themselves, believing that the government would defend them and ultimately buy or drive out the red nomads. Some had taken claims, urged by the same mood of vague longing which had actuated Richard and David, but others had openly proclaimed their desire to drive out and destroy the primitive people who held, but could not use, the land. They were speculators and not home-builders. Now, in a panic of fear, all were hurrying to evacuate the invaded territory.

The commander of the district, in driving back the squatters, was merely carrying out the order of the President, who was seeking to avoid a war with a tribe which up to this time had been friendly and with which the State Department was conducting negotiations in the hope of peaceably obtaining the land. In such wise began "The Black Hawk War" and many another in the past.

Of all this, Richard, like his companions, was aware, but only obscurely. He had no notion of the exact stage of proceedings. To him, the case was simple. He was in need of land and here it was, oceans of it—flowery plains whereon the redmen only infrequently pursued game. As part of the conquering race sweeping over the continent like an ever-swelling tide, he believed that the primitive races must ultimately give way. That the Sioux loved this glorious hunting-ground he could well believe, "but they can't use it—at least they don't use it," he argued. "They'll have to let the white man have it."

To this, Captain McRae, as representing the Federal Government, replied, "I've no doubt we'll take the country, as we have all the other lands east of the Mississippi River, but that's none of my business. Just now I'm under orders to see that you squatters are herded back to safety. If it was my own say, I'd let you and the redskins fight it out, but luckily I'm not Secretary of War—yet."

Richard was much taken with McRae, who in his more than twenty years' experience had been stationed so often in garrisons on the border-line, that he had taken on some of the characteristics of the scout and the redman, retaining, withal, the bearing of a soldier. He rode like a plainsman with easy slouch, but his uniform and side-arms were in military order. His speech at times was that of a scout, but his discipline was unrelenting. Though but a captain with a squadron he had the air of leading a regiment, not in a pompous or boisterous way, but in a precision which indicated the natural commander.

He liked Richard and answered his questions concerning Kansas and Texas and Oregon with vivid phrases of description and comment. " 'Tis a big country," he said with an inflection which was Irish. "Sometimes I wonder will it ever be settled up. Why not let the redskins have the land beyond the Missouri? There's plenty on this side for all of you."

Upon reaching the long winding road which led from St. Louis to St. Paul, McRae sent his straggling column of fugitives forward with a parting word of warning. "Here's your trail. Keep going till you cross the river and don't come back till the government notifies you that these tribes have been placated or removed."

David and Richard obeyed his command to the full, but others of the fugitives, finding the scare dying out along the river, remained among the settlers, having in mind to return to their claims when the Indians had calmed down. "Washington will never consent to our being driven off our claims. Congress will do as it has always done, make a treaty and move the red devils to the wilder country farther on. There's a world of hunting country out there."

CHAPTER XX

Richard Wins a Bride

MEANWHILE Isabel and other relatives of the wanderers were greatly concerned about them, for fugitive settlers from the west had been arriving at La Crosse, and stories of massacres (mostly imaginary) were current. It was impossible to get the truth of the situation from these panic-stricken farmers, and there was nothing to do but to wait and hope.

With no understanding of this anxiety on the part of their friends and relations, the explorers returned one day too crest-fallen and disappointed to give any attention to the words of joyous relief with which their mothers and sisters greeted them. "We didn't see hide nor hair of a redskin," said Richard; "I don't believe we were in any danger at any time."

Isabel was not amused by David's laughing account of their arrest by Captain McRae. With more of asperity than Richard had ever before heard in her tone, she said,

Richard Wins a Bride

"Served you right! You had no business out there, anyway. It was all a piece of foolishness. I won't move into that wild country among the Injuns. There's plenty of land right here. Why don't you buy a farm around here?"

Richard admitted that she was right. He perceived that glorious paradise from a woman's point of view. She was sweet but she was firm. "I will never go on the other side of the river, Dick, I can't think of it."

With that remark his hope of a level farm vanished. Notwithstanding his memories of the Minnesota prairies, notwithstanding his vow never to plough another hill-side furrow, he put aside his dream country and purchased from his old friend, Ben Plummer, a quarter-section of land in Green's Coulee, about six miles from the home of the Mc-Lanes and some five miles north of the county town. It was a sad "come-down," as he confessed to his mother. "But what can I do? Isabel will not move away from her folks, and I can't blame her much."

It was a pleasant little prospective farm and sheltered by wooded bluffs, but its level acres were few and marshy. Furthermore, the price demanded obliged him to place it under mortgage, a condition he had hoped to avoid by locating on the lands of Minnesota. To him the word "mortgage" had a sinister connotation. It was a monster which fed on the flesh of the poor. It was a writing which put a farmer into the hands of a relentless town-dweller.

Isabel was delighted with his purchase. She had no fear of the debt involved. Her faith in her future husband was unquestioning. "We'll soon pay off that old mortgage," she declared. "I'll work and save till we do."

Childishly eager to see the place, she went with him one Sunday afternoon to select the site for the house—"our first home."

They fixed upon the spot, the sunny side of a knoll on the west-eighty, from which they could look eastward across the meadow toward Sugar-Loaf Hill, and which commanded a view of the vale from north to south. It was a bare and windy plot, but with the eyes of youth and love they saw it sheltered by trees and adorned with flowers.

This selection of a farm so near his own pleased old Hugh. It removed all his objections to Isabel's marriage, and David and Luke at once volunteered to haul lumber for a house, and to help break up some of the sod land in preparation for the next year's crop.

In making this choice of a homestead Richard had been influenced by Plummer's remark, "When work on the farm is slack, you can get work on the booms," and his farm was only two miles from Onalaska which was a veritable "Boom-town," for it had been built at the mouth of Black River and was a home for the mill-hands and a point of supply for the men at work on the "booms" or yards in which the logs from the pineries of the upper river were caught and sorted.

These water-yards were formed of hewn logs laid upon the water and chained end to end, with here and there a raised length to serve as gate for entrance or exit. During the spring drive, the runways of these booms swarmed with skilful red-shirted rivermen with cant-hooks in their hands, walking the gates, riding the logs, scanning each for its brand and assigning it to its proper place. Below these booms, on an island in the river, several saw-mills with ceaseless, cheerful howling received the logs and worked them into planks, boards, lath, and other building materials, most of which was then rafted down the Mississippi River.

In "boom-times" it was a rough and riotous little village crowded with sawyers, uncouth and lawless hardy rivermen, off-duty lumber-jacks. Groggeries abounded, but two churches and a school-house indicated the will of a saving minority who were bravely keeping alive the traditions of New York and New England. Certain streets at

Richard Wins a Bride

night roared with battle, but the warriors fought with their fists, and no lives were lost. The era of the revolver had not reached the river. The tradition was Donnybrook or Queensberry. It was no place for a timid man, but then neither Richard nor his father was timid.

In this turbulent little town Clinton was a frequent visitor, for he, too, had shifted his lumbering operations from the Wisconsin to the Black River. Though he still lived in Galena he had acquired an interest in a lumber company whose office was in Dubuque, and when he learned of Richard's plans for a new home, he promptly offered to contribute the lumber for it, an offer which Richard declined in a way which made Clinton laugh. "I knew you'd take that attitude. That's why I talked so large. However, I want to make a wedding-present. Why not accept the shingles for the roof?"

He was now an employer of labour and looked the part of a prosperous young lumberman; but, though as handsome as ever, he remained unmarried, much to Richard's wonder. "You can better afford to marry than I. Furthermore, you're getting to be an old man, over thirty."

To this Clinton only smiled, volunteering no reason for his celibacy. "What you want to do, Dick, is to stop working your arms and use your head. Make yourself into a boss. Let the other fellows swing the axe. Come into my mill and I'll work you into the firm."

To this Richard replied with the same curious, stubborn pride he had always manifested, "No, Clint, I'll go my own gait along my own path."

It was probably this attitude which had led Addison to walk aloof. He now wrote a cordial letter and asked Isabel to name what she needed most. Richard, replying for her, said, "We're not in need of anything, but will like to see you and Hannah."

Robert Graham came over to help build the new house, and his frequent visits to Onalaska led him to give up his home in Burnham Valley and to establish a small grocery-store in Onalaska, a plan which did not strongly appeal to Richard. He anticipated that his father's "notions" would make it difficult for him to succeed as a trader. He discouraged the idea for another reason: it threw upon him an extra burden at a time when he had need of all his resources. He had succeeded in gaining old Hugh's outspoken consent and Isabel had set the day of their marriage. "I'd like it to be on your birth-day, the first of September," she had declared.

She came down every Sunday to see the growth of the house, and her joy in it was very sweet to Richard. The cottage was a tiny structure, a storey and a half in height, with a living-room fourteen feet square, a bedroom and a pantry at the back, and a lean-to which contained the kitchen-stove and churn, but to Isabel it was enchantingly complete. She loved the smell of new lath and shingles and fresh mortar. Many of her young married friends were still living in log cabins, and to have a frame dwelling of such neatness and completeness was more than she had hoped for. "Think of it! Every room is lathed and plastered and there's a brick chimney rising from the roof!"

In the midst of the work of building his stable of poles, the harvest bustle called Richard away to his rented farm, and for six weeks he had no time to give to his homestead. Reaping, binding, stacking, he toiled from dawn to dark and often on moonlight nights returned to the field after supper, there to set up sheaves or to bind such swathes as had been left by the cradlers. He took a kind of fierce pleasure in thus driving his tired body to the highest point of service. Too busy to think of Isabel during the week, his joy in her companionship on the Sabbath was all the sweeter for the reason that it was associated with his hours of rest, and his freedom from the heat and grime of his labour.

In this stern, unromantic fashion he approached his marriage and his twenty-eighth birthday. Sometimes he saw himself as he was, a man in debt after eight years of life in the Western paradise which he had so hopefully sought to share. "For the life of me," he said to Belle, "I don't see how I could have done better. I could earn more money on the river than on a farm and so I stayed on the river. Maybe I should have gone into business with Addison, but I'm no good at waiting on people or figuring. Clinton wants me to go into his mill, but I can't think of that as a job. I've always been just a year too late in getting land, except in the trip over into Minnesota when I got too far ahead of the game. I guess there's only one way for me to get rich and that's just plain hard work. I give you fair warning! If you come with me you'll come to a home where work is plenty and money scarce."

He meant this as a warning. In that mood he honestly wanted her to know that he was a failure as a money-getter, but his candour of statement only increased her love and admiration for him.

"I know what I'm coming to," she replied, but she didn't know, she couldn't know, mercifully, the work, the worry, the pain to which she was bound. She only knew that this handsome, valiant, unconquerable trail-maker loved her and wanted her to help him make a home. When he lifted his graceful head and fixed upon her his big grey eyes nothing else mattered. Having him, she was not afraid.

The wedding-day was one of those silent, golden, September days, when the sun's rays are tempered by a thick haze and the odour of grain in shock is mingled with the smell of ripened melons and tasselled corn. The birds were songless, but the crickets were chirping innumerably as

Richard set out on his way toward the McLane farm where the wedding was to take place, with only the relatives and a few friends as witnesses. The new house was complete and furnished, with a long-legged stove set up on the bright yellow kitchen-floor filled with wood and ready for action. Other articles, presents and necessary furniture were at the McLane farm, ready to accompany the bride.

It was a merry, crowded house to which he came that day. Fortunately the warm sun permitted the men to lounge on the grass under the trees whilst the women set the table in the living-room and laid boards across kitchen-chairs to provide seats for the feasters.

At noon precisely, the preacher called the men to the ceremony which took place on the porch and was brief for he was hungry and the wedding feast ready to serve. What a feast! Fried chicken with cream gravy, mountains of mashed potatoes, cords of corn on the cob, wild honey, blackberry short-cake, pitchers of cream, mounds of butter, and stacks of biscuits, but better than all these the hearty voices and comely faces of the McLanes, who were always at their best on festal occasions. All the comfort, hope, kindliness, and good-cheer of the border was in this dinner.

Hugh sat at one end of the table and his good wife at the other—the end next the kitchen, so that she could the more readily slip away and serve. She *always* served, but with no time to stand or wait. The bride, following her habit, would have risen to assist her mother, but her brothers and sisters, even Deborah, insisted on her being "the Queen of the Day." "This is your picnic, Belle. We'll wait on you for once."

She was a bit uncomfortable in her grand dress, but concealed it very well, submitting to the kisses and compliments of her friends with native dignity. She was a handsome girl; not pretty, but nobly graceful.

As the men filled up they left the table and returned to

the shade of the popple trees before the door, leaving the women "to rastle with the dishes" and gossip. Harriet Graham (who had not ridden so far since leaving Burnham Valley) sat in an easy-chair on the porch with Isabel beside her while the girls put the house to rights; and the men talked of freeing the negroes and other political matters.

It was a quiet, peaceful hour, like a Sunday afternoon, but no one was disposed to talk loudly or foolishly. It was not a moment for music, not until after three did the McLanes "tune up with a wedding-song." It was a typical union of East, South, and West, of the Old World and the New. These two families, beginning in such diverse conditions, travelling widely separated roads, had joined at last, here on the bank of a placid little river in a community of blended nationalities. Who will say it was not foreordained?

Somewhere about my desk I have a sadly faded ambrotype portrait which reveals with moving fidelity the kind of man Richard Graham appeared when (adorned to meet his bride) he confronted the camera. As I study the face in this tarnished frame it remotely suggests the countenance of a youthful judge. His expression is severe, almost stern, and he stares up at me through that plush-upholstered oval with such piercing intentness that I turn away. It is difficult, almost impossible, for one to identify this austere individual in a high collar and black stock, with "Yankee Dick," the pilot of Big Bull Falls, whose red-shirted figure appears in another and earlier portrait, muscular and rowdy, a handsome boy with smooth face and powerful hands. If Isabel McLane ever saw him in his riverman's garb, I marvel that she had the courage to accept him as a husband. He looks entirely competent, but a savage and dangerous citizen.

A careful study of these two pictures leads me to wonder

if he ever wore for a second time that Websterian collar and that long-tailed coat. If he did not actually "swap it for a yellow dog," as he afterward laughingly declared he had done, he must have discarded it immediately after the wedding, for it vanishes from his history at this point and never again reappears in his account or Isabel's.

At four o'clock the groom brought his oxen round to the door, where all the McLanes and Grahams stood ready to load in their presents and to send the two adventurers forth upon their bright, uncharted sea.

To me there is an element of pathos in the fact that Isabel, passing from her father's doorstep, mounted to a seat in a lumber-wagon and was drawn to her coulee home by means of an ox-team, with her meagre store of wedding-gifts heaped in the box behind her, but there is no record of any expression of disappointment on her part, and I doubt if she saw the slightest incongruity in the picture presented by her stately, high-chokered bridegroom as he walked beside his cattle. Wedding-journeys of this character were all too common to excite remark. The slow-stepping span occupied three hours in the journey, but ten minutes later Isabel had lighted a candle and was at work in her kitchen.

Perhaps the pathos of this infare festival lies in our present-day outlook. It may be that these young lovers were wholly content with their bare little box of pine. So far as I can judge from Isabel's own story, she had no regrets and no envies, and the neighbours who came in to greet her, expressed no pity. The roof was low, but it sheltered her valiantly from the rain. The walls were narrow, but they defended her from the winds. No, no, it will not do to read back into the minds of these young pioneers the discontent, the bitterness, the flippant envy of the present day. Richard's world was hard and his life laborious, but I am assured by many a rich man of my acquaintance that he would give his city house, his shining motor-car, and some part of his stocks and bonds to be back in that joyous era driving an ox-team toward such a cabin on such a farm with such a bride.

As I look back along the trail of Richard and Isabel Graham I long for the spirit of the border, the hospitality of the latch-string. I would re-enter that cabin if I could and blow upon its embers till its flames returned and shadows of mournful beauty danced upon the walls. I would call back David and Luke, Rachel and Deborah, and ask them to sing once more for me, knowing that from their chorus Isabel's voice would rise in clear familiar sweetness, restoring for me a world that is gone—the world of my youth, the land of the pioneer.

THE TRAIL-MAKERS

BOOK II: IN WAR

As a tribute to those brave and silent men, soldiers and civilians who served without adequate reward and without public commendation, as scouts and guides to Grant's armies in the West, I dedicate this the second part of Trail-Makers of the Middle Border.

CHAPTER I

The Cabin in the Coulee

GREEN'S COULEE, the minute valley in which Richard Graham had at last taken root, was hardly more than a ravine. Less than three miles in length it provided room for only four other farms, and as each of these was narrow and only the central acres level it was very far from being the prairie land for which he had left Boston and, from a sympathetic point of view, was but a pitiful ending of high hopes and of seven years of unremitting and savage toil.

The first house, at the mouth of the coulee, belonged to the Widow Green whose husband had been the earliest settler in the region, and who quite naturally chose the best land. Mrs. Green was the head of a noisy, hearty, vigorous, and lovable family of the sort who form the solid substratum of a state, but the two farms above Richards were owned by Bushrod Brown and his son-in-law, Albert Crandall, all of a somewhat ruder type, but Isabel was glad of any kind of neighbours. Mrs. Crandall, who was only a girl, aspired to be a little more refined than her mother and often reproached her.

Mrs. Brown, who smoked like a man and swore like a pilot, came early to call and Richard was highly amused by her. She shocked Isabel, however, at the same time that she made her laugh, as when one day she reproved her grandson for swearing and then querulously added, "I don't see where in hell that boy learnt to swear."

She was short, broad in the beam, and deep-bosomed. On a clear morning she could be heard "jawing" with Bushrod, but her bark was reported to be worse than her bite. She was in truth a good neighbour in many ways. She and Richard were on good terms, although he had begun by disciplining her. She had a habit if calling the attention of her guests to the disorder of her house and the poor quality of her cooking, expecting, of course, that her visitors would exclaim, "Why, Mrs. Brown, your dinner is delicious." It was her way of extracting a compliment, for she was an admirable housekeeper.

One noon, as Richard came in to dinner along with the men of the threshing-crew, she met them with her usual phrase, "I'm sorry for you men. There ain't a thing in this house fit for a dog to eat."

Richard, who had just taken his seat at the table, rose abruptly and started for the door.

His hostess turned a startled glance upon him. "Hold on, Dick Graham, where are you going?'" she sharply demanded.

"Home," he replied darkly. "I'm no dog."

The old harridan's broad face turned a brick-red. For a moment she could not find voice, then she burst out, "Damn your hide, Dick Graham! Go back to your place or I'll take a broom to ye."

The crew broke into a roar of laughter as Richard with resigned look permitted himself to be pushed back into

The Cabin in the Coulee

his chair. "Think you're devilish smart, don't ye?" his hostess bitterly remarked.

"I always take cooks at their word," he retorted.

The lesson was effectual. She never again tried that form of boasting with Richard.

She was capable of fighting like a wildcat, but she was amazingly gentle at a sick-bed. Having grown up in the Michigan backwoods almost without schooling and surrounded by rough men, it was natural that her habits should be uncouth. She knew some of her failings and acknowledged them, and, like old Hooper, she had wept buckets (if not barrels) of tears over them.

She took Isabel to her heart at once, and was of the greatest comfort to the young wife when, in the deep of the winter, she fell ill of a fever.

Thereafter Richard spoke of the old woman with tenderness.

The Graham cabin was a desolate place in winter. The snows fell deep in December and over the ridge, behind the cottage, the wind blew the flakes in clouds to lodge in great drifts before the door. By January the cabin was almost buried. Day after day Richard was obliged to tunnel into the barn, and the road was almost impassable for oxen. At Isabel's request he traded one pair of his cattle for a horse, and his father having built a hickory sleigh, they were able to ride out with an approach to comfort. This committed him to a change in locomotion. Oxen were going out of fashion.

On pleasant days he wallowed through the snow to the wooded hill-sides of his farm to cut firewood and to split rails. In this he worked alone. Accustomed as he had been to the bustling of logging-camps and the excitement of mill and river, chopping by himself was dreary business. It was a lonely winter for Isabel, too, for only now and then could she find time to call upon her neighbours.

Occasionally David or Luke drove over with Deborah or Rachel, and sometimes she and Richard went to Onalaska to church or to call upon his mother. In spite of all ameliorations, the winter was dreary and she longed for spring. Richard repeated the old rhyme, "March the twenty-first is spring, and little birds begin to sing," to cheer his young wife's heart, but realized that this confident assertion of spring was born in some milder climate than Wisconsin and that April tenth was as early as spring could possibly arrive. They were not unhappy, but March was a hard month to bear.

At last snow began to melt, the sunward sloping fields grew warm and dry, and Richard with but few acres of his own to sow was able to go forth upon the fields of his neighbours.

The mechanical seeder had not yet been imagined and Richard's skill in broadcasting seed was in high demand. To see him marching with steady stride, maintaining an unswerving course, while from his fist a golden, semi-circular, evenly divided spray of seed intermittently gushed, was to witness a noble action. Fixing his eyes on a stake at the farther side of the field, in order that he might not overlap his previous spread, he strode erectly, the wheat falling from his hand with such fine precision that no barren streaks could afterwards develop to make weedy accusation of his fault.

He loved this work. While spreading seed upon the soil, he sensed a kind of majesty in the action, as if somehow he had taken on a partnership with God. He delighted in it, also, by reason of the warm noons and still sunsets which April brought to the valley. In early red mornings, while robins rioted in the mist, and water-fowl were winging their confident flight into the north, he went to his task with delight.

A different but equally rewarding pleasure came to him

The Cabin in the Coulee

in the hushed, resplendent after-supper hour when, from neighbouring thickets, the hidden thrushes rang their sentinel bells. At such moments he forgot his hatred of stumps and his resentment of ridges, and rejoiced in the swelling cloud of hill-side foliage, foliage which presented at this moment all the colours of October in delicate, diminished scale with exquisite refinement of leaf and bloom.

It was good to go from such magic surroundings, weary and hungry, to sit at a homely laden kitchen-table, there to be waited upon by grateful and smiling women. Their hot biscuit, their heaps of mashed potato, flanked by salt pork or sausage, and their shining dishes presented something rewarding, and the doors, standing wide to the wind, let in the sounds and odours of sunset almost as if the meal were set in the open air.

Sometimes Isabel shared these meals and afterwards they walked homeward in the fragrant dusk, planning improvements in their home and farm. At such moments the trail-maker's eyes were calm.

Brave and serene as Isabel was, she was only a girl and she suffered from loneliness while Richard was absent. He realized this and every night, no matter how far away his work was, he returned to her. Sometimes this caused a walk of several miles across the hills and a dawn-light return next morning, but he made no comment on that. He was accustomed to early rising.

"Changing works" in this new land was a method of co-operation in getting seed sown, houses built, barns raised, and grain harvested. The stocking of hay, the cutting and threshing of grain (all done by hand) took on the character of a "bee." In such neighbourhood assemblies Isabel and Richard were welcome members, for he was skilful and she a tireless cook and always ready when the time came to sing.

Poor as they were in other ways, they were rich in the

good-will of their neighbours, most of whom lived quite as humbly, to tell the truth. Few had a spare room in that period of pioneer privation, but all, looking into the future with confident glance, planned houses that should have the comforts of the houses they had left behind them in the East.

The task which Richard most cordially hated was "grubbing," a process of chopping out the stumps of the small oaks that cumbered a part of his lands. I mention this again, for it has an important bearing on his future. It was not so much the back-breaking labour of this job as the indignity of it.

He spoke of this to Clinton. "It gravels me like the devil to think that, after leaving the rocks and hills of Maine, in search of land that didn't stand on edge, I should now be digging out grubs on a Wisconsin side-hill! It's as bad as digging stones. But what else can I do? Belle won't go to Minnesota and I can't afford the price of the level farms around Neshonoc. I stuck to the river just about three years too long. I should have located here in '54."

His mood turned sour whenever he had occasion to drive his waggon over one of the ridges or when he bogged down on his marsh. Sometimes when swinging a cradle against a field of wheat in some windless "pocket" between the hills, he broke out in furious resentment. These clouds occasionally shadowed his home, but not for long. His anger was as quick to go as to come.

In this stern routine he walked during the years of '58 and '59 while the valley filled up to its remotest nooks and the town of La Crosse grew to the dignity of two banks and a newspaper. Three small saw-mills arose at the mouth of Black River, and each spring the lines of the booms on the still water extended themselves like swift aquatic vines, and lumber-camps thickened on the head-waters of all the streams. Settlers from Norway, tall, blue-eyed, flaxen-haired, and hardy, acquired homes in the narrow coulees, and a colony of Germans, seeking a liberty they could not find at home, built a church on the ridge over which the Grahams had entered the valley three years before.

Deacon Graham was already a leader in the little church in Onalaska and Harriet, his wife, in spite of her failing health, was counted a useful spirit in all matters which concerned the school and the congregation. She remained cheerfully content with the new country and only spoke now and again of her home and friends in the East. She spent more and more of her time in an arm-chair in a corner of her sitting-room where she could arrange her sewing materials within the reach of her hands. She still helped with the housework, but was not able to remain long upon her feet. She accepted her pain as she accepted her privation, with lofty philosophy, and continued her reading with growing rather than with diminishing interest.

Her influence, her suggestion led Richard to subscribe to the *New York Tribune*, "Horace Greeley's paper," and to keep in touch with what was going on in Congress. Together they often discussed the Slavery Question, and shared enthusiasms over speeches and actions of their leaders. Small as Robert Graham's home was, it took on dignity by reason of the patriotism and the high purpose of its owners.

"Yankee Dick," no longer the boy, had grown graver and less of the dare-devil, naturally, but he still threw himself into any task with a reckless disregard of his long-suffering body. He chose the dangerous places at barn-raisings and the hardest jobs around the threshing-machine.

He loved to muse in moments of leisure on the life he had led as a pilot and riverman, and he often repeated with vivid phrase the outstanding incidents of that life.

He was a natural story-teller, and while some of his neighbours were a bit suspicious of his method and accused him of drawing the long-bow, the truth was he could not have overstated the daring and the hardship of the life he had led. The deeper he settled into the routine of his coulee farm the more alluring became "the days on the Old Wisconse" as he affectionately called them. His boyhood was there, his freedom was there, and his period of boundless expectation was there. It was in the nature of the man that he should recall with a wistful tenderness his daring deeds with canoe and raft.

Meanwhile, all around him the trails were becoming roads, and some of the roads were in process of becoming turnpikes. Bridges were being built, fences were being run, and frame cottages were taking the places of the log huts. Most important than all, railroads were being projected all over the state and one such plan promised a track down the valley through the village of Neshonoc. It is true that Dick had little to do with these larger matters outside his little valley, but he had the imagination which makes a citizen proud of his state no matter how small his own concerns. From his cabin on the hillside he kept informed of the stir and progress of the outside world.

If he perceived the pathos between his boyish dreams and his present actuality, he said nothing of turning back—quite the contrary. His eyes were now turning to the level lands beyond the Mississippi River, lands that were reported to be under purchase from the Sioux Indians. He was still the trail-maker in spirit. Grumbling at grubs and railing at ridges, he continued to walk his narrow round in Green's Coulee while his mind roamed the Minnesota prairies.

He had no doubt of his future, and in spite of his occasional moods of resentment and regret, he was happy. He enjoyed the meetings with his neighbours. He was a wel-

The Cabin in the Coulee

come figure at all the bees and log-rollings, as Belle was welcomed at the quiltings and sewing-circles. He especially enjoyed the season when he ran with William's threshing-machine, for that took him all over the valley and brought him in contact with many of its citizens.

There was poetry in this threshing job. It offered drama. He loved companionship, and he loved an audience. He took delight in "routing out" his farmer neighbours while yet the morning sky was grey and the frost lay thick on every rod and rail. He gloried in the sound of clattering wagons on the frozen roads, as the "hands" came hurrying to the threshing-field. To rally the laggard ones as sleepy-heads gave him joy, and when he mounted the feeding-table he commanded like a triumphant chieftain.

They both took a singular pleasure in the moving of the machine by night. There was charm in the darkness, in the clear starlight, in the silent houses and the voices of dogs. To be awaked by the morning bugles of the cocks signalling from farm to farm, was a glorious beginning of each day.

Isabel, who worked as hard as her husband, had little joy in early rising. The sound of the roosters at dawn was harsh music for her. As cook, tailor, spinner, knitter, and housekeeper, her days were full. She carded wool, spun yarn, knit socks, made jackets, trousers, gowns, bonnets, butter, sausage, rag carpets, quilts, candles, and sauerkraut. She churned butter, dried fruit, and picked chickens. She had no sewing-machine, no help of any kind, and though seldom called upon to milk the cows, she did most of the churning and some of the gardening.

As I review these years of farm-building, I can see that Richard and Isabel lived like campers and toiled like galley-slaves, and yet they were happy. I am certain of this, for they have assured me of it. "In winter we nearly froze to death," Isabel used to say, "and in summer the flies and mosquitoes plagued us terribly, but we were young and soon forgot each worry after it was over. I didn't mind any part of it but the lonesomeness. When Dick was away I found the days forty-eight hours long."

"A man's job runs from sun to sun, but a woman's work is never done," is an old saying which was composed by some such wife as Isabel Graham, who, in spite of her drudgery, remained the smiling, sturdy girl whom Richard had married for "speed and durability," as he used, jokingly, to declare.

To this she was accustomed to retort with gentle sarcasm, "I married *you* for a fine home and an easy time."

In addition to her many other duties and trades, she now took on the pain and the ecstasy of maternity. In the spring of '59 a baby girl came into her busy life on the hill-side, and for several weeks she knew the luxury of lying abed while others did the housework and took care of the child. To be a pioneer wife is not enough. The land must be populated, and so these toiling women became the mothers of a new generation. Themselves daughters of other states, they became the source of the new generation of Wisconsin citizens. They were not conscious of any heroism in thus carrying on the life of the border, the purpose of the government, the destiny of the republic, but to me there is more to commend, to revere in their labour and care than in all the toil and care of the men.

Isabel's house had become a little roomier, her furniture a little better, and her yard a little more cultivated, and when one day Richard said to her, "Belle, Clinton has written me, asking me if I don't want to boss one of his camps this winter," her protest was instant. "Oh, Dick! You promised you wouldn't go back to logging."

"I know, but I've still got a thousand dollars to pay on our farm, and I'm not getting ahead as fast as I expected to do. I've strained every nerve——"

The Cabin in the Coulee

"I know you have, Dick, but I can't live here without you. I can't stand it! Women can't live alone in this valley. You know how deep the snow falls, and think of the baby. Suppose she got sick? I won't stay here and freeze. I'll go with you."

Her tone startled him. "You can't do that! What would you do with baby?"

"She'll be safer there than here. You talk of needing money. Well, I can help in that way. I can cook for your crew. That will save you the wages of a man."

Though secretly delighted at the thought of having her with him, Richard argued against it. "You'll find it dreadfully lonesome up there. You won't see another woman from November to March."

"I don't care. It won't be as lonesome as it is here when you are gone," she stoutly replied.

CHAPTER II

Isabel's Winter in the Woods

KNOWING nothing of a lumber-camp, Isabel kept bravely to her purpose. No warning prophecies or doubting smiles could persuade her, and when at last at the end of a long November day's ride to the north, she found herself in a rude log hut, surrounded by nearly a score of men with the appetites of walruses, "men with the bark on," as the saying was, she could not rightfully complain.

It is only fair to Richard to explain that Clinton had provided a separate cabin for Isabel and the baby, and had hired an assistant in the person of a sturdy Norwegian woman, the wife of one of the teamsters. Furthermore, the choppers were not as rough as they appeared. Some of them she knew personally and all of them were self-respecting citizens, who rejoiced when they learned that the boss's wife was to be in charge of the kitchen. They not only praised her cooking amongst themselves; they boasted of it to the other crews.

Isabel's Winter in the Woods

In addition to these mitigating circumstances, Isabel had the promise of an occasional visit from David, who was freighting along the Black River. The work was hard, but as she said with a smile, "It's like having a threshing-bee every day in the week."

The winter came on gently, beautifully, with deep, soft, snow-falls alternating with brilliant skies and windless nights. Isabel, who had never lived in a forest before, found its sights and sounds of such interest that whenever she had time to look and listen, she experienced both joy and terror. From early dawn, when Richard called her to the newly uncovered fire, till nine at night, when she put the kitchen in order and set the batter for the early-morning meal, she hardly had time to put her head outside the door. Simple as the housekeeping was it was incessant and taxed her severely.

David's visits were as sweet as they were unpredictable, for he not only brought news of what was going on at home; he created a momentary glow of poesy and art. He carried his beloved violin on these trips and was always ready to play, but it was not alone his skill that made him so welcome a visitor. Something in his face and his voice created a pleasant mood in his listeners and drew smiling greetings from the most reticent of them. He was never especially witty, but his spirit was so essentially well-wishing that he had no need of other graces.

When the fiddle began to sing, nothing else mattered to him or to Isabel. In the golden land of melody, politics seemed far away and over-due interest of small account.

To the men, David was a minstrel, a messenger from valleys in which no wars rage, and when Isabel sang to his accompaniment of the violin:

"Oh, islands there are on the face of the deep
Where the skies never change and the clouds never weep.

'Tis there, if thou wilt, our loved bower shall be
When we leave for the greenwood our home on the sea.
Then wake, lady, wake, and away o'er the blue sea,
This night and forever, my bride thou shalt be,"

the sound of her voice subdued the profanest of their hearers to a momentary mood of wonder.

Another song which Richard especially loved to have them unite upon was a ballad called "Maggie, air ye sleepin'?", in which the wandering lover laments his loneliness:

> Oh, mirk and rainy is the night,
> An' no' a starn in a' the cairy.
> The lightnin' flames athwart the lift
> An' cry o' howlets makes me eerie.
> Oh, air ye sleepin', Maggie,
> Oh, air ye sleepin', dearie?
> Oh, let me in, for lood the linn
> Gaies roarin' o'er the moorland craggy.

As David's violin and Isabel's voice rose on the refrain, "Oh, let me in, for lood the linn gaies roarin' o'er the moorland craggy," the log walls dissolved into Scotland's rain-drowned hills and at the close of it no one applauded and for a time no one spoke, so deep was the impression it had made.

This assault upon the forest was, in effect, a measure of the hurrying Western Settlement. As the need of walls, roofs, and windows intensified; as the towns grew and railways spread, so the logging-camp thickened and the chorus of the saws increased. The spoliation of the forest subtended the building of homes. The one foretold the other. The need of lumber was anticipated by men like the Coopers, who were becoming rich in the business of providing building material.

Clinton perceived it also and was beginning to take on the look and tone of a successful business man. In all his letters and in all his talk he urged Richard to drop his farming and join him in cutting and marketing pine. "I'm on the road to being a millionaire," he said laughingly as he sat by the fire, with Richard and Isabel. "If you had worked your head more and your hands less, you'd be a great deal better off."

Richard could not deny this and yet he could not bring himself to abandon his dream of a noble farm. To enter upon Clinton's way of life would be a very sharp break in his plan of action. This timidity in business ventures amounted, in his case, to an inhibition. He was still willing to dare any physical hazard, he could still set his jaw in a resolution which put his magnificent body into battle against flood and wind and rock, with magnificent bravery. He had been bitten of frost, smothered by whirlpools, burned by harvest suns, and beleaguered of snow, and still retained his undaunted youth, but he could not or would not bring himself to any commercial chance other than that of sowing and reaping. To own and improve a piece of land was still his dominant ambition.

I do not set this down in praise of him, but in order that my readers may understand his perversity, and sympathize with Clinton in his good-humoured criticism. "Why, Dick," he exclaimed, "it's foolish for you to stick in that little coulee, while all these chances for making money in lumber are going to waste. You have been in the state nine years, and yet you are just about where you were when you landed here. I am not a rich man, but I've got sixty men working for me, including you," he added. This slur was uttered for a purpose; he wished to sting Dick into action, into change, and before the discussion ended, he said, "I guess you are right, Clint, and if Belle will consent I will sell my farm and go into business with you."

This promise gave Clinton such satisfaction that his handsome face glowed with affection. "Now I am done with criticism, Dick," he said, with frank kindliness. "I won't say another word—I consider this a bargain," and to Isabel he remarked, "You needn't move away from your home, you can live in Onalaska, I will buy or build a mill there and put Dick in charge of it."

After he went away, Richard said to Isabel, "Clint is right, I've worked my feet and hands so hard that my brains haven't had a chance. I came West to be a farmer, a big farmer, on the prairie, but maybe I've taken the wrong trail. Maybe I've missed my chance just as Clint says."

Isabel sat in silence. She, too, lacked the spirit of daring in business matters. She could toil, she could go without the things she needed, but she could not say to her husband, "Follow Clinton's footsteps, speculate in lumber." Trade was not in her blood. She did not openly oppose the plan, but she sadly and wordlessly expressed her doubt of the change.

Clinton returned to the attack in a letter. He wrote easily, in a beautiful script, almost as clear and regular as print, and whenever Richard looked at it, his face clouded with self-contempt. "If I could only write like that," he said, "I'd go into business with better heart. What a fool I was not to take Enoch Lawrence's advice and go to night-school. Well, it can't be helped now."

In spite of his good resolutions, Clinton returned to the matter at heart. "Can't you see it, Dick? The whole state is a field for new enterprises. We are all trail-makers out here; no matter which way you look, there are open chances for success. Just because you failed to find exactly what you started for is no reason for giving up in despair. I came out to mine for lead. You must take a new road—break a new road, just as I have done. We are going to build a great state here. It is true half of it is fine farming land, but the other half is forests. You have lost out on the farming side of it, but there is abundant opportunity in the lumber business."

Richard did see it, and he realized also that his youth was passing. As a man of twenty-nine, it was folly to retain the dreams of the boy.

As the weeks passed, Isabel ceased to miss her home. She was too busy to be lonely and she professed to love the forest and her work. Richard, like other young husbands in similar cases, believed her. He went about his own duties, day by day, in full reliance upon her expressed contentment with her lot. She was in good health with a smiling baby girl to care for and to amuse her. Why should she be lonely?

If she had been called to tell why she was not perfectly happy she could not have answered, but the cause of her unexpressed weakness, if it was a weakness, lay in the fact that her entire life up to her marriage had been passed in the midst of a happy, tumultuous family. She had never been alone as a child for a single instant. The McLanes moved in merry tumult. They maintained an open house even while they were in themselves a houseful. It was for this reason that Isabel, superbly fitted in other ways to be the wife of a pioneer, was never quite happy when alone. Richard's absence was always a somewhat serious hour for her. She never sang when alone, as other wives do, and she counted the hours of his absence quite as definitely as during the first year of their marriage.

Here in the forest she was not merely lonely, she was awed by the mystery around her. Harriet Graham, frail wisp of a woman that she was, would have tranquilly sewed her seams while hearing the owls and the wolves. But Isabel could never forget the helplessness of her child.

Her Celtic imagination imaged the woods and its denizens as an ever-present danger. Her physical courage was almost as great as her husband's, but her schooling had not been such as to fit her for solitude in the forest.

One morning she said, "Mrs. Larson is going away, Dick; I shall be all alone today."

"I'll have one of the boys stay and help you, if you need help."

"Oh, I can do the work; it isn't that. I don't want any of the men around, but I wish you could stay."

"I can't very well do that. I am needed in the cutting, but I will come in occasionally and see how you are getting along."

She said no more, but he went away to his work with a feeling that she was more unhappy than she cared to express. "It isn't right to leave her alone. Something might happen to the child."

As the morning wore on he became more and more uneasy, so uneasy that along about ten o'clock he slipped away from his crew and started for the camp strongly moved to assure himself that all was well. He had a sense of guilt in leaving her with so much work to do. "It's too much for one woman."

Just as he came in sight of the cabin, his ears were assaulted by an uproar of whooping and laughter, and a moment later forth from the door of the cook-shanty surged a dozen or more Chippewas, men and women and children, all screaming and shouting, while close behind them and wielding a broom with formidable action, came Isabel.

"Get away from here" she commanded, flourishing her weapon. "Stir your boots!"

This scene did not amuse Richard; on the contrary, his eyes blazed with wrath. Like a young lion he charged. He was upon the intruders before they were aware of him. Singling out the biggest man in the group, he struck him

Isabel's Winter in the Woods

with the full weight of his powerful shoulder. Behind the blow the redman went down in a limp heap and Richard worked havoc among the others. He slapped the women and booted the men, shouting in their own language, *"Puck-achee! We-wip Wa-sah."* "Git out of here! Git!"

He was like a wolf among sheep. They scattered precipitately, all except one, a pacific old fellow who held up his hands in a gesture of entreaty and tried to explain. "Injun no hurt 'im squaw. White squaw heap brave. All same chief."

Isabel called out, "Don't hurt him, Dick. He didn't touch me. None of 'em did."

"Then why did you drive them out?"

"They wanted bread and I gave them all the old bread I had, but they started to help themselves to my new bread which I'd just taken out of the oven; then I went at 'em with the broom."

Isabel and a broom made a dangerous combination, and Richard, as his wrath cooled, began to see the comical side of it. He smiled and the wider he smiled the angrier she got. "If you don't stop laughing, I'll give *you* a taste of my broom," she stammered in her fury.

This sobered him. He saw that she was really hurt by his laughter. "When I saw that gang backing out of the cabin screaming and whooping, I didn't feel a bit like laughing, I'll admit. I thought of McMahon and his fight with old chief Otter and his gang. I was fighting mad. That big chief got a taste of my fist he'll remember for a while. Where's the baby?"

"Asleep in her crib, luckily—but, oh, Dick, don't leave me alone again! I don't mind the work, but I can't stand the loneliness. I don't like deep woods, anyway. I never did, and with baby, I'm terribly uneasy."

He put his arm about her. "I'll never leave you alone again," he said.

263

CHAPTER III

Richard's Last Raft

ALTHOUGH Clinton's business office was in Dubuque, he continued to make his home in Galena. He remained unmarried for some reason which he had never made plain, even to Richard, who rallied him about it occasionally, but he only laughed and said, "Time enough yet."

He frankly confessed his ambition to be a great lumberman. "I'm going to make a fortune—and I am going to do it without stealing from Uncle Sam." He added this with a touch of bitterness, as though honesty imposed a handicap.

He was already part owner of a log-boom and mill at Onalaska, influenced, no doubt, by Richard's partial agreement to come into the enterprise with him, and when Richard came down with his winter's harvest of logs, he was met by Clinton with a request to take charge of a raft of lath and shingles, which he was sending down the river.

The pay was tempting and Richard consented, with the

provision that he might have a few days to visit his farm and arrange for the sowing of his land.

In the course of their conversation, Clinton said, "I am seeing a good deal of that brother of yours and I like him. His store is a meeting-place for a lot of Abe Lincoln Republicans and I enjoy sitting in with them. A few weeks ago I met a soldier there whose talk gave me a sharp jolt.

"Addison and I were in the middle of a hot debate on the best way to handle the situation in Washington, when he was called upon to tend a customer, a man who came in leading a little boy by the hand. A few minutes later, as I started to go, Addison called me over and introduced the man to me as Captain Grant.

"The captain was about forty, a red-bearded chap, with pleasant blue eyes. He was civil enough, but not especially enthusiastic in meeting me. He stood quietly by while Addison explained that he had recently come to Galena. 'Orville Grant of Grant & Perkins is the captain's brother,' Addison went on to explain, 'and the captain is going to enter the firm. He has been living in St. Louis since his resignation from the army three or four years ago.'

"Grant was not a talkative man, I could see that, but Addison got him going, finally, by saying, 'You know the South, captain. Will the Southerners fight?'

" 'Yes, they will fight,' the captain said, and he spoke like a man who knew.

" 'What about Missouri?' I put in; 'will she go with the South?'

"He considered this for a moment, then said, 'I think she will. Southern feeling is very strong in St. Louis.'

" 'It must have been a bit uncomfortable for you down there.'

"This made the captain smile. 'It was, that's why I came North.' He was very fair to the Southerners. 'They were my neighbours,' he said. 'I know their problems.'

Then he said something that had a big effect on me. 'So long as slavery is confined to the states where it belongs I wouldn't interfere with it, but if it is to be used as a means of disrupting the Union, I would destroy it.' He meant this, I can tell you, and I warmed to him. He was reasonable, however, for he added, 'Many Southerners are just as anxious to get rid of slavery as we are.'

"I was greatly interested in this soldier, and after he went out I asked Addison to tell me more about him. It seems that he's the eldest son of old Jesse Grant who is a leather dealer back in Ohio. Grant & Perkins is a branch of his business. The captain's wife is Southern—that's how he came to go to St. Louis after his resignation from the army —her people all live there. The gossip in Galena is that old Jesse hates 'the whole Dent tribe' as he calls 'em, and so long as his son Ulysses lived among them, refused to help him or visit him. It was a hard position for the captain, but he struggled along on a farm till finally his wife consented to come North. He's book-keeper and general factotum for Grant & Perkins and takes a hand at anything which needs to be done. As I came down the street the morning I left I saw him taking in a load of hides. He's not above snaking a hide by the tail.

"A day or two after our meeting in Addison's store, I dropped into his office in hopes of another chat with him. He was sitting on a stool before a high pine desk, smoking a pipe and posting accounts. His clothes were seedy and he looked discouraged, but I liked him. His eyes are fine, and little wrinkles come into their corners when he's pleased. He never laughs, never raises his voice, and has no use for cuss-words. He doesn't even use slang. Think of that for an ex-soldier and quartermaster! I never saw any one just like him. He won't talk about himself and never complains of hard luck. His interests are all in the Mexican War, the settlement of the Western Coast, the slavery question—things like that. He's a queer case. I'm told he's only getting fifty dollars a month, and I guess that's right, for he lives in a little house high on the hill. 'By working my legs, I save rent,' he said to me.

"He seemed interested in me and I told him all about our coming West and our first winter on the Wisconsin. It seems that lumbering of this kind is something he has never seen although he knows the states from Lake Ontario to Oregon. 'My father thinks West Point spoiled one of his sons, and I guess that's true,' he confessed. 'Education as a soldier don't seem to help a man in making a living as a civilian.'

"He asked me to walk home with him, and it was surprising to find a man of his experience and ability living in such a place. He's able, no question about that. I've developed a great liking for him, and I think he likes me, although he is not outspoken about it."

Richard was interested in this ex-soldier, but sympathized with his father. "The captain should have settled in the North."

"But he couldn't force his wife to leave her people."

"It was her duty to go with him."

Clinton smiled. "I know another man whose plans are sometimes changed by his wife. In fact I'm not a bit sure he will take my raft down the river, if his wife objects."

Richard acknowledged this but said, "I think Isabel will be won over by your offer."

Isabel was bitterly disappointed but did not oppose his going. She knew he liked the job. After his intense activity in the woods and on the river, rafting below La Crosse was a delightful relaxation. He was only a half-way farmer, after all. He set off in cheerful mood, for David had taken charge of his seeding and for a day or two he luxuriated in the sunshine and rest.

The river was high and the going good and one morning, as the raft was swinging along in noble ease just above Dubuque, a man in a passing boat shouted, "Hey, men! Heard the news? The war's begun! Lincoln has called for troops!"

For a few moments not a man on the raft uttered a word, then Richard remarked grimly, "They've done it now! They've started something that will make 'em sorry."

He thought of his brother, and a desire to see him and learn more of the situation led him to a decision to visit him. As the raft reached a point opposite Galena he ordered the men to tie up for a day. "I want to see Addison, and find out what has happened. I'll run over and get the latest news."

It was about six o'clock in the afternoon when he arrived, and Addison, who was at supper, greeted him warmly but gravely. "You've heard the news?"

"Only a report. What's the latest word?"

"Lincoln has asked for troops, and you are just in time to attend a mass-meeting in response to his call. We had a meeting the other day which came to nothing for the reason that our chairman was a politician. We're going to have a soldier preside tonight and we intend to enroll a company of volunteers before we sleep. The whole town is up in arms, figuratively speaking, and we believe Captain Grant will put the shouting into something concrete."

"Clinton's been telling me of Captain Grant. Is Clinton here?"

"Yes, he's here and full of fight, but why aren't you on your farm? Isn't this seeding-time?"

Richard was a bit nettled. "It *is*, but rafting pays better."

"Does it? You've been on the river ten years; why haven't you more to show for it"

"I don't know."

"I do. It's because you've been somebody's hired man

268

all the time. You've used your muscles and not your brains."

"I haven't any brains to use."

"Nonsense! You've been on the wrong track, that's all. Either quit this lumbering business or go into it on your own hook."

"I've been working on shares for Clinton this winter, and I hope to clear the mortgage off my land in two years."

"I can't understand, Dick, why you at the end of ten years in a new country should be carrying a mortgage on a hill-side farm. You don't drink or gamble and no man has worked harder, and yet here you are, bossing a camp for Clinton who tells me that dozens of your chums have gone into lumbering for themselves and are getting rich while you are still running a raft. They flatter you, tell you what a trusty pilot you are, and keep you breaking the roads for them."

Richard admitted all this. "I'm timid about managing a business. I feel my weakness when it comes to writing and figuring."

"Now you've hit it! When you were young you wouldn't learn to cipher and now you've got where you can't. You'll be handicapped all your life, just as Enoch Lawrence told you you would be."

Richard began to smart under the lash. "You must remember," he retorted, "that I've had father and mother on my hands for all these years."

Addison's clear gaze wavered a little. "That's true, but you will recall I wanted them to come to Galena. Mother told me she preferred going to La Crosse County. It was her own choice."

"I admit that, and I'm not complaining, but I want you to remember it when you're giving me particular Gowdy for not getting ahead."

There was not much more to be said on either side, and

Addison ended by agreeing to help his father to run his little store. "In this way I can ease your burden, providing, of course, father makes a go of the grocery business. But, come! It's time to go."

Dropping personal matters they rose and together walked over to the County Court-House where a tense and quiet audience of men had gathered.

As they entered, Clinton, who was sitting on one of the back seats, waved a greeting and indicated a vacant place beside him. This Richard took, but before he had a chance to explain his presence, one of the leaders rose to call the house to order.

"Fellow-citizens," he said with blunt candour, "some of you attended our first meeting and you all know how it fizzled out and all because our chairman was a sympathizer with secession. We are determined that this meeting shall have a different outcome. I rise to nominate a chairman who is not only loyal but competent for this particular job. I see in this room tonight a man who has had nine years' experience as an officer in the regular army. His advice at this time should be invaluable. I move that Captain Ulysses Grant be made presiding officer of this meeting."

A majority applauded the suggestion, not because they knew the soldier, but because of the chairman's earnest commendation. The action carried, but the captain, taken by surprise, shook his head and said, "I can't do that. It lies outside my training."

His reluctance, his modesty only caused the audience to insist. Calls for "Grant!" "Grant!" kept up. The speaker had struck the right note. The men wanted a soldier, a leader.

At last the captain rose, probably with intent to ask release, but as the urging continued, he slowly made his way up the aisle.

On reaching the open space in front of the judge's desk,

he turned and for the first time confronted his fellow-citizens in mass. Many of those present had never before taken note of him. Some had met him on the sidewalk or in the store. All were now minded to discover what sort of a man he really was. Richard's eyes were fixed upon him with especial interest because of Clinton's report.

A little above middle height and of powerful build, the soldier's attitude expressed a quiet dignity. His face was square, his nose straight, and his brow broad and white. His beard, close-clipped and reddish brown in colour, covered his cheeks and chin. His general appearance was that of a fine, sincere, and earnest physician. There was nothing military in his dress or his bearing.

"Fellow-citizens," he began in a clear voice which reached every ear in the hall. "Your chairman has stated the purpose of this meeting which is to enlist a company of volunteers. Before calling you to enroll, I think it only fair to state what will be required of you. First of all, obedience—unquestioning obedience—must be given to your superior officers. The army is not a pleasure-party. You are not entering upon an excursion. You are going to war. You will have hard fare. You will be obliged to sleep on the ground after long marches in the rain or snow. You will often go hungry. Many of the orders of your commanders will seem unjust and yet they must be borne. If an injustice is really done you, however, there are courts-martial where your wrongs can be investigated and the offending officers punished. If you put your name down on this roll it should be with full understanding of what the act means. In conclusion let me say that, so far as I can, I will aid the organization of this company and I intend to re-enlist in the service myself."

The cheering at the end of the calm, concise, and honest speech was less in volume than that which followed the flights of oratory of other speakers, but it was applauded.

There was something in this serious, plain-spoken talk which brought the meeting down to realities. This soldier's feet were on the earth. Quietly, authoritatively, without a useless word, he had let the wind of bombast out of the proceedings, and had put in its place a resolute, intelligent devotion to the Union.

In answer to questions concerning military regulations, he replied with masterly brevity. At last he said, "Now, men, here is the roll. Who of you will put his name down as a volunteer?" Nearly one-fourth of the young men rose, Clinton among them. He was indeed among the first to rise, and Richard, equally hot with patriotic fire, was about to follow when Addison laid a restraining hand on his arm. "Hold on, Richard. Let the unmarried men go first. You don't belong here, anyway. You should enlist in a Wisconsin regiment."

"But Clint is going in and I want to sign with him," replied Richard.

Addison was firm. "Don't be precipitate. Wait a while. Remember your wife and children," he added. Richard, his mind filled with a vision of Isabel, his baby, his cabin, his farm, resumed his seat and waited.

Nearly half the requisite number signed that night. All agreed that Grant was the man to head the company, all were surprised when he feelingly declined the honour. "I am a West Point graduate," he explained. "I held for several years a captain's commission in the regular army. I can't afford to go into the volunteer service as the head of a company." He hesitated a moment and then modestly added, "The truth is, I believe I am fitted to command a regiment, and I intend to go at once to Springfield and ask the governor for a commission as colonel."

"You are right," said Addison, but others, who knew Grant only as an ill-paid clerk and book-keeper in a leather store, were outspoken in their belief that he was making a mistake. "You'd better take what's offered. You may fail of getting a commission," they said with well-intentioned bluntness.

At the close of the meeting, Clinton joined the Grahams and walked part way home with them. "Well, Dick, I'm in for it. For a year at least."

"A year? You don't suppose this war will last a year?"

"Captain Grant says it may last two," interposed Addison. "The South has been preparing to fight for a long time. She will fight desperately to repel what she will call an 'invasion' of her territory, and in that action of repelling an invader they will have a great advantage."

"But we have more money and more men than they."

"Yes, we can call out more men, and we have more money, but they are united and they are prepared. Captain Grant says we should move quickly and strike hard. He says the South has the best leaders. She has sent many cadets to West Point. She will have many officers who served in the Mexican War, men of ability. If they go with their states, as they undoubtedly will, the South will have nearly all the skilled leaders at the start."

Clinton turned from national affairs to personal. "By the way, Dick, how do you happen to be here? I thought you were bringing my raft down the river?"

"I was, but I tied up opposite here and came over to see Addison."

"Well, you'll have to go on and deliver that lumber. This war business has upset all my plans and calculations. We start right in drilling tomorrow. There's talk of making me an officer. I don't know a thing about war, but then nobody else does, except Captain Grant."

"Good thing you aren't married. It wouldn't be so easy for you to step away," said Addison.

Clinton made no reply to this, and Richard, who had often wondered at Clinton's "single blessedness," merely said, "I wish I could go with you, Clint, but I can't just now."

"No, you stay with Belle and the babies. That's your job. I don't know how I'm going to leave my business, but I'm off."

He had been made a second lieutenant and was so deep in military tactics that he listened to his partner's report with absent-minded gaze.

"We're in luck to have a drill-master like Captain Grant," he said. "He won't take the captaincy, but he has given a lot of his time to whipping us into shape. He has helped us arm and clothe ourselves. He knows the business, that man! He ought to have command of a regiment. I'd like nothing better than to be on his staff."

Meanwhile the raft was tied up to the bank, and on Clinton's order, Richard waited over to see the "Jo Daviess County Guards" start on their way to Springfield. They marched down the street to the railway depot preceded by the city band with young Captain Chetlain striding at their head, whilst a crowd of cheering men, women, and children filled the sidewalks or moved along beside the column. Richard and Addison, standing on the corner, observed at the tail of the company, in the middle of the street, a civilian with a lank carpet bag in one hand, and carrying a faded military overcoat folded across his arm. It was Captain Grant on his way to Springfield, to see the governor and ask for a commission.

Addison, seeing him thus obscurely trailing in the dust of the company he had helped to form, voiced Richard's judgment as he said, "He belongs at the head and not at the tail of that procession."

The situation was highly significant of the left-handed fashion in which the North went to war. Here was Captain Chetlain, a young civilian who knew nothing of arms or military discipline, leading a column with lofty confidence, while Grant, the trained soldier of many campaigns, modestly, soberly brought up the rear with only one or two of his friends, like Addison Graham, bestowing on him the honour of a second glance.

CHAPTER IV

The New Interest

UP to this time the dominant interest, the consuming interest, in all this new country, had been the question of "improvement"; that is to say, the clearing of fields, the opening of roads, the building of bridges, and the creation of towns. Every man was a boomer, confident and boastful, looking to the future with joyous anticipation. Now a new and disturbing conception intervened. The call to arms turned the faces of explorers like Clinton Helmstock and Richard Graham from the West toward the South. For the moment, they were like wild geese suddenly arrested in their normal course, confused and hesitant.

Their New England training was fruitful soil for the seed of Captain Grant's warning. That the war was not to be a summer excursion ran parallel with their own conviction. They parted with emotion and Richard took his way back

276

The New Interest

up the river in a very serious mood. He felt the call of duty strongly, and whenever he caught the sound of martial music in the villages along the river, he wondered if his own town would be as prompt in raising troops as Galena had been.

He was gratified to find La Crosse equally ablaze with the spirit of war. Drummers were thumping, fifers calling, and squads of new recruits marching to and fro upon the square. One of the first men he recognized in the ranks was Luke McLane and later he learned that Sam Blanchard and several other of his friends had signed the roll. He was again almost overpowered by an urge to enlist. He held the impulse in check, however, and hurried on to consult his mother and Isabel.

Harriet Graham received her son with her usual serenity, but there was a light in her eyes which showed the inward pain. "It has come," she said solemnly; "the controversy is now to be fought out."

"The question is, shall I go?" he replied.

Her voice was firm as she said, "If the cause of freedom needs you, yes. You are the only soldier in our family. Addison is too frail and your father is too old. Wait a few weeks, however, and see how matters turn out. I am not one of those who think this is to be a short war. It has been too long coming on."

From her arm-chair in that small cottage, she had quite accurately gauged the growing fury of the war spirit in the course of congressional debate. Her casements had been shaken by the national storm. Her husband, equally warlike, was much more outspoken in criticism of local leaders. He bluntly denounced certain of them as Copperheads and hinted that he would gladly join a posse to march upon one of those editors and ride him on a rail.

Leaving the date of his enlistment still undecided, Richard set out for his farm, so emotionally exalted that he hardly felt the sand under his feet. He walked with bent head and reflective eyes.

David who was at work harrowing his corn land raised a shout and waved his hat in recognition. "What's the news?" he called as soon as he was near enough to get Richard's reply.

"They are drilling in La Crosse, I saw Luke in the squad and I felt like enlisting myself. Clint has gone in, enlisted in Galena, three or four days ago."

David was interested, but did not share in Richard's intense conviction. He took it all as a bit of exciting news. Like William his attitude towards the question of secession was apathetic. He loved his native land, he adored it as a place of boundless opportunity, but he possessed little of that intense patriotism which involves going to war against seceding states. "Let them go," he said jovially, "they will come back."

Richard quoted the editorial of the *Tribune* to him, and also repeated as well as he could the words of Captain Grant; but David remained irritatingly undisturbed. "Luke went in more for the adventure of it, and as for Pap, he's working out a new line of prophecy and can't be interested in a small war away down South."

Thus while the tired horses dozed in the mellow sunlight and the golden woodpeckers called resoundingly, the two young pioneers leaned against the fence and argued the question of military duty. "You can't go now, Dick; you can't leave Belle with two small children. Addison is right; let the men go who are free to go."

In spite of himself Richard found his martial spirit evaporating. All about him the warm brown soil was calling for seed. The hills were putting on their ever-renewing robes of green and blue, and in his cottage-yard small Hattie was playing, while Isabel kept her spinning-wheel abuzz.

The New Interest

Then, too, the question of clearing away the mortgage from the farm came up. How could he go to war leaving that hanging over his household? At this stage of his mental reaction, Clinton's enlistment seemed precipitate. He had given up too much to become a soldier.

Isabel was not expecting Richard, and when he called to her with little Hattie on his shoulder, "See what I found," she turned upon him a surprised as well as a delighted face.

He soon found that she shared her brother's aloofness from the heat of the conflict. She sympathized with the poor blacks and thought they ought to be set free, but her concern did not go much deeper. Her interest was in people, not in states. Furthermore, she was expecting another child, and the disability and pain involved in this condition deepened her love of home and increased her need of protection. "I hate to have Luke go to war. I tried my best to keep him from it."

Richard perceived in this a warning. He realized that she would strenuously oppose his own enlistment, and he passed to an account of his meeting with Captain Grant, whose story aroused her sympathy. "I hope he gets a commission. With all those little children to feed and clothe he will need the pay."

"He'll get it," Richard assured her. "He is about the only experienced soldier in the West. They're going to need him from the very start."

In this he was mistaken. Clinton wrote from Springfield to say that the captain had been unable even to reach the governor. "No one pays any attention to him. Having no political influence and no money, no one takes any trouble to advance him. All he can do is wait around the governor's ante-room, hoping for an interview. I saw him today at work at a little three-legged table, ruling blank paper into forms for military requisitions. Think of that!

Here is a man with ten years' experience in the army, part of the time quarter-master, and yet is unable to obtain any kind of command. I guess he wishes he had taken the offer of the captaincy of our company. Gus Chetlain has kept in touch with him and has tried to help him, but the governor is so surrounded by political wire-pullers, that Grant has no chance."

A few days later Addison forwarded a letter which he had received from Clinton, wherein he spoke of finding Captain Grant sadly discouraged. "Chetlain tackled the adjutant about Grant. 'What's the chance of his getting command of a regiment?' he asked. 'Not a chance in the world,' said the adjutant. 'The woods are full of men wanting command, and a 'decayed regular' like Grant hasn't the ghost of a show. If he's a friend of yours you'd better tell him to go home. There's nothing I can do for him, and the governor has no time for an interview.'

"The captain has given up hope, I guess, for when Chetlain told him what the adjutant had said, he answered, 'He's right. There's no place for me. The politicians have got everything here. I'll go to Ohio, my native state, and try for a regiment there.'

"I'm afraid his chances are just as poor in Ohio. Commissions are not being given to poor men with no influence."

Richard shared this bitterness, but the gloom lifted when Clinton wrote that Grant, during the absence of the camp commander, had been put in charge for a few days. They found he knew the military game.

Soon afterward Addison sent a copy of the *Galena Gazette* which contained an editorial which Richard read aloud to Belle and his mother with an exultant ring in his voice. It was the first public recognition, so far as Galena was concerned, of Captain Grant's qualities. "Our fellow-citizen, Captain U. S. Grant, who has been employed for several months [he had been gone only three weeks] by

The New Interest

the state in superintending its military operations" (that is to say, ruling military blanks for orders and clearing muskets out of the state-house cellar), "is at home on a visit. Captain Grant is a regular graduate of West Point and has seen service in the regular army, having been an officer all through the Mexican War, and afterwards was in command in Oregon. He resigned the captaincy about six years since. We are now in want of such soldiers as he, and we hope the government will invite him to take some high command. He is the very soul of honour and no man breathes who has a more patriotic heart."

The editor had at last come to know and to value Captain Grant, for he ended his comment with these significant words, "We want among our young soldiers the influence of the rare leadership of men like Captain Grant."

On the margin of the paper Addison had pencilled these words, "Politics is in every military appointment and that makes hard sledding for Grant. He's been to St. Louis to consult Fremont, but Fremont wouldn't even see him. He is going to make a trial for a commission in Ohio."

On June 20th Clinton wrote that Grant had obtained a colonelcy at last and in another editorial the *Gazette* said, "We are glad to learn of the probability that Colonel Grant will accept the appointment by Governor Yates of the Twelfth District Regiment. Colonel Grant is a modest man from principle, which of itself is worthy of mention in this day of pretentious impudence."

Two days later the editor wrote, "Colonel U. S. Grant who is in the city has accepted the colonelcy of the Seventh District Regiment."

This news Clinton confirmed and corrected. "The truth is the Twenty-first Illinois Regiment which Grant mustered in and which has been stationed at Mattoon held a convention of its officers some days ago, and selected Grant as their first choice for colonel. A committee called on Gov-

ernor Yates and notified him of this choice. He approved
it and Grant was commissioned. He is in command at
last. I have asked to be transferred to his regiment. He
has offered me a place on his staff. I'd rather be orderly
sergeant under him than captain under one of these high-
chested political colonels. This war can't be fought out by
regiments led by a gang of orators."

Addison wrote of seeing Colonel Grant in Galena. "He
has the commission but no money for his outfit. I let him
have some goods. Collins of the firm of Grant & Perkins
let him have a horse. Young Burke contributed a saddle.
Grant said to me, 'I haven't a dollar in the world, but my
pay as colonel ought to take care of my family. This appointment is more of a satisfaction to me than you can
realize, for my father has all along believed that West Point
had ruined one of his sons and up to this time his opinion
appeared justified.'

"Collins, in talking to me about his former clerk, remarked, 'If Ulysses can hold his present command we will
all be satisfied. Old Jesse is astonished at his son's good
luck.' I hope he is as pleased as Colonel Grant thinks he
ought to be."

The truth is Addison and Richard, because they had
seen Captain Grant and liked his voice, were more concerned in his fortunes than with those of any other officer
in the army. As one behind the scenes, Addison said, "I
understand something of Jesse Grant's attitude, for I know
the little frame cottage in which the captain lived and from
which he started out, valise in hand, to march at the tail
end of the Jo Daviess County Guards. It's hard to estimate a man's ability as a soldier in times of peace."

One very amusing letter from Clint detailed the changes
in discipline which took place after Grant assumed command at Mattoon. "It seems that the recruits have been
skylarking like a lot of hoodlums, purloining chickens and

all that sort of thing, and Colonel Goode who looks like a cross of Buckskin Bill and a pirate was unable to enforce discipline. All kinds of rowdyism, drinking, and deviltry went on under him. I wish you could have seen the faces of the men when Colonel Grant at the close of our first drill made his little speech to us. He said, 'Hereafter no man will be permitted to leave camp without a pass. I shall expect order and discipline in this camp. You are soldiers, not picnickers!' Jeems Rice! The row that broke loose!

"We had seventeen men in the guard-house that night. In the morning Grant called all the commissioned officers in and gave them a talk that left them stunned. 'This regiment is not a mob, it is a military unit,' he said. 'It is a machine for marching and fighting. Every infraction of discipline will be punished no matter who the offender may be, and I shall expect every officer to insist on proper soldierly obedience.'

"They went out, awed. 'By the Lord, he's right,' said the major. 'He's a soldier, we're only a lot of rowdy patriots who think we can fight a battle in mob formation.'

"I am acting as adjutant. My handwriting has done this for me, and I wouldn't swap places with anyone but a lieutenant-colonel. Colonel Grant is a soldier. He knows the military game. For instance, the governor didn't know just how he was going to get transportation for us across the state to St. Louis. 'I'll find transportation,' said Grant. 'I propose to *march* to the front,' so here we are, going to the front like an army, the first regiment to play the game. Every night our camps are guarded by armed sentries. Discipline is rigid, but we like it. We are perfectly certain we've got the best regimental commander in the Western Army."

As Richard read this letter, a longing to be a part of the regiment came over him, and Belle, who sensed that longing, gravely said, "After this I'm going to burn Clint's letters before you have a chance to read them."

What a summer that was! Day by day, week by week, the flames of sectional hatred mounted higher. On every farm, in every grocery-store, men debated war plans and congressional action. David and Richard made hay, cut wheat, and husked corn in quiet routine, apparently, and yet underneath every day's employment throbbed a growing sense of change.

Richard's desire to explore was gone. His eyes were turned to the South. Every day brought news of enlistments. In his little cabin in the coulee, the storm of strife made echo, as the ocean's voice resounds in the hollow chamber of a shell.

It was not a time of depression. Enlistment offered a delightful excursion into a strange and beautiful country, a land of flowers and romance. None of the volunteers expected to be gone long, and a rising demand for lumber, corn, and cattle brought a growing prosperity to the farmer and the logger.

In the midst of the martial excitement of this summer, whilst news of the armies and the deeds of President Lincoln were all-absorbing subjects of discussion, a young woman came into David's life with such allurement that he assumed an unexpected relationship with the daughters of his neighbours.

Up to this time he had been the smiling, unattached cavalier. On kindly terms with all the girls of his acquaintance, he had manifested no marked desire for a proprietary interest in any one of them, and this fraternal attitude had been sadly puzzling to some of them. "He cares more for his fiddle than he does for any of us," they said, and in this they had been correct. But now, all was changed. He not only gave to Adele the larger part of his free time, he neg-

The New Interest

lected his violin on her account. Small, dark-eyed, with just enough of alien colour to stir his imagination (she was Canadian), she conquered without effort. The charm of her intonation, her childish gaiety, her remarkable taste in dress, set her apart as something finer, something different, something more precious than any of her rivals.

Richard thought her a nice little thing, but perceived nothing of the witchery which had reduced David to a willing slavery, and Isabel, amused at first to see her proud brother so worshipful, so adoring, ended by resenting his submissive attitude. "No girl," she said, "is good enough for Dave."

David seldom spoke of his sweetheart, even to his mother, and when William or Franklin ventured to joke about it, he silenced them with a look. He loved as he played the violin, with poetic imagination and with noble singleness of heart. In this he was at once the Celt and the Saxon. His love was a sacred thing.

One day he came to his mother and gravely told her that Adele had promised to marry him and that the wedding would fall on Thanksgiving Day. She made no reply in words; she only put her arms about his neck and laid her head for a moment upon his shoulder. She loved him above all other of her sons.

All through September and October Richard read the war news carefully and awaited letters from Clinton. For several weeks he heard nothing. Then came a jubilant note saying, "Grant has been made brigadier-general and is in command at Cairo. We are not doing much at present, but while we were over in Missouri, the general sent President Lincoln a plan for opening up the Tennessee and the Cumberland. He is for moving at once on Forts Henry and Donelson. He sits all day in his office studying maps, and smoking like a wet rag. If he could only get permission to move! If somebody would only let President Lincoln know

285

that Grant is the only seasoned commander in the West, we might get action."

He enclosed a photograph which showed Grant in full uniform standing at the door of a post-office. He looked strong and well, a graceful, soldierly figure. The stoop of his shoulders was no longer noticeable. Active campaigning had given him an air of command, a bearing quietly authoritative. In spite of the opposition of envious rivals, he was slowly winning recognition.

At the end of October, Richard's fall work was finished; but he had no heart for a return to the woods. With his infant son in his arms, he seemed to Isabel quite safe from the war madness. At other times she feared, for even in the McLane household "The Battle-Cry of Freedom" with its marching swing had taken the place of "Rosalie" and "The Pirate's Serenade." All the magazines reflected the war spirit, and the note-paper of the time, with flags for ornaments, incited to enlistment, and although Manassas and Bull Run were almost as remote from the citizens of Neshonoc as Waterloo or Wagram, many shared the feeling of dismay with which the President received the news of McClellan's reverse. Luke, who was in these battles, wrote, "The South has the best of it so far. They have all the generals."

Nevertheless Lincoln proclaimed Thanksgiving, and David and Adele were married in the homestead on that day. It was not a day of general rejoicing, for the war was being taken very seriously.

All through the long, cold winter, Richard worked at anything to which he could turn a hand. He teamed to La Crosse by day and split rafting-pins at night. He cut and sold firewood. He helped his neighbours get out fence-rails and framing timbers. From daylight to dark he toiled while Isabel ran her spinning-wheel, pieced quilts, moulded candles, and nursed her children. She was gravely in sympathy with her husband, who was ever more deeply concerned for the fate of the Northern armies and the Union.

The first note of encouragement came in a letter from Addison. "General Grant has taken Paducah! They say the President has become interested in our general. I hope this is true, for very few people in Galena have any use for him. Houghton has urged our congressmen to back up his claims, but not with much success. It's a wonder that he has been able to get where he is."

Through the influence of Addison and Clinton, Richard was so given to talking about Grant that his neighbours smiled at his confident predictions. "Grant will take Henry and Donelson, if the division commander will let him. He is for action. Clinton says the general will march straight through Kentucky if Halleck will give the word."

One day in February while Richard was in his wood-shed busily splitting blocks of oak into rafting-pins, he heard the jingle of approaching sleigh-bells. Recognizing them as belonging to his neighbour Alfred Crandall he stepped outside the door, and waited for him to approach.

Crandall pulled his team to a stand and called out, "Hurrah for your man Grant! He's taken Donelson!"

Richard, thinking Crandall was making game of him, answered calmly, "Has he?"

"You bet he has! He's captured General Buckner and over twenty thousand men. La Crosse is wild over the news. Ged-dap!" and he drove on with a jingle of bells and a whoop.

Too excited to go on with his work, Richard hitched up his team and drove to Onalaska to share the good news with his mother. Then, eager to know the latest report, he and his father went on to La Crosse. The nearer they came to the source of information, the greater the victory appeared. The town was ringing with the conqueror's fine, heroic name. "Grant! Grant! Grant! *Grant!*" What a fine name it was. To Buckner's question, "What terms do you propose?" he had replied, "No terms but unconditional surrender. I propose to move immediately upon your works," and these words were being repeated by every man in the street. The resolution of it, the grim sententiousness of it, thrilled the nation. No such phrase had hitherto been uttered. Something new had entered into the conduct of the Western campaign.

In a single day this friend of Clinton, this unknown Western commander, had become "Unconditional Surrender Grant." Heralded as a man of decision, of action, of genius, his name swept over the North. The people clamoured for news of him. "Who is this man Grant? Where does he come from?"

The President was reported as asking, "Who is this man Grant who fights battles and wins them?"

Richard became to his neighbours a valuable source of information concerning Grant's origin and personality. As he visited Onalaska, men gathered round him, eager to learn more about the general's home in Galena, and when Richard quoted Editor Houghton's eulogy, written when no one else knew or cared who Grant was, his auditors remarked, "I guess that editor is the son of a prophet."

Richard drove home filled with envy. "I wish I was serving under Grant," he said to Isabel.

He was marching to and fro on the east eighty of his farm, flinging seed-wheat from his hand, when David came hurrying to tell him that Grant's army had won another great battle." I've just come from La Crosse and they say the loss of life was terrible. Thousands of men were killed on each side."

This scene was typical of many others all over the West that day. Here on the same spot, in the haze of another April afternoon, these young men stood. Richard, with a bag of wheat hanging from his shoulder, and David with eyes of sombre reflection telling the story of Shiloh.

"It appears that the battle lasted two days," David went on. "The first day was a draw game, but the second day Grant was up and at 'em harder than ever. He saved the day, but he lost thousands of men. They don't know how many."

In the pauses of his story the songs of birds and the whistles of the gophers went cheerily on.

Richard unslung his grain-bag, and David watched him with anxious eyes. It was as if he were about to go to war but he only said, "I've got to know more about this." Maybe they'll get out a special edition of the paper. I guess I'll drive down after supper and see."

Isabel knew what both these beloved men were thinking. *The time had come for them to go in* and she was terrified. If Richard went to town in that mood he might return in uniform as Everett Ripley had done. "Don't go down to-night, Dick," she pleaded. "Wait till tomorrow. They'll have more news then."

Richard made no answer to this appeal, but after she had gone into the kitchen, David said, "I know what you're thinking, Dick, but I can't go. Adele is not well and Dad is depending on me to run the farm. Frank is too young and flighty."

"You mustn't go," replied Richard. "I'm depending on you to look after Belle and the children. We'll wait till I hear from Clinton. I ought to market my crops and pay off the mortgage, but I'll go when Clinton says the word."

In the midst of the lurid accounts of the battle which followed, Clinton's letters were of the greatest comfort. "The slaughter was frightful, but what could you expect? The plain truth is, most of our regiments are mobs, not troops. No one knows what the general has had to contend with. He was held at Donelson, by the order of Halleck, so long that he had no part in placing the armies at Shiloh. Halleck restored him to command too late to make any changes. There was no team-work. Buell didn't come up as expected and Wallace got on the wrong track. That left us with only thirty-eight thousand men to oppose Johnston's army. All the same, we won.

"The general was on a gunboat, conferring with Commodore Foote, when the attack began. I wish you could have seen him arrive. He came sailing in on that old claybank of his like a whirlwind. It's always a pleasure to see him ride, but his time—well, he was magnificent! He was perfectly cool when he questioned us. His voice was quiet, but I tell you he got every man into action. His orders had a quiet ring which put a spur into every officer."

Shiloh sobered the Northern editors and orators and filled wives and mothers with terror and dread. Long lists of the dead brought agony to thousands of homes. All levity remaining in the minds of those who had hitherto regarded the war as a romantic excursion vanished utterly. It was now certain that other and bloodier battles were about to follow. Grant's words of warning to the people of Galena were now recalled with respect. His serious view of the contest was justified. The second year had opened with larger armies and with increasing fury. Soldiers were being made out of excursionists, and officers were being sifted to find those best fitted to command.

Richard returned to his farm-work with almost mechanical persistency, moody and silent in the house, and dangerously truculent among his neighbours.

He said nothing of his purpose to Isabel, but with his mother he was more outspoken. "I've written Clinton to find a place for me under Grant. I'd rather curry a horse for a man like Grant than serve on the staff of a man like Halleck."

Harriet was profoundly moved, but advised him to wait

till after harvest. "Make sure of your crops and your farm before you go."

He had finished corn-planting when Clinton reported that Grant was again in full command. "Old fuss-budget Halleck has been called East and Grant is in control. With greatly reduced forces, we are marching on Corinth."

With one absorbing purpose Richard harvested his hay, talking of Grant and his campaign until even William made fun of him. "Dick, you're wasting time running a farm; you ought to be a general. Seems like Grant needs your services."

"I know he does," retorted Richard; "that's what bothers me."

As the tragic effect of Shiloh died away and the wheat-harvest came on, he was less troubled by his conscience. Having definitely decided the date of his enlistment, he gave all his energies to the gathering of his grain.

A wonderful new mowing-machine had just been invented, and David, who was always watching for such novelties, had purchased one. It was drawn by two horses and was called the "Buckeye." It could cut more hay in a day than ten men as David proved by cutting Richard's entire field in two days.

As the machine dropped the gavel directly in the way of the horses on the next round, it was necessary that a crew of men stationed at equal distances around the field should bind the grain as fast as it was cut. This led to "binding on a station," a new phrase in the world.

In the bustle, the excitement of this work, Richard regained his natural cheer, and when David reported a new and greatly improved threshing-machine, he perceived that the war was having a stimulating effect on the raising of grain. Even with enlarged acreage, the price of wheat was rising, and this made certain the payment of his debts. "I'll swing clean and clear this fall," he assured his mother.

It would be giving a false idea of the time to say that war remained the only interest of the country-side. It is true that it was always in the consciousness of men and women of larger growth, but to the young and careless, it was only at times a near presence. Susan, who had grown into a studious, thoughtful girl, was one of the subscribers to *Godey's Lady's Book*, and she and Isabel often studied the gaily-coloured plates with entire forgetfulness of the war.

Most of the women of the villages and some of the farmer's wives and daughters followed the New York fashions, as nearly as their means and materials would allow. They tattied and crocheted in distant collusion with their sisters in Philadelphia and Boston. Hardly a hint of the war was to be found in all the pages of Godey's delightfully feminine publication. Its life, so exquisitely hooped, flounced, and laced, was the antithesis of the life their husbands, sons, and fathers led campaigning in the South.

It was well that one periodical offered release from the horrors of Shiloh and Chancellorsville, for *Harper's Weekly* and *Leslie's Weekly* were filled with war scenes and war news. *Harper's*, the *New York Tribune*, and the county paper formed Richard's entire source of information. He snorted with contempt of the *Lady's Book*, a contempt which Susan met with the quiet smile she had inherited from her mother. Once she said in justification, "It is a great help to mother in her needle-work," and Richard was reasonable enough to admit that to a woman shut in as she was it could be of decided use and advantage.

Susan, who was a teacher part of the time, and housekeeper for the rest of the time, took the keenest delight in the pages of this magazine which seems so placid to us now. It was in truth a kind of dream-world with its stories, poems, and songs mainly of England.

It depicted ladies in gorgeous silks and laces and its chil-

The New Interest

dren were like exquisite dolls. Its entire absence of men
and men's attire gave to it a remote and stately elegance
which absorbed and soothed its women readers in the West
as it did for thousands of anxious women in the East.

Susan, engaged to a fine, thoughtful young man from
Maine (one of Richard's companions on the river, and now
in the army of the Potomac), had some of the Spartan courage of her mother, but she suffered agonies of fear after
the telegraphic news of each battle until she heard directly
from him.

She sang in her small, sweet voice all the war songs, and
when she dwelt on lines like these:

> "On the grass, the little major
> Dropped his drum that battle day,
> On the grass all stained with crimson
> Through the battle night he lay,
> Crying, 'Oh, for love of Jesus
> Grant me but this little boon,
> Can you, friend, refuse me water,
> Can you when I die so soon?' "

her heart contracted and tears filled her eyes. "It might
be my Tom," she thought.

Another song which depicted a soldier in prison awaiting
rescue by his comrades was also sad but less harrowing:

> "In my prison cell I sit,
> Thinking, mother dear, of you,
> And our bright and happy home so far away;
> And the tears they fill my eyes
> Spite of all that I can do,
> Though I try to cheer my comrades and be gay.
>
> "Tramp! tramp! tramp! the boys are marching,
> Cheer up, comrades, they will come,

And beneath the starry flag
We shall breathe the air again
Of the free land in our own beloved home."

Crude as these songs may seem to us now, they expressed the essentially rustic and serious character of the volunteer troops of 1862, and they were sung in almost every household.

Isabel knew them all and sang them as soon as they came out. Richard, rough of hand and intensely active of foot as he was, loved any song whose sentiment was put into words. Songs like "Lorena" which had nothing to do with war, he liked equally well, and in this he had many companions, for this particular ballad was popular on both sides of the battle-line. Its serene melody, sad as an autumn wind, suggested something fateful. Its lines were full of regret as well as of love:

"The days pass slowly by, Lorena,
The frost is where the flowers have been.
A hundred months—'twas flowery May
As up the hilly slopes we climbed
To watch the dying of the day
And hear the evening church-bells chimed."

Isabel sang these ballads willingly enough, but "The Battle-Cry of Freedom" was of such warlike appeal that she always dreaded the effect of its marching swing:

"We are coming, Father Abraham,
Three hundred thousand strong,
Shouting the battle-cry of freedom!
We are coming from the hill-sides,
We are coming from the plains,
Shouting the battle-cry of freedom!

294

The New Interest

"The Union forever, hurrah, boys, hurrah!
   Down with the traitor, and up with the star;
While we rally round the flag, boys,
Rally once again,
Shouting the battle-cry of freedom!"

Separated from their melody these lines seemed poor enough, but I am not sure that they suffer as much as some of the modern topical songs would suffer in like case. And when David and William and Isabel and Deborah voiced them, they suggested the swing and power of a conquering regiment.

The autumn of 1862 was a most depressing period of the war. After Shiloh, which shocked the West inexpressibly, a grim determination took the place of the confident and careless mood of the early spring. "More men, more men! the armies need men," orators and editors repeated with growing emphasis and to Richard these appeals had more and more of a personal application. He did not say so to Isabel, but to his mother (from whom he made no concealment of his plan), "Just as soon as I market my crops and pay off my mortgage I am going into the service."

CHAPTER V

Richard Goes South

ONE morning late in November, 1862, when his threshing was done and his produce marketed, Richard said,
"Well, Belle, let's go to La Crosse tomorrow. I've got the
money to pay off that mortgage."

It was a sunny day with a fall of new snow, and Isabel,
glad of this invitation, was happy in the knowledge that the
farm was about to be cleared. She rejoiced in the sound of
sleigh bells, whose music put the war out of her mind. She
got the children ready at once and they set forth.

The sun flamed along the summits of the hills with dazzling glory and the sleigh-tracks in the road shone like twin
ribbons of satin as they spun from under the broad steel
shoes of the bob-sled. The shadows of fences and trees
were everywhere steel-blue in colour and vivid as stains of
ink.

Al Crandall, who always drove like the wind, passed them
with a shout and a challenging flirt of his gloved hand, but

Richard Goes South

Richard refused to be drawn into a race. He grew more and more preoccupied as they approached the town, and Isabel, believing that he was again brooding over the question of his enlistment, lost a part of her pleasure in the ride.

It was Saturday and the principal street was lined with sleighs whose boxes were bedded with straw and filled with quilts or buffalo-robes, and among these teams huge loads of hay or cords of stiffly frozen porkers moved. Light and graceful cutters occasionally dashed by, the bells on their horses uttering a merry chime. Men in shaggy garments stood about the corners and women in their best gowns, expanded by hoops of fashionable size, loitered along the pleasant sidewalks. It was a busy, cheerful, and friendly street, with no hint of war except when a man in uniform came by. The war was now accepted as a necessary evil, but some regarded it as a good thing, for it was quickening invention and pushing agriculture. It also stimulated enterprise and raised prices.

Finding a place between the other bob-sleds, Richard hitched his team to a ring set in a plank of the raised sidewalk—a ring which Mons Anderson, the Norwegian merchant, had thriftily provided. The children, roly-poly figures in their shawls and caps, were so filled with wonder of two iron lions keeping sentinel on either side the door of the "General Store" that they could hardly be induced to enter.

Several of Isabel's neighbours, similarly swathed in long knitted shawls, were seated about the glowing stove in the back part of the long room and while she unwrapped her children, rosy with health, and big-eyed with wonder, old Mons, a hearty soul, presented to each of them a stick of candy. His unaffected kindliness was very grateful to Isabel.

Richard said, "I'm going over to Plummer's office and pay off the mortgage. I don't want anything to happen," he added.

Plummer, who had been made provost-marshal of the military district, was sitting in a big, bare room swarming with soldiers, and men who were about to become soldiers. "Hello, Dick," he called out. "Don't tell me you've come to pay off that mortgage!"

Richard assured him that he had, and that he had the money ready for him.

"You can have another year, if you want it."

"I don't want it. I want to pay it today."

"All right. Go to my private office and wait for me. I'll come over in a few minutes."

Richard no longer dreaded to meet his neighbours in uniform.

His self-respect was restored, and when a man in blue called out, "Hello, Dick! When are you going to get one of these suits?" he was able to reply, "Tomorrow. I'm paying off the mortgage on my farm today."

"Good for you! It's tough on our women, but there's no help for it. When is Dave going in?"

"He would go now if I said the word, but somebody has got to stay and look after the folks."

"It seems to me he ought to go and let you stay."

"I won't consent to that, and, besides, he don't feel exactly as I do about it. I can't stay out any longer."

Although he said nothing of it to anyone, it hurt him to have old Hugh and his sons slurred in this way, and the worst of it was, he could not quite justify them. They were not cowards, no one could be braver in many ways, but they were not warriors. It was not a part of their religion, their way of life.

The provost-marshal met him as plain Ben Plummer, lumberman and banker, and their talk was all of mills, the price of lumber—for a few minutes, but only for a few. Richard was impatient to cancel the mortgage. "I want to put my affairs in order. I'm going into service. I should have enlisted long ago but for this money which I owe you."

Plummer studied him gravely. "You really think you ought to go in?"

"Yes, I have been uneasy about it for a long time. I hate to be counted a shirker."

"How many children have you?"

"Two—at present."

"You oughtn't to go. Why doesn't Dave go in your place?"

"He has a wife and one small baby, and is trying to pay for a farm. Besides, I don't want him to go; I want him to stay and look after Isabel."

"Why don't you sign on with me? I will make you an orderly and you needn't go South at all."

This offer was a surprise and a temptation. "That is mighty good of you, Ben, and I will consider it, but first of all I want to buy back that signature of mine."

"You always were a determined cuss—all right! all right! I'll cancel it but I want you to understand that I'm perfectly content to have it run."

With his fingers on his money, Richard watched the big fist of his creditor as he wrote the word "cancelled" on the outside of the mortgage. Pushing the money across, Richard said, "Better count it before you surrender my note."

Plummer laughed. "Count it! I'll bet you've counted it twenty times. I can smell the sweat you put into every dollar of it. It makes me think of my own first indebtedness. No, I'll take your word for it." As he tossed the mortgage over to Richard, he added, "Now, what about serving with me?"

"Give me a little time to decide that? I don't feel like deciding it today."

"All right, come in as soon as you get ready, and later if you want to go South I can let you go at any time."

With a promise to think it over, Richard went back to Isabel who was anxiously waiting for him. "It's done," he announced, "we don't owe a dollar."

In a mood of remorseful tenderness, he urged her to buy a new dress for herself and some shoes for the children. But his urging only added to her uneasiness. She read in it the decision which she had dreaded. There was something new in his face.

The day, which had begun so brightly, darkened gloomily with the dusk. They rode home in a restraint so marked that the children felt it, as they felt the bitter wind. The next day Richard drove to Onalaska to confer with his father and mother concerning Plummer's offer.

"What shall I do?" was his question.

His father urged him to accept. "You will be doing your duty and you can supervise your farm at the same time."

His mother said nothing against this arrangement, but Richard was not entirely convinced of her agreement. "It is a powerful temptation," she said. "Most people will tell you that with three small children you are honourably exempt, and that you would be doing your full duty by serving under Plummer, but others will not take that view."

He ended by sending word to Plummer that he would soon come down and sign, but before the end of the week, little Harriet developed a virulent sore throat, and he was so worried and distracted by her suffering that he failed to report. Had he been actually enlisted it is probable that he would have left Isabel to struggle through this crisis alone, but as a civilian, he remained where his most pressing duty was. There were no antitoxins to assist in the struggle against diphtheria, and the battle was to the strong in all cases of this disorder.

It was not until late in December that he was able to report to Plummer. "I will sign with you," he said, "provided that you will agree to release me when Clinton finds a place for me, as he has said he would."

Plummer considered. "I will tell you what I will do, Dick; I will put you on the civilian roll and assign you to guard-duty. Any time you want to go to the front I can release you."

On this understanding he signed the roll as civilian guard and went home to let Isabel know what he had done.

She surprised him by cheerfully consenting to the arrangement. In truth she was so relieved that a girlish smile came back upon her lips. All danger of his going to the front seemed over, and while she dreaded the loneliness of the winter, she took comfort in the thought that he would be only a few miles away.

Richard's life in La Crosse was pleasant. He was not required to wear a uniform and his duties were light. His experience in handling crews of men came into use, for at times the guard-house was full of recruits who had broken bounds, and once or twice a strong test of his quality took place. Plummer had such confidence in his judgment and courage that he seldom interfered or advised.

He had a natural aptitude for military tactics and though not required to drill he volunteered to do so for an hour or two every afternoon, and soon became so proficient that he could command an awkward squad as well as any of the sergeants. Occasionally the marshal granted him a half-day leave and he was able to see that Isabel was provided with fire-wood and groceries.

For nearly three months he served in this semi-military capacity, to the entire approval of the provost-marshal, but did not succeed in quieting his own conscience. It hurt him to have his envious neighbours say, "You're in luck! I wish I had a soft job like yours. You'll never be called upon for front-line duty and you're safe from the draft."

When he spoke to Plummer about this, the marshal only

laughed. "Let 'em talk. What do you care? If I'm satisfied I guess you should be. Somebody must act in your capacity and I don't know a man I'd rather keep in that position."

In a letter to Clinton, who was in Memphis, Richard told of the criticism to which he was occasionally subjected, and again said, "Remember your promise to give me a job under your command. I can't stand much more of this backbiting. I want to be nearer the spot where fighting is going on."

It was in February when a letter came from Clinton commanding him to report. "I have volunteered for a tough job and I need you. I'm not saying, 'drop everything and come at once,' but I do say that the quicker you can get here the better. I have waited till now so that it won't be so hard on Isabel, but I guess the time has come for you to take a position on that front line you've been talking about so long. You'll never be satisfied till you've had a whack at war and here's your chance. I am enclosing a pass which the general signed at my request. He remembers you as my partner and as a brother to Addison and understands my reasons for wanting you."

A stir went through Richard's hair as he looked at that signature, so potent now. The thought that he might possibly see the commander in person was an inspiration. It was not easy to make the connection between the Captain Grant of that Galena war-meeting and this man who signed "General Commanding," but Clinton's letters had kept the way open. Furthermore, he knew that strong and simple signature, for Addison had once sent a letter from U. S. Grant. He was aware that the distinction of this pass came through Clinton, but he was exalted by it nevertheless.

Going at once to the marshal, he said, "Ben, here's my marching order," and extended the letter and pass.

Plummer took them and read them with care, reflecting

on them for a moment before he asked, "Any idea what the service is?"

"Not a hint. Clinton has said that he would make me his orderly if I came down, but I don't think it's just that kind of job."

Plummer returned the pass. "Well, when General Grant wants anything done a hint is as good as a kick. I'll write out a release at once."

With his discharge and his pass in his pocket, Richard went to his mother. "Well, mother, I'm going South."

Harriet's thin face grew graver, but her voice was firm as she replied, "Very well, Richard. Do your duty. We will look after Belle and the children." Her body was a withered reed, but the spirit which had made her an uncomplaining pioneer now enabled her to send her son to war, especially on such a summons.

His father was very curious about the duty at which Clinton hinted. "I wonder what it can be."

"I don't know what it is, but as he knows how hard it is for me to leave Belle and the children, he must consider it important."

Harriet did not question. "Whatever it is I hope it will be service of the highest sort of which you are capable."

"I don't think he expects to keep me in the rear, mother, but if he asks me to be his hostler I'll do it. He's at the front and he'll carry me along with him."

The nearer he got to his own home the less his exalted mood served him. He faced the ordeal of telling Isabel with a heavy heart. It all seemed unreal in the presence of his small cottage deeply banked with snow, and still more unreal as he entered the sitting-room and found his children playing on a sheep-skin spread under the high-stepping stove.

They scrambled up and ran to him with cries of joy, but Isabel instantly read in his face something which robbed the meeting of joy. "What has happened? Why have you come home today?"

"I've got my marching orders, Belle."

She confronted him with startled eyes. "What do you mean?"

"Clinton has sent me a pass, and Plummer has transferred me. I'm going South at once."

With a piteous, whimpering cry she went to him and put her arms about him. "Oh, Dick, I can't bear it! I can't let you go!"

Poor girl, she had not Harriet Graham's stern philosophy of sacrifice, and besides, Richard had been shockingly abrupt in his announcement. Perhaps he had expected her to thrill at the honour conveyed by a pass from General Grant. He had anticipated her protest, but he was not prepared for her despair.

He tried to make light of it all. "The fact is, Clinton needs a new hostler. I'm not going to fight. Somebody must curry the colonel's horses. He can't do it himself."

She found no comfort in his jesting, and the general's wonder-working signature failed to exalt her. She turned away to comfort her frightened children, the love of the mother rising, for the present, above that of the wife.

She was not of those who buckle on a husband's sword, sending him forth to conquer or to return a corpse upon his shield. Like her brother, she was a Celtic dreamer, one to whom the words "Confederation" and "Secession" connoted something very vague and far away. She had not been schooled in New England traditions like Susan. She had no deep-laid political convictions like Harriet Graham, whose impersonal emotions lifted her, in times like these, to heroic self-sacrifice. She was just a young wife who loved her husband and counted upon his protection. He was her government, her country, and her future.

Her fears for him were intensified by the fact that for

many days her brother Luke had not been heard from. When last he wrote he was a captain, serving in Virginia. A persistent conviction of his death saddened her. "Luke is gone," she now said, "and you are going. Soon Dave will go, and I shall be left alone. I can't stand it! I won't let you go."

She grew calmer as she went about her wifely duties, but her cloud did not lift. Her night was filled with visions of the dangers to which she believed her husband was deliberately addressing himself, and in the morning she insisted that he drive over to consult with her father and mother.

To this Richard agreed, although his decision was unalterable. "That pass is a command for me," he declared. "It is hard to leave, but I must obey."

The McLane household had suffered many changes. William, Rachel, Jane, and Deborah now had homes of their own. Only Frank, pretty Samantha, and David with his young wife were living at the homestead. The broad-roofed cottage had weathered into grey, and in the yard the stalks of hardy flowers were standing stiff and brown above the snow, but in his accustomed chair at the window sat Hugh, his thatch of white hair a little thinner, his eyes a little dimmer than they had been when Richard knew him first, but he was still of massive frame.

Mother McLane, looking bent and sad, came to the door to meet her daughter, and as she took her grand-children in her arms, Richard derived comfort from the thought that she would be their stay in case he should not return from the front.

In answer to questions, Mrs. McLane said, "We still hope to hear from Luke. I can't bear to give him up. Why will men go to war when the Day of Judgment is so near?"

Her voice expressed a bitter humour, for she was not yet wholly convinced that the new date of the Second Coming had been accurately determined. The "horns" and the "beasts," the "chariots" and the "wheels" were still more mystifying than convincing to her. Her world was concrete, homely, cheerful, or rather it had been up to 1861. Now it was falling to pieces, but not as her husband saw it ending.

Hugh greeted them with remote gaze, kindly, abstracted. Not till small Harriet climbed to his knees and put her arms around his neck, did he disengage his thought from his visionary world.

Isabel burst out. "Dick's going to war, pappy! Make him stay! He won't listen to me."

The patriarch's face lost its genial lines. "Strange that men should fight when the Day of Judgment is at hand," he mused.

Richard smiled as he replied, "The trouble is, grandpap, the slavery men don't believe in the Day of Judgment. They won't admit that they are the stubble. The Southern armies go on flourishing and fighting. The President is calling on every able-bodied man to come down and fight. I can't stay out any longer, for Clinton has asked me to come in, and has sent a pass signed by General Grant."

"Would you leave Belle and the little ones?"

"Yes. I have cleared my farm and I'm going in. You must see that Belle and the children do not suffer."

It was well that Richard had that call from Clinton and that magic signature to steady his resolution, for though old Hugh's faith seemed a rank futility and his prophecies had no weight, yet something in his lofty unconcern with military affairs took the edge from Richard's fighting temper. Hugh's attitude explained the aloofness of William. Brave as a lion though he was, his willingness to enter an army and march through another man's country to burn and kill was not keen. Nevertheless, when at Richard's request, he and the girls sang the grand new song, "The

Battle-Cry of Freedom," his voice carried something of its heroic emotion.

At the end David was moved to say, "You stay, Dick, and after the spring crops are in, I'll go in your place."

"I can't wait," said Richard. "This pass means *come now*. No, you stay and look after both families. We can't all go. Some of us must keep on raising wheat and corn to feed the armies."

It was a beautiful winter afternoon. Outside a dazzling sun made a world of blue and silver. The snow on the south side of the roof melted, creating icicles which the children broke and used as swords, but within the gloom deepened. At times they talked of pleasant, homely things or joked to relieve the tension, whilst Grandmother McLane, the most composed of them all, went about her preparations for supper with unfaltering feet, finding a measure of consolation in her wonted tasks.

In spite of his denials, Richard could not entirely escape the feeling that his wife might be right. "This may be the last time I shall sit at this table."

David's sombre face, Adele's fitful gaiety, Hugh's abstraction, and the grandmother's care of the awed children all united to take the steel from his resolution. His baby's face, fair as a flower, weakened his will so that he spoke of delaying his departure. In this understanding he and his little family rode away to their home.

The routine of his life was hard to break, and perhaps if it had not been for the power of another letter from Clinton, he might not have gone till spring. I cannot be sure. I only know that a few days later he wrenched Isabel's clinging hands from his neck, and went away into the sinister South. He suffered; God knows he suffered as a husband and father should, at the moment of parting, finding the unconscious attitude of his little son at play upon the floor even more poignant than his wife's silent grief. It seemed a kind of treachery to kiss his unconscious children and walk away from them as if only for a day.

Isabel followed him to the road where Crandall's sleigh waited, her sweet face quivering with pain, but she made no further protest. She lifted her lips to him in a final resignation which was like that of a child, very lovely and very moving. At the moment of parting, a comforting conviction came to her. "You will come back to me," she said with solemn intensity. "You'll be wounded, but you'll come back. I feel it. If you need me, send for me. Write to me! You will write often, won't you?"

"I will write as often as I can, Belle, but don't worry if you don't hear from me. Clinton will write if I can't."

In this spirit they parted, and as he drove away, she was standing in the door of the snow-covered cottage with the baby in her arms.

CHAPTER VI

Richard Reports for Duty

RESTLESS and roving as his life had been, Richard Graham was singularly ignorant of railroad trains. Since leaving Massachusetts, thirteen years before, his travelling had been entirely by way of stages, steamboats, or lumber rafts. Even in this Southern trip he would have gone by river had the upper Mississippi been open to traffic.

The passenger equipment had changed marvellously and for the better since that day in 1850 when he rode to Hoosac, but even so, its service was dirty and poor. The rails were rough, the coaches low and grimy, and the wood-burning engines, which carried enormous smoke-stacks comically disproportionate to their boilers, belched out clouds of smoke. Sleeping-berths (a new contraption) were hardly more luxurious than the bunks in a logging-camp and cinders filled the train when the wind was dead ahead. Stops for meals were uncertain and very short; nevertheless, notwithstanding all these discomforts, the railway was supplanting the stage and retiring the steamboat.

Richard found the county seat of Sparta still unsettled. The railway had not made much change there, but a bridge spanned the river at the foot of the Dells and he was curious to see how the gorge, which had been such a terror in his rafting days, would look when seen from above. He was amazed to find that the river, once so like a lion in his path, was only a very pleasing bit of scenery when studied from a coach-window. The falls were hardly more than ripples and the walls of the canyon an interesting "view" to his fellow-passengers. Thirteen years had tamed the whirlpools and subdued the falls.

The car was filled with volunteer soldiers on their way to training-camps at Madison and Milwaukee, and in their talk the spirit of the country was revealed. "Our head generals are all failures" was their verdict, "but the right man will be found and the country saved. We've got to win! What kind of a nation would we have, split right through the middle the longest way, with slavery on one side of an imaginary line and abolitionist farmers on the other? Our states would be like a lot of tom-cats tied together by the tails and flung over a pole."

This was a homely way of putting it, but it expressed the general feeling. The North had no intention of quitting the field until the Union was assured.

It saddened Richard, however, to find that few of them shared his admiration for Grant as the great Western soldier. He was in truth almost forgotten. One or two alluded to him as a man who had done good work at Donelson, but who had been beaten by whisky, a judgment which aroused Dick's anger.

"What do you know about that? Nothing but what his enemies put into the papers. My brother lived in the same town with him and found him a good citizen. He won

Henry and Donelson, and he saved the day at Shiloh. No matter what the papers say, he's a soldier. He knows his business. He's no politician, and if they'll let him alone he'll take Vicksburg. You can bet your hat on that."

It was folly to argue, but in this way he raged while a crowd of jeering, shouting recruits surrounded him. A few agreed with him; others said, "I hope you're right," but the majority were openly derisive. "What's your 'great general' doing now? Why don't he go ahead and take Vicksburg? Why hang around Memphis?"

"I'll tell you why! Halleck took command after Shiloh and robbed Grant of half his men, so that Grant couldn't move in any force. He's in full command now, and he's going to make a noise that the whole country will hear."

He was tempted to show them Clinton's letter and his pass, but restrained himself, and after the recruits left the train at Madison Junction, he rode the rest of the way to Milwaukee in sober reflection. How could Grant make headway against all this envy and doubt?

Milwaukee had grown into a little city since his landing there in 1850, but Chicago, which he had never seen before, was a booming metropolis and he was very glad of Addison's presence in the city. He met him at the station and took him to his hotel.

"I envy you," he said. "If I possessed your health and strength I'd go, too. I've had my chance. Grant told Rawlins to find out what I wanted to do, and commission me to do it, but I refused to make capital of his friendship. Thus far I've never asked him for anything. Have you any intimation of what Clinton intends to do with you after you report to him?"

"Not a word. He just said he had a place for me."

"You won't get as far as an aide, and your handwriting will keep you from being made an adjutant. Stable orderly is more in your line."

"His horse will shine, if that's my job, but I hope I'll have a chance to handle a gun."

Addison became serious and sympathetic. "That's the spirit. My greetings to Clinton."

Richard rode away toward Springfield on his mysterious and dangerous mission with such martial exaltation that his wife and children became strangely vague and far away.

There are men who decry patriotism. To them this abstract emotion which lifts a man out of his furrow and sends him forth, away from his wife and children, into the mud and misery and imminent danger of the battle-field, is an ignoble passion, and yet I suspect it will be a long time before love of country fades into the paler sentiment of "International Amity." Richard was not going to war for Wisconsin, not even for the North. He was going to aid in the preservation of a national ideal. For him the flag stood for a Union, not a section; a Republic, not a confederation of colonies. Lincoln was his leader and Grant his warrior. Both were Western in spirit and training, breaking out new ways in government and in war.

He spent that night in Springfield where all the perplexities and campaigns of the state were seething. As the home of Lincoln, it possessed orators who believed him to be the greatest man in American history, but it contained others who regarded him as "a lucky country judge." One man said in Richard's hearing, "Abe Lincoln is no more fitted to command armies than Deacon Adams or Amos Flint."

Enemies of Grant were equally outspoken, and this added to Richard's resentment. That the victor of Donelson and Shiloh should be condemned by these stay-at-homes (many of whom had shouted his praises after the surrender of Buckner) was a bitter injustice.

A Galena man whom he met sadly confirmed these impressions. "Every Western politician, even Senator Washburne, has deserted Grant, but Lincoln still believes in him. To a senator who wanted Grant removed, he said, 'I can't spare that man—he fights.' "

To this Richard could add a word of cheer. "My friend, Clinton Helmstock, who is on Grant's staff, says he's in full command and is moving on Vicksburg."

At St. Louis he found a familiar boat, the *War Eagle*, just ready to start south, and soon after he went aboard he met the captain, who knew him and saluted him jovially.

"Hello, 'Yankee Dick!' Aren't you boarding the wrong raft? I'm headed south this time."

"So am I," replied Richard. "I'm on my way to Memphis. You remember Clinton Helmstock, who used to run the river with me?"

"Perfectly. What's become of him?"

"He's serving under Grant. I'm on my way to him with a pass from the general himself."

The captain was impressed. "Can I see the pass?"

With boyish pride Richard showed Clinton's letter and the pass. After studying it closely, the captain handed it back. "That's good for a ride on this boat. Don't you pay a cent for passage."

"But I've already done so."

"Come with me," commanded the captain and led him to the purser's window. "Return this man his money," said he. "He's a Wisconsin River pilot and a friend of mine," and as he turned away he added, "Any man with a personal pass from General Grant is a star-boarder on the *War Eagle*."

The boat was crowded with traders, speculators, gamblers, money-changers, and missionaries, a motley gang trailing at the safe end of an advancing army, many of them concerned only with plans for making money. "The war is their chance," thought Richard with smouldering resentment. "They are all on the make."

He was glad of the captain's invitation to sit in the pilot-house and he put in much time there listening to the endless stories of the river which the commander and the pilot interchanged. One story which the captain told concerned a plot to capture General Grant.

"I live in St. Louis, when I'm on land, and one of my friends, a second cousin, is a farmer out where Grant used to live. Jeff Safford, that's my cousin's name, gave me a full account of the scheme. It all took place last year while Grant was in command at Cairo. It seems that an old German who lived near Jeff was in the business of smuggling medicines through the lines to the Southern armies, and had learned of the general's intention to visit his cabin on the Gravois a few miles from St. Louis, and believed he could be captured. So he passed the word around among the Knights of the Golden Circle and a special meeting was called. They were to meet in his barn near Grant's old cabin. On the night appointed, Jeff was on hand. The German called the meeting to order and stated his plan. 'Grant is in St. Louis tonight. He intends to drive out here tomorrow in a single-seated buggy without military escort. It would be a fine job, almost like capturing an army, to put him out of commission. Half a dozen men can do it at any lonely point on the road.'

"His idea created a stir. According to Jeff, every man was on his feet hot to be one of the posse.

"In the midst of all this jubilation Jeff got up and called for silence. He's a big fellow, strong as a horse, one of these slow-spoken chaps whose words count. 'Now hold on a second,' he said. 'Let's arguefy this thing. It's a fine scheme, a mighty fine scheme. It can be carried out just like you say—no doubt of that—but what I want to ask you men is this. What is the Northern Army going to think of our smart little trick? You can yank Grant out of his buggy as you've planned, but have you considered what comes next? I'll tell you what. The Yankee troops won't leave a house standing in this valley and they'll hang every man-jack of us.'

"This dropped a wet blanket over the proceedings, and while they sat with mouths open he went on, 'Furthermore, I want it understood that I won't stand for no such low-down scheme. Grant's my friend. He was my neighbour. We've harvested wheat side by side. We've eat at the same table. You can't waylay and rope and tie him if he is a Union general, not while I'm alive and healthy. If Johnston or Pemberton can't get him, it's not your job to sneak up behind him, like a lot of burglars, and hit him with a sand-bag. I'll advise you to let this project die right here!'

"It did just that," ended the captain with a chuckle. The meeting broke up and Grant visited his old neighbours, Jeff among the rest, and so far as I know has never been told how near he came to being ambushed. I sometimes wonder what he would do for Jeff if he did know."

In Richard's mind Jefferson Safford took on something of the character of William McLane. "I'd like to meet that man," he said.

The captain introduced Dick to a merchant from St. Louis who really knew something of Grant and his problem. "He's one of the most reticent men in the world. Nobody knows what his plans are. He's as silent as an oyster. Every reporter finds him unyielding as granite."

"Why should he publish his plans?" demanded the captain of the boat. "Seems to me a general who tells his plans is giving his enemy a chance to defeat him."

At Memphis, a small, unkempt town on the first high ground south of Cairo, Richard left the *War Eagle* and went in search of Clinton's headquarters. Here for the first time he came in touch with the South and its negroes. The streets swarmed with them, many in rags, and all stained with the red clay of the fields. To this son of a New

England abolitionist they were as amazing as they were disheartening. Wide-nosed, thick-lipped, and as ugly as gorillas, they shocked and dismayed him. "Are these the creatures our men are fighting to set free?" he asked himself. Their shambling walk, the colour of their skins, and their clouded animal eyes repelled him. "Why, they are savages!" he exclaimed. "It will take a thousand years to make them into men. Nevertheless they are human beings and should not be bought and sold."

A few of them, however, were curiously attractive by reason of their smiles and their musical voices. There was something childlike in their notion that the Union armies had come to set them free. They resented being put to work. "Why should we work? We is free."

Richard asked his way of a white man who was standing at the door of his shop. He pointed out a store building on which a flag was flying. "That's Grant's headquarters —so I'm told," he added with a grin. "I keep away from it. You'll notice another flag draped over the doorway. No one can enter without taking off his hat to the flag, so I jest naturally keep to the other side of the street. Not that I have anything against Grant. He's treated us well."

Richard passed only one sentry and at last reached General Rawlins, Grant's chief-of-staff, whom he remembered as the eloquent young lawyer at the war-meeting in Galena. Authority had made him brusque.

"Well, what do you want?" he demanded.

Dick was nettled. "I want to see Captain Helmstock. I have a pass signed by General Grant."

Rawlins modified his tone. Calling an orderly he said, "Take this man to Captain Helmstock."

Clinton was seated at a desk in a room which looked like a business office. With a shout of delight he greeted Richard. "You infernal old river-rat!" he exclaimed. "On what saw-log did you arrive? Gosh-all-hemlock, but you look good to me! How is Belle? How are all the Mc-Lanes?"

As Richard answered these questions, Clinton lost his smile and became reflective. "It all seems a long way off to me now. My business has gone to pot up there—you can't go to war and manufacture lumber at the same time. I don't think about it, except when somebody comes along and reminds me of it. This war is in a low stage of water just now. These old-time West Point officers are all jealous of one another and our political generals are after glory and ballots. Some of 'em are good men, of course, but you can't make a soldier out of a lawyer or shoe merchant without a lot of waste effort. We've got the only great soldier right here, and I guess our President knows it. Anyhow, Grant is in full command of the armies in the West and Vicksburg is our objective."

"What are you doing?"

"I'm nominally attached to McRae's engineering corps, but I'm actually a kind of map-builder for the general. You see nobody knows anything about the Southern roads and streams and somebody must find out about swamps and bridges. As the army is now organized there's no one to do this work. People back home wonder why we don't move right on down to Vicksburg, horse, foot, and cannon, but before we do that we must know the best way to get there. That is my present job, and you've got to help me. The general wants some exploring done and I've volunteered to do it. I said, 'Here's the place where Dick can be of service. It isn't spy duty, exactly; it's a kind of survey for roads. Sometimes this is done by a detachment, a company, or regiment. In this case you and I are going to try it with some negroes to guide us. But come! Let's go and see the general."

Richard's eyes betrayed uneasiness. "He don't want to be bothered by me."

"It won't be a bother. He sees everybody. He's the friendliest man in the world. Anybody from Georgetown or St. Louis or Galena can always see him. 'Pears like he's home-sick for news of the home-town; besides, he knows and likes your brother."

After leading the way up a flight of stairs and down a long hall, Clinton opened a door. "We'll find the general in here."

As the time came for confronting the commander of a great army, Richard was as near scared as he had ever been. He followed Clinton like a reluctant boy.

The room they entered was big and bare and at the back end of it, an officer was sitting beside a table and gazing out of the window. It was General Grant musing on the problems which confronted him.

As Clinton advanced, the commander looked up with a remote expression which changed to a cordial smile as Clinton said, "General, this is Richard Graham, a brother of Addison Graham."

"I'm glad to see you. How did you leave your brother? I hear he is planning to leave Galena."

While he talked of Galena and various homely matters, Richard studied him closely. He had changed, of course, since that war-meeting in Galena, but not by way of taking on pomp and ceremony. He appeared care-worn but his close-cut beard showed the firm line of his thin lips. His hair which was parted rather low on one side was neatly brushed and his uniform was new and shapely.

In repose his face was like a mask, stern and cold, and his eyes, partly concealed by narrowed lids, were piercing, but as he talked of old friends his eyes twinkled with kindly humour. His voice was low, friendly, and musical.

"Have you paid off that mortgage?" he asked.

"Yes, I cancelled it just before I left home."

"And your wife and children are well?"

318

"All well, general."

"Then you are ready for service?"

"Yes, general, I am ready to do whatever is required of me."

Indicating a map which was spread out on the table, the general continued, "Clinton tells me that you are particularly expert in finding your way in a swamp."

"I do seem to have a special gift that way," admitted Richard. "I cruised the head-waters of the Wisconsin River for six years without getting turned around, as they call it."

"So Clinton tells me. He is responsible for your being here at this time." His voice became more impersonal as he went on: "We are without detailed information concerning this region," he pointed out on the map the country opposite Vicksburg, "and Captain Helmstock has volunteered to go into it and survey it for me. The special duty for which he is assigned is of vital importance to me. You will act as his aide with the pay of orderly sergeant. There will be many hardships and some danger in this expedition, for much of that ground is under fire of the Confederate guns, and all the lower part of the peninsula is overrun with small guerilla bands." He glanced at Clinton. "Report only to me." To Richard he added, "Remember me to Addison when you write."

Richard left the room with a sense of having been called to aid in a most important task. Friendly and simple as the general's manner had been, Richard could not forget that this quiet man was the head of a vast army and that the survey which Clinton had volunteered to make might determine the march of that army. Neighbourly as Grant had been, his tone was authoritative.

Clinton now took command. "Understand this, Dick. No one must know when we go or where we go. I picked you to help me do this work because you can take care of yourself in the swamps better than any man I know. Our experiences as timber-cruisers and rivermen in Wisconsin should count for something now. The facts are these: Sherman's land forces have failed to carry Vicksburg from the north, and Porter's gunboats have failed to silence the Confederate batteries commanding the river. The general now wants to know exactly what the chances are for marching an army across this loop of land which lies between Milliken's Bend and New Carthage. We are something more than scouts. We are to make a woodsman's survey. We are to study streams, roads, and bridges, but technically we are spies, and must take care of ourselves. There is a considerable Confederate force on the west side of the river, and many small bands of grey-coats roaming about. It will be necessary to proceed with the greatest caution. We are to move as rapidly as possible and report at the earliest moment." Here his expression became boyish, jocular. "Dick, it's a whale of a job! It's a case of turning swamp-fox for a week or two. Are you game for it?"

Richard looked at him with the familiar blaze of his gray eyes which expressed his sternest resolution. "What you can do I can do."

Clinton laughed. "I knew you'd say that—or something like it. Well, now, for preparation. This work while not as spectacular as charging a line of breastworks, is important—and it's dangerous, I won't say it isn't. There is always the liability of capture. You will act as guide, commissary and cook just as you used to do when we were cruising for pine-land. Mostly we'll live off the country. I am depending on the negroes to help in that regard."

This commission not only appealed to Richard's adventure-loving spirit, it ran parallel with his training. The value of this survey and the need of doing it swiftly, secretly and with judgment filled him with resolved pride. He put aside all thought of home and its concerns, and turned to the task of outfitting for the expedition, whole-heartedly almost joyously. His conscience was at rest. He was at last serving his country and under the men he most revered.

At every opportunity he questioned Clinton about Grant whose rise to power became each day more miraculous. "Some of the papers back home print stories about his drinking but I have never believed these yarns."

"There never was a general more abstemious," Clinton replied. "He lives as simply as a Quaker. He won't stand for roystering of any sort. He hates dirty stories and he won't have men tell them in his presence. He's the kindest man I ever knew but he can be stern. One night several of his subordinates were having a rip-roaring time in their quarters when suddenly the Commander appeared in his night-shirt. "What's the meaning of all this?" he demanded, and they froze. Two of 'em had to go, by reason of that spree.

"Another thing, you'll hear it said that Rawlins or Wilson or some other man is the brains of Grant's Army but let me tell you there is only one head to this army and that is U. S. Grant. Rawlins may think he's running things but Sherman and McPherson know better. *Nobody* tells Grant what to do. He listens to everybody, McClernand, Wilson, Dana—he's a wonderful listener; but when he goes, he goes his own way! Rawlins argues and roars, but Grant just smiles and smokes till the storm ends.

"For instance, one day last fall, while we had our headquarters in a little country church over to the east of here, the chaplains of the army cast eyes upon the building Grant was in. They wanted to hold a series of religious meetings in it. They called a conference and delegated an Illinois man to beard the lion in his den. The reverend gentleman was pretty nervous, I expect, but he faced the general and made his wishes known in a fine little speech.

Grant's face was blank as a stone-wall while the preacher was talking, and I was flabbergasted when he said, 'Why, certainly, chaplain. We'll move right out. A tent will serve our purpose just as well as the church.'

"Rawlins, who was listening, let out a roar you could hear a mile. 'I won't stand for any such nonsense. I won't give up my head-quarters for a dash-dashed lot of preachers. Let 'em preach in the open air.'

"When he stopped to catch his breath, Grant said to the scared minister, 'Don't mind General Rawlins, Mr. Smith. He's not as fierce as he sounds. We keep him to do our swearing for us.'

"That's the General! He's the strangest man I ever knew. There never was such a chief. He never parades, never raises his voice even when giving an order. I've never heard him use a slang word and he never 'slops over,' not even to his friends, and his ability to sit down any minute and write is wonderful. His orders are expressed fluently yet in the fewest possible words. How did he get where he is? People talk of this man or that man helping Grant, and so they do—after he has helped himself! What would Jack Rawlins be if it were not for Grant? He'd be practising law in Galena and Rowley would be a shop-keeper in St. Louis. That's the general's weakness. He has carried a lot of these fellows to high command that aren't worth it.

"I won't say they're *all* undeserving their rank, but some of 'em wouldn't be deuce high without his help. It makes me weary to hear some little squirt talking of 'influencing Grant.' Just because he's friendly and gives his orders in a conversational tone of voice, some people are fooled into thinking he's slow and commonplace. Commonplace! Good Lord! I don't think his career can be matched in all history.

"Talk of his being 'made by circumstances.' The fact is *he makes his circumstances*. Did you know that President

Lincoln went back on him last fall? He did. He went so far as to commission McClernand to raise an army and move on Vicksburg. When Grant learned of this he saw that his trusted Sherman was about to be superseded. He knew that McClernand hated Sherman and that McPherson distrusted McClernand, a nice mess! There was only one thing to do. By taking command in person he subordinated McClernand, placated Sherman and pulled the army together. That's what I mean by creating circumstances. Grant does things. He's a kind of inventor in military strategy. He's breaking out a new trail right now. All his experiences in the Mexican war and on the frontier are coming into play. He could do this scouting job himself if he weren't needed at head-quarters. That's the kind of general he is. He's one of us.

"Now as to our job. The more inconspicuous we are, the better. I'm going to take no one else but a couple of negroes. We'll have some high-class Injun scouting to do, mostly at night, and you'll have plenty of water to paddle in. The whole country is flooded, and we may have to ride alligators the way we used to ride logs. Furthermore, the swamps are full of bears, wild hogs and snakes. Our job is not what old Cooper used to call a 'sine-a-cure'; it's a dirty, dangerous undertaking."

Richard knew nothing about war, but he very naturally asked, "Supposing an army can be marched over this swampy neck, how can it ferry the river and get at Vicksburg?"

"That's our problem. We've got to find a place to cross."

A few days later, a small gun-boat took Clinton and Richard on board and set off down the river. They were accompanied by two negroes, big silent serious fellows who said they belonged in or near Grand Gulf, and claimed to know all the country below Milliken's Bend and around

Vicksburg. "We'll find them helpful when we come in contact with the plantation negroes," Clinton explained.

Work on the canal which the general had half-heartedly sanctioned in order to keep the army employed, was languishing. Part of it was under fire, and the officers began to suspect that the chief had lost interest in the project as impracticable, but no one knew this to be a fact.

"Our job is to find, not only the best road, but the best approach to unfortified ground on the east side below Vicksburg. Pemberton must not get wind of Grant's plans. He must be fooled as to what our army intends to do. The army can't ferry in the face of enemy cannon. Once on the east bank, however, our men can live off the country."

With all his seeming austerity, Grant was curiously confiding in those whom he knew and liked. He made much of the human relationships. The fact that he had known Clinton in Galena had led him to trust him with this task. For those he loved, no honour was too great, but to those who betrayed his trust, he was relentlessly unforgiving. Gentle as he appeared, generous as he was, he could be granite when a charge of duplicity or disloyalty was preferred. His employment of trusted friends, in high command, was at once a weakness and a source of power.

Out of the scouts at this moment detailed, Captain Helmstock was the one he most relied upon. The peculiar schooling which he had undergone, gave him peculiar value.

At Milliken's Bend a regiment of engineers, fore-runners of McClernand's Division, was encamped, and the boat touched there long enough for Captain Helmstock to visit head-quarters. The colonel in command reported that "the upper part of the peninsula was pretty clear of the enemy, but that it was necessary to be watchful." "I couldn't hold this position twenty-four hours if the roads were not under water," he said.

In accordance with Clinton's orders, the commands of the

gun-boat waited till darkness fell, then steamed quietly
down the river to a deserted landing just above Ducksport,
from which point (so his negro guides declared), a turnpike
ran all the way to Grand Gulf.

Here in the deep of night, the boat landed Clinton and
his companions and stole away up-stream, leaving them
perched on top of the levee close to the enemy's lines, and
with rations for a ten-day march.

CHAPTER VII

Exploring the Lowlands

DESPITE his many harsh experiences as woodsman and river pilot, something very like fear seized upon Richard as the boat made off up the river, leaving him and Clinton standing on the edge of a swamp in the enemy's country exposed to attack and without any clue to compass-points. For the first time in many years his sense of direction failed him. His world, hitherto so definite and sunny, had become a chaos, warm and wet and black. A sinister world without north or south or east or west. He felt as helpless as a child.

Clinton was almost equally at a loss, but concealed it better. With a note of bravado in his voice he said: "Well, Dick, here we are; on our own resources in a region where every white man's hand is agin' us. Every step south adds to our danger."

"And we don't know which way *is* south, at least I

don't. I infer that the boat is going north, but I don't know it."

"As a general deduction, I think you're right, but the river makes a big bend here."

Slowly the sound of the gunboat died away and one by one the voices of water-fowl and water-beasts arose in broadening chorus. Bull-frogs croaked, toads trilled innumerably, and in the midst of these familiar spring sounds a monstrous bellow broke with appalling suggestion.

"What's that?" asked Clinton.

"Gatahs," replied one of the negroes.

"What do you mean? Alligators?"

"Yes, marster captain. Gatahs mighty plenty in dis swamp."

"Well," Clinton remarked with humorous inflection, "we won't bother them so long as they don't bother us. Let's make camp. We must get under cover and stay there till we can reconnoitre and plan our advance."

They had two small tents, a double blanket apiece, and enough coffee, sugar, hard-tack, and bacon to last for ten days. Beyond that they expected to forage on the country. At Clinton's order the negroes carried their outfit to a deserted warehouse which the light of the steamer had dimly revealed to them. It was in decay but offered a part of a roof. "It will screen us from observation," Clinton observed.

Spreading their blankets on the floor they went to sleep; that is to say, the negroes and Clinton slept, but Richard, too excited to close his eyes, listened to the weird noises of this strange land till long after midnight. Much of his uneasiness arose from the tales he had heard of the swarming serpents and fever-breeding fog of the region in which he was about to cruise. In his snatches of slumber he dreamed of slimy pools, copperheads, and monstrous lizards.

The weather was very mild, like April in Wisconsin, and

all the scaly beasts in the water surrounding the warehouse were alert and vocal, and listening in disgust to them, he recalled with affection the sweet woodland streams of the North. The thought of surveying these swamps, under trees festooned with water-moccasins and over streams swarming with saurians, gave him a bad hour. With no notion of retreating or even of complaining, he conquered his repugnance and finally fell asleep, and when at dawn Clinton asked him if the 'gators had kept him awake, he replied, "Not very long." His tone was firm and his glance keen. Richard was himself again. His homesickness and panic had passed.

The outlook was hardly less sinister by daylight. To the west the country, all of it below the level of the river, was mainly overflowed, but a strip of moderately firm ground surrounded the warehouse. A group of empty cabins a little farther back gave evidence of a plantation. A winding canal of sluggish water led past these cabins toward a grove of trees already touched with the green of spring. One of the negroes who knew this plantation had located a clumsy boat beneath the warehouse and was bailing it out for use.

"Now, Dick," said Clinton, "we must slip into yonder wood before any lurking spies are aware of us. You make the coffee. We don't want to advertise our fire."

As soon as they had finished their breakfast, they loaded their outfit into the punt and silently slid into the swamp.

This was the beginning of an exploration which tried Richard's skill to the utmost. Every road was under water and a week of almost incessant rains continued to keep them so. Each night they rowed silently along a bayou or splashed through swamps in which water-beasts made hideous clamour. Each day they camped in secluded spots and studied their surroundings.

At times Clinton took one of the negroes to explore a stream while Richard with the other black surveyed a turnpike or foraged for provisions in the smoke-houses of deserted plantations. They saw no white men during the first days of their quest, and only a few negroes, faithful old fellows keeping guard over the property which their masters had deserted, a fact which gave Richard a kindlier conception of the race.

Loyal as they were to their trust they were glad to contribute any food which their masters' pantries or smoke-houses still contained, and in this way Richard added to their rations as well as to their fund of information.

At last the sky cleared, the floods began to recede, and one by one the pikes emerged, muddy and full of wash-outs, but passable for mounted men.

Several times they caught glimpses of Confederate scouting parties or bands of guerillas, and once they were saved by the prompt action of some negroes who concealed them till the enemy had passed. Every mile they went increased their danger, and yet they pushed on. "This is the most essential part of our trip," Clinton said. "We must know where the army can ferry the river after it has crossed the peninsula."

Having mapped the upper end of all routes, they moved on toward Vicksburg with utmost caution, for the number of planters still clinging to their homes increased. The negroes of these plantations all knew of the expedition, but Sam and Tom assured Clinton that all black men were friends. Moving on at night, the path-finders reconnoitred landings on both sides of the river at Carthage and secured information concerning the fortifications on the eastern bank which decided them to go farther down.

In these dangerous expeditions Richard and Clinton took turns. Richard and Sam usually scouted together and Clinton made use of Tom. For the most part they kept to the thickets, but occasionally they came out into the sunshine of a cotton-field where mocking-birds were singing from cherry trees in bloom. The air was soft and the soil firm. Such days saved their lives, for they were able to wash and dry their clothing, and so recover something of their self-respect. They were ragged, hairy, tanned like leather, but astonishingly well.

Richard's skill as timber-cruiser had served him well. He had never lost his sense of direction since that first night and at moments of indecision his word was taken. Fine and loyal as the blacks had proved themselves to be they had their limitations. A map meant nothing to them. The farther they went the more care Clinton exercised. He drew every map in duplicate, and gave one copy to Richard so that the chances of its loss should be lessened.

It seemed to Richard that they had been in this low country for a month and though he seldom spoke of the Northern woods, they were always in his mind by way of contrast. He wondered if this region represented the South. Where did they get their fighting men?

At last when they had roughly explored and mapped two possible roads to New Carthage, another even greater problem arose. Could the army cross the Mississippi at this point? Was the bank opposite a good place to land? In his simplicity Richard believed that Clinton's report would be the only report, and his sense of responsibility increased.

After careful questioning of the negroes who knew the opposite shore, Clinton came to the conclusion that it would be necessary for the army to proceed down the river to some unfortified point. "An army couldn't cross in the face of a fort."

One of the negroes whom Sam brought to camp, an intelligent fellow, said that he had once lived in Jackson, Mississippi, and knew the country well. According to his account, the best road inland started from a town called Bruinsburg and ran north-east to Fort Gibson. "Dey ain't no cannons at Bruinsburg," he declared.

Exploring the Lowlands

This statement, which was of the greatest value, brought Clinton to a most momentous decision. The information he now had was invaluable to General Grant, and to make sure of his possessing their knowledge of the routes they agreed to separate.

"One of us must cross the river and check up on this negro's story and the other get back to head-quarters," said Clinton. "You're the best trailer, Dick. You take Sam and go back to Milliken's Bend while Tom and I go on down to Hardtimes, or as near there as we can get. I'll cross the river, if possible, and reconnoitre Bruinsburg. If you're in danger of capture, destroy your map. Show your pass to the first commanding officer you meet, and tell him to help you to reach Grant. Get to the general as quick as the Lord will let you. Tell the general what I am trying to do and say that I'll report within a week if it is humanly possible."

"I hate to leave you here," answered Richard, "but you're the boss."

As soon as dusk fell they shook hands. "Good luck, old man," said Richard with husky tenderness.

"Same to you. I think you'll make it, for unless the guerillas have got wind of us they're not likely to be ranging the upper half of the peninsula. They know the Northern army is at Milliken's Bend. You should reach the Union outposts some time tomorrow, but don't take any unnecessary risk, Dick. The Lord love ye!"

Richard estimated that from where they were it was not more than fifty miles to the Bend even by the Roundaway Bayou, and he decided to travel fast, covering the more dangerous section before dawn. It was a lovely spring night, and as he set off at a swinging pace he thought of the many nights he and Isabel had sat on their porch listening to the frogs in the marshes, and watching the moon come over the hills. It seemed that he had been months in this steamy, unwholesome land. He was muddy and ragged and weather-beaten, but his courage was still high and his vigour unimpaired.

Hour after hour he kept that devious, broken levee trail, the negro following close upon his heels, gamely, silently keeping pace. Occasionally they came to a break in the pike and were obliged to go down into the mud and water and everywhere they went they produced a silence. "If guerillas are alert, they can follow us by the hush we put on the frogs," he thought, "but that's their job. Mine is to go on."

About eleven he came in sight of a camp-fire, and after cautiously reconnoitring it, decided that it belonged to a Confederate scouting party in bivouac on the pike, the only dry land. There was but one way to pass them. He must slip from the path into the mud and slime of the swamp and this was a test of his own soul as well as of the loyalty of the black. "Sam," he said, "we've got to get into the swamp and go round that camp. I hate it, Sam, hate it as bad as you do, but it's got to be done. The general is expecting us to bring these maps. Now I'll go first. If anything happens to me, you take the papers in this piece of rubber cloth back to the Northern soldiers. Do you understand?"

"Yes, marster," answered Sam, with a readiness which showed his devotion.

It was slow work in the detour, for they had to move as silently as possible and at times the way was so black that Richard kept his hands extended while slipping and stumbling over roots and bogs. When he regained the turnpike and could look back at the camp-fire, he was glad to rest a moment. "The swamp," as he afterward said, "had taken the tuck out of me." His comfort was that every mile took him nearer the Federal pickets. "We won't meet any more Rebs. We're nearly half-way now."

Exploring the Lowlands

With mind set on getting out of the danger zone before daylight, he pushed on relentlessly, and sunrise found him within ten miles of Ducksport, and two hours later he reached the outpost.

A sentry halted him in the path. He showed his pass. "Take me to your commanding officer at once," he said,

The sentry, a stalwart youth, was very curious. "You look like a man of grief. Where do you come from?"

"I'm a hungry man. Who is your commander?"

"Colonel McRae, Forty-fourth Engineers."

"Take me to him."

"McRae," thought Richard, "it would be queer if it should turn out to be Captain McRae."

The colonel received him with keen glance and impassive face. "Who are you and where have you been?"

Richard smiled. "You don't know me, colonel, but I know you. You broke up my farming operation some years ago, in Minnesota."

"Were you one of those fools that I rounded up in the Sioux country?"

"I was. I'm Dick Graham, the man from La Crosse County."

"I remember you. You were with a big, black-eyed musical boy. Mud and hair make a good disguise, but I recognize you now. Where have you been?"

"I'm an aide to Captain Helmstock of General Grant's staff. I've been on scout detail. I'm under orders to report to General Grant at the earliest moment. Can you help me reach him?"

"I can that. There's a small gunboat lying at the bank. I think the captain can be induced to take you to the general, but you're not very presentable. Come to my tent and clean up a bit. I infer you've been where mud was plentier than rations."

"You're right. I'm as hungry as a wolf. Have some one

look after this black man. He's a good scout and as empty as I am."

Richard's relief was greater than he could express. With Colonel McRae's aid he would soon be able to hand over his map.

The morning was grey, but after those weeks in the swamp, this camp of "saps" seemed a pleasant city, miraculously orderly, celestial in its comfort and safety.

As Colonel McRae approached the wharf where the gunboat lay, the sentry at the gang-plank saluted respectfully and passed Dick, but refused to admit Sam.

"The black man belongs with us," said the colonel, and Sam followed them on board.

To the officers who met them McRae explained that Richard was on scout duty and under orders to reach the general as soon as possible.

The natty young officer studied Richard with amused glance. "He looks like he'd been consorting with alligators," he remarked with humorous inflection.

"I have, or rather I've been dodging 'em," he answered.

"I'll take care of him, colonel," said the ensign, and with a kindly word McRae turned away and left the boat.

Filled with eager haste, Richard faced the captain. "I must reach General Grant at the earliest moment. I have papers to deliver to him."

The captain looked at him curiously. "Where have you been? Through the lines?"

Richard hesitated. "Yes, but I'm under orders to report only to the general."

"I see. Well, you can report very soon. He's on this boat. He's been here two days. Come to my cabin and wait while I tell him you are here."

Richard's heart filled with boyish pride in his mission and with awe of his commander. He was no longer the husband and father; he was the soldier.

The captain soon returned. "Come with me; the general is anxious to see you."

Richard, indicating Sam, said, "Take care of this black man. He's been our guide. Don't let anybody question him."

"I'll look after him," replied the captain; then, with a note of friendly concern, "you've had a hard trip?"

"I have. It was a tough experience, but I lived through it."

Opening a door, the captain motioned Richard to enter. "The general is in there," he said.

The general's face remained impassive, but his eyes showed pleasure. "I'm glad to see you," he said with sincere inflection. "I was beginning to be alarmed about you. Where's Captain Helmstock?"

"He's still in the field, general, but he's all right, or he was when I left him last night. He sent me back to report to you and to hand you this." He presented the maps.

The general took the packet eagerly and spread it out on the table. After a careful study of it, he asked, "What can you tell me?"

"We've explored every possible route across the peninsula, general, and you'll find them all set down there as accurately as Clinton could draw them, but I can tell you more in detail if you want me to do so."

"Tell me all you can. Sit down and go over the maps with me. Your verbal report is as valuable as the map."

With the paper under his hand, Richard told their story, tracing their wanderings with a pencil, explaining in detail just what the conditions of each route were. He omitted nothing that he considered essential, but tried not to exaggerate the difficulties in the way of marching an army. As he talked, Grant listened, his head bent, his eyes on the map.

At last Richard said, "I'm not a soldier, general. I'm

only a Western timber-cruiser, but it seems to me that no army, at least no army with artillery, can cross this country at the present stage of the water, and even after the water falls away many bridges and corduroys will have to be built. Captain Helmstock agrees with me. The best route leads by way of Richmond, the Roundaway Bayou, and Vidal Bayou to the river at New Carthage."

"Are there many wash-outs?"

"Yes, general, there is a very bad place between Bayou Vidal and Bushy Bayou. It is absolutely impassable at present for about four miles. It is impossible for the army to cross the river at New Carthage and Captain Helmstock is exploring a lower crossing. A negro from the east side of the river told us there are no cannon at Bruinsburg."

The general considered deeply. "Captain Helmstock thinks the army should keep on down the river?"

"Yes, general. If the negro's report is correct, the army should ferry at Bruinsburg. Captain Helmstock is going to cross at that point and reconnoitre. We separated to make sure of getting our maps to you."

"Did you meet any scouting-parties on your way back?"

"Yes, general. I had to make one wide detour in the swamp to get past a camp on the pike."

This drew Grant's attention to Richard's clothing, which was clammy and crusted with mud. His face softened and his tone was again that of Captain Grant of Galena as he said, "You don't look as you did when I saw you last."

"No, general, and I don't feel as I did then, but to see that map in your hand makes me forget all my troubles. If Clinton gets safely back I shall be happy."

Grant's face grew grave again. "I'll ask McRae to send a scouting-party out to meet him. He must be rescued at all cost."

"I'm ready to guide such a party, general."

Grant rose, "That you shall do, but you need a rest."

"I'm able to go now, general. I'm worried about Captain Helmstock."

"Very well. Return to Colonel McRae's headquarters. Take the negro with you and warn him not to talk. As soon as the roads will permit I shall take McRae and go over the route myself."

Richard saluted and went out, leaving the general looking after him with an amused glance. Dick's salute, I fear, was not precisely according to tactics but it expressed his desire to be a soldier.

CHAPTER VIII

Clinton's Rescue

ON the following morning while Richard was eating his breakfast with McRae's aides, one of them said, "The colonel wishes to see you. He has instructions from General Grant to send out a detachment to make sure that your fellow-scout is not captured."

That the general was anxious about Clinton was evident, and Richard, worn as he was, reported to McRae not only as a soldier under command, but as a man alarmed for the safety of a comrade. "I was about to ask permission to go back to meet Captain Helmstock, colonel. I want to warn him of that band of guerillas. He's almost sure to come back the way I did, and those Confeds may nab him unless we get them first."

"Very good," said McRae. "I have detailed Major Compton and a force of picked men to proceed to the rescue under your guidance. From your condition when you

Clinton's Rescue

reached here, I assume they'll swim part of the time and wade the remainder."

Within an hour Major Compton and a detail of fifty men in light marching order started over the route, led by Richard and his black companion.

The sky was clear and the air genial and for several hours the road was fairly firm. The gaps in the pike were not wide but they were deep, and in several instances the men were forced to ferry their rifles on rafts of logs and swim.

The wide breaks, however, were shallow enough to wade, and as they were getting into the enemy's country, Richard advised a halt while he reconnoitred. "That camp I saw was not far from here and they may be working this way."

Moving with great caution, he and Sam made frequent detours which enabled them to spy out the turns in the pike and to signal the major when to advance.

Along toward mid-day, while lying in the sunshine, waiting for the troops, Richard detected a column of smoke rising above the tree-tops to the south. It increased in volume so rapidly that it formed a cloud, and when the men came up he indicated the smoke. "I don't understand that, major. These Johnnies wouldn't burn their own people's houses, and yet that is a burning building. There are no Northern troops in here. It looks to me like the work of guerillas."

"How shall we advance?" asked the major.

"We can't march down this turnpike, that's sure. We'll have to work our way slowly. For some miles here the country is covered with water and the grey-coats will keep to the pike just as we are doing."

As Richard left the pike and slipped into the forest, he believed that he was leading the detachment into battle, and his keen eyes were alert to prevent an ambush. That the enemy was ignorant of the presence of Northern troops

339

was evident. He imagined them absorbed in looting a plantation. "We should be able to surprise them."

He remembered the plantation which stood on a small mound in the middle of a low-lying area of rich cotton-land, and Sam reported much bacon in hiding there. "De gorillas help deyselves," he said.

Suddenly he stopped and said, "Grey sojers comin'."

Richard's confidence in the black's keen senses was so strong that he turned back to warn Compton, who was advancing slowly a quarter of a mile behind. He understood Richard's signal and his men instantly dropped out of sight.

"Where are they, Sam?" asked Richard.

"Dey on de pike, marchin' dis way."

Richard decided to fall back to Compton. Bloodshed was near. Those unsuspecting men must be shot down and he dreaded to witness it.

Compton, experienced warrior, had no qualms. "If they are Rebs and a larger force than ours, our only safety lies in taking them by surprise."

His men were crouching in the mud of a reedy covert, and every face was tense as he said, "Boys, the enemy is reported marching down the pike. We don't know in what force but probably not large. Hold your positions and don't move till I give the word. "To Richard he said, "If it is a small force it will surrender on demand."

Richard, who had drawn his revolver, was ready to fight but in dread of it. It was his first touch of warfare.

The enemy came into view, a dingy crew, marching in open order, straggling along, each man with a load of provisions on his back, while at the head of the column rode an officer on a small mule. They all looked weather-beaten and unkempt, but they were clothed in Confederate uniform.

"They are regulars," whispered Compton. "A scouting

detail. We must take them into camp. Down, down!" he motioned to his own men. "Lie low and keep still."

As the Confederates came carelessly on, he estimated them to be about as numerous as his own force and decided on a bold step.

"Halt!" he called authoritatively.

The column came to a stop; then to his own men, "Make ready! All up!"

They rose as one man with levelled rifles before the astounded Confederates could unshoulder their guns. "Hands up! Surrender, or I fire!" shouted the major.

The commander of the scouts was no thick-head. He took note of the levelled rifles and shrewdly counted the odds against him; then, lifting his hands, drawled out, "We surrender. Don't fire."

Compton ordering his men to keep their guns ready and to follow him, marched straight toward the enemy, and Richard's feeling of relief was very great. To his civilian mind, shooting those men would have seemed like murder, and yet he realized that they would have done the same thing to his company if the positions had been reversed. That was what war meant, but he was so recently from the farm!

In all his rough life on the border, he had never seen a man shot down. Many brutal assaults and several stabbing affrays had taken place under his observance, but no shooting, and he walked beside Compton in the firm conviction that no treachery would be attempted. The Confederates were almost comical in their stupefaction. They stared with unwinking eyes, leaning on their guns, an uncouth lot, but powerful and resolute.

Compton made treachery impossible at once by disarming every man. In answer to questions the commander, a blond young lieutenant, said, "I'm out after one of your scouting parties. I captured one feller back here a piece. He'd been making maps of the country, so I put him under guard and sent him back to New Carthage. He's on his way to Vicksburg right now."

"How far back is he?" asked Richard.

The Confederate grinned. "You'll have to find that out for yourselves," he defiantly answered.

Richard turned to Compton. "That captive is Captain Helmstock. Give me a few men, stripped to running weight, and I'll overtake that guard. Those maps must be recaptured."

Compton called a sergeant. "Take six of your best runners, drop everything but your rifles, and follow this man," he said, indicating Richard. "He's in command."

In a few minutes Richard was off at double-quick, accompanied by Sam and followed by the sergeant and six of his hardiest men. The closer he dwelt on Clinton's danger, the more relentlessly he pushed forward. He hardly glanced at the smoking plantation; his whole mind was on the road and the possibility of overtaking the guard. With his gun in his hand and swinging in rhythm to his step, he trotted swiftly. The sergeant followed with his men in even pace.

Richard was surprised that Clinton had got so far on the way back. "He must have been alarmed last night by news of this scouting column."

They came at length upon the trail of the captors. "The party is small, not more than ours, probably a corporal and four men," said the sergeant. "They are going easy. We'll overtake them before night. Don't use the men up, so they can't fight."

Richard perceived the good sense of this and consented to a momentary halt. "Men," he said, as they stood panting before him, "the maps which Captain Helmstock has made are of the greatest value to General Grant. We must recapture them. If any of you fall out, follow on as fast as you can. I'm going to push on. I'm going to overhaul them if possible."

The men declared themselves ready to follow, and with the sergeant beside him and Sam at his heels, Richard again resumed pursuit.

"Clinton's captors will make two, or at most three miles an hour. We are going five. We should overhaul them before they reach New Carthage. We *must* reach them before they take to the river."

He was greatly encouraged to come upon the place where they had camped for mid-day snack. "The ashes are still hot. They have not been gone over two hours," he said to the sergeant. "We'll overtake 'em soon."

The pace was telling on the men and especially on the sergeant who was no longer young. Two of the men had fallen behind. One of the others had dropped his rifle and was carrying his revolver in his hand. The road was firmer but the air was hot and another downpour of rain threatened.

The captors were plainly pushing for New Carthage, and when about three miles from the landing, Sam stopped like a hound. "Sojers!" he said softly and pointed.

Just vanishing around a bend in the pike a half-dozen grey-coated soldiers with their muskets over their shoulders, were leisurely marching along, with Clinton in their midst, a captive.

"Here is where some killing *must* be done," thought Richard as he waited for the sergeant to come up. "We are the weaker force. Counting out Sam there are only three of us ready for business. We can attack them from the rear but I'm afraid the sergeant is too near petered to cut across and head 'em off."

In this surmise he was right. The sergeant was limp and the two men who had kept pace were in distress. They brightened when told that the enemy had been sighted, but when Richard outlined his plan, they looked troubled.

The sergeant was game. "I'll do my damndest," he said, "but I'm too near forty to keep pace with you and that black."

"Sam, can you shoot?" asked Richard. The black shook his head.

"Well, you can carry a gun and yell when I fire. All right, sergeant, Sam and I are going to head those fellows off. You push on in their rear, but don't attack till you hear my guns, then you fire even if you're not in sight of them. They'll think they are surrounded and may surrender."

"Wait a minute. Give me time to catch my breath, and I'll go with you," pleaded the sergeant. "Here come two of my men. I'll tell them what to do and join you."

Richard recalled this stretch of road. It had a curve, so that by making a line through the swamp he could come out in advance of the enemy.

The going was comparatively easy, for the water had receded from it. At one point an open field increased the danger of being observed, but there was no help for it. He and Sam started and the sergeant and two of his men followed.

In less than twenty minutes of rough going, they came out upon the pike almost opposite an old cabin with a fragment of rail fence before it. New Carthage was less than three miles to the south.

"Sergeant, you get behind that fence," Richard suggested, "Sam and I will attack from this side."

"Very good. Shall I open fire the moment they come within easy range?"

"I leave that to you," replied Richard, who, as a civilian, still hoped to avoid bloodshed. "Fire as soon as you think best and Sam and I will open up. But be careful you don't shoot Captain Helmstock."

With this arranged, each man sought cover. The sergeant and his man on the left knelt behind the fence, the negro and Richard cowered in a clump of cane on the right. "Will I ever get out of mud?" complained Richard as he sank into the wet ground.

The corporal leading his little band came into view, and Richard, knowing that in this case shooting was inevitable, was tempted to fire his gun in the air in the hope of stampeding the enemy without bloodshed, but the thought that such a plan might prove a treachery to Clinton, kept his hand. A moment later the sergeant's weapon blazed out and the leader fell. As Richard fired and Sam uttered a war-whoop, the Confederates, believing themselves outnumbered and surrounded, left their prisoner and took to the woods like rabbits.

When Richard reached the spot where the Confederate corporal had fallen, Clinton was bending over him and searching his pockets.

"Hello, there!" called the sergeant. "What are you doing?"

Clinton did not answer him, but with a grin at Richard flourished a packet in the air. "Here they are. I knew he had 'em and I had made up my mind to free my bonds—I knew I could—and take my chances on a mix-up before we reached the river. You got here just in time."

"I came as quick as the Lord would let me," Richard replied.

The sergeant bent over the wounded man. "I reckon this man won't march much more this year."

Richard was concerned. "What can we do to help him?"

"Not much. We'll have to leave him here for his men to pick up. I'm for retreating."

"So am I," said Clinton. "Now that I have my maps it's my job to hot-foot it to the north. I am under orders to return to Grant's head-quarters at the earliest moment."

The sound of a gun and the whistle of a bullet cut him short and decided the matter.

"I guess we'll all retreat and double-quick," said the sergeant. "Seeing how few we are, they're disposed to pot us at long range."

"There are more of our men up the road a ways," Richard explained to Clinton. "Our pace was too hot for 'em."

A few minutes' run brought them to the other men who were moving down the road cautiously with rifles ready. They had heard the shots and expected attack.

"What happened?" asked Richard as they were all marching up the pike.

"Shortly after you left, some negroes came in to say that a force of men had landed at New Carthage and were moving up the Roundaway Bayou road, and seeing that my plan for crossing the river was dished, I set out for Ducksport. Tom had left to do a little scouting for me and I couldn't wait for him. Now tell me what happened to you."

Richard told him of his surprise in finding the general on the boat, and of his anxious care that Clinton should be saved from the Confederate scouts.

"That's like him," said Clinton. "He never forgets a friend. It's marvellous the difference our Galena association makes in his relationship to us. Think of the million things on his mind and yet he never forgets your interest or mine."

"He told me that as soon as this route was possible for a horse, he intended to inspect it in person. I hope we are to be his guides."

The return was made leisurely, for Clinton was both tired and sleepy. It was a hellish road for a hungry and weary man, and they were all glad when they came back to Major Compton and his captives.

That night Clinton slept in Compton's camp and the next day he returned to McRae's command. Two days later he reported to Grant.

CHAPTER IX

The Eyes of the Army

TO claim that the army's approach to Vicksburg was based entirely upon the information brought back by Captain Helmstock and his aide would be claiming too much, but that the chief was decisively influenced by these reports is certain. Anyone who has studied Grant's career will understand why he selected men like Clinton to do this work, and why he accepted his maps and estimates as determining factors.

Ulysses Grant was himself a man of the frontier. He was born in Ohio when it was the border. As a lieutenant he had been stationed on the Great Lakes, at Sackett's Harbour, and at Detroit, and later at Jefferson Barracks in Missouri. In the Mexican War he had served as quarter-master under General Tayler, struggling daily with mule-trains and mule-drivers. As a farmer he had been accustomed to the muddy pikes of Missouri, and he had driven along the winding trails of southwestern Wisconsin.

In asking the question, "How are the roads?" he expected the answer which a shrewd teamster would make. He knew that these Western woodmen would think in terms of transportation and leave the military problem to him. As he listened to his surveyor there came into his face that shut-in, grim, and lonely look so characteristic of him, when taking council with himself.

Clinton reported this look to Richard exultantly, saying, "This army is going to move! U. S. Grant has taken command."

Upon the General's order, he returned to McRae's headquarters, taking Richard with him.

In this period of rest, Richard's mind turned back to his own concerns. Minute as they now seemed, they were, after all, vital to his happiness. He was worried about the seeding and about the children. Spring always brought so much croup and coughing. He wrote to Isabel telling her a little of what he had been doing. "I haven't seen much war yet. I've been in the swamps but I think we're going to start on a big advance soon. Don't worry if you don't hear from me for some time. Tell Dave to sow wheat, mostly. These soldiers are great on hard-tack, and flour is going to be high. No telling when I'll get back, not before fall. Clint has been detailed for special duty and I'm going along as handy man. If you write in his care I'll get your letters as regular as anybody. I don't like this waiting around. I want to see the army pushing ahead."

The army was about to advance, as McRae and Clinton fully realized. A shiver of excitment ran through the ranks, as under the commander's orders the brigades began to move to a common centre, ready for the prodigious adventure of entering the enemy's country, for it began to be dimly understood that this was the general's perilous project, Napoleonic in its daring, nation-wide in its significance. This plan was opposed by Sherman and most of Grant's subordinates, but the army as a whole was eager to try it out. Subordinate officers were confident. It seemed impossible that any Confederate force could withstand the power of the blue-coated host which was encamped along the river-bank for many miles and day by day augmenting.

To myriads of these sons of the West, Grant was a superman, and those who knew something of his humble origin held a belief in his genius which was fatalistic in effect. The fact that he, an ex-captain of the regulars, a kindly, thoughtful Galena book-keeper, had, in two years, gained supreme command of the armies of the Mississippi created in many minds an unquestioning faith in his decisions.

Few had seen him, but all had heard of his unassuming dignity, and all were eager to catch a glimpse of his person. An opportunity came to Richard on the ninth of April when, in grand review, the troops moved before the chief, in preparation for the long-expected march. As they passed with "eyes right," thousands of his admiring men saw him for the first time.

He looked the commander-in-chief that day. In full uniform and sitting his horse with the easy, unconscious grace of a lifelong rider, he saluted from time to time in recognition of the regimental colours, maintaining a grave immobility of countenance which many noted and admired. They felt the power and concentration of his mood. Not many men in human history have spanned, in two years, a greater gulf than that which lay between his seat on that stool in his father's leather shop, and the position of power and the responsibility he now held.

Richard was awed by this mystery. Without power of analysis, he could not understand it—he could only bow in loyal admiration. An emotion greater than any he had ever known filled his throat. He could not define this feeling, but Clinton, more analytic, and with fuller knowledge of his chief, read in his impassive face and in the line of his firm lips a mood of inflexible resolution which predicted disaster to the South.

That night as they sat in McRae's tent, he talked of the problem as he saw it. "The general is breaking out a new military trail. He's going to put his army below Vicksburg. How he's going to ferry the river or feed his men, I don't know. They say Admiral Porter is to run transports past the Confederate batteries. He must get by with boats enough to ferry the men, to say nothing of feeding 'em. No one knows the roads below Vicksburg. It's all unknown territory to us. It is a little like starting a raft into the Dells; there's nothing to do but go on, meeting the dangers as they arrive. There's no going back. It will either make or break the General."

"Going on suits me. I'm sick of lying about in camp," said Richard, thus voicing the common soldier.

Ten days later orders were issued giving the date of the start, and assigning positions in the marching column. McClernand's division was to move first with McRae's engineers leading the way. Clinton was in command of the advance-guard and with him went Richard as orderly and guide. The whole army was vocal with exultant anticipation. Their long inactivity was ended. Drums beat, bugles called, bands blared exultantly, and commanders harangued their men.

Clinton as well as Richard had achieved a high admiration for McRae. His experience on the plains, his fine voice, and his soldierly figure made him an ideal commander of trail-makers. He had the indomitable will, the daring, the power to endure hunger and pain which Richard delighted to emulate, whilst he, on his part, realized that in Helmstock and his orderly he had two experienced pioneers.

Riding well in advance of the regiment, Clinton led the way, which he had mapped. The road was fairly firm for

The Eyes of the Army

the first brigade, but it soon became a quagmire under the feet of the horses and the wheels of the cannon. The whole army travelled light with "pup" tents and restricted rations. That night as they camped mid-way, the sky to the east was lighted by the flame of burning transports. Porter's men were running transports past the Vicksburg batteries in the same spirit in which McRae's command was marching overland.

Richard's reckless joy in this march was typical of Clinton's entire command. He cooked his bacon, boiled his coffee, ate his hard-tack, and made his bed on the ground with the adroit ease of a timber cruiser. It was all in line with his Wisconsin experience. He had no doubts, no hesitations, no backward glances. He was again among the path-finders.

After crossing the river at Bruinsburg Clinton's men became in very truth "the eyes of the Army." Upon his report depended the direction of advance.

In order to march an army must see its way. No commander in the Union army knew in detail the territory into which they were marching. They had no detailed maps, no reliable information as to roads, swamps, bridges and towns. Some trusted individual must ride ahead, observe and make report concerning these important matters, and as at this date there was no regular scout service, men like Richard volunteered or were detailed to act in this capacity.

For several weeks, while the army was assembling at Bruinsburg Richard and other of Clinton's command were studying roadways and skirmishing with Confederate detachments. To this force Richard acted as scout. For twenty days he was in the saddle, part of the time alone, part of the time with Clinton, part of the time guiding bands of skirmishers, winning possession of a bridge or defending it from counter-attack. In all of this he took a peculiar pride and satisfaction. He was doing what he had been trained to do. He knew little of what was going on behind him, but he did understand that Grant had cut loose from his base of supplies on the river and that he was marching swiftly to attack Johnston at Jackson, a town east of Vicksburg, and that he intended to get between the two Confederate armies and prevent their combination.

At times Richard rode alone, stealing forth to find a Confederate camp or to spy out a ford or bridge. Occasionally he carried reports from Clinton to McRae, or from McRae to Grant who was riding with his men, camping in the field, sleeping under a tree or in any chance shelter, stern, silent, hard as iron. In all this Grant showed his training on the frontier. News of the fact that he was sharing the common hardships, spread among the troops, and an affectionate admiration for him developed. "Boys, we've got a *working* general."

It was not easy to recognize him in his muddy blouse and slouch hat but when they did, a cheer broke from the ranks. "Here comes 'the Old Man'!" He was only forty, but to them he was old.

McRae realized the desperate character of the game Grant was playing and knew the importance of its success. To fail would mean not only personal ignominy to the commander, but a national calamity of terrifying magnitude.

"He is sharing all our hardships and doing our thinking besides," he said to Clinton with the Irishman's power of poetizing a plain fact.

Richard had come to love as well as admire McRae, who, though one of the oldest officers in the army, kept his place at the front with the spirit of the plainsman. "It's like an Indian campaign. A dash into unknown hostile territory," he said and his face was lit with martial enthusiasm for the plan.

He and Grant had known each other on the coast and

for that reason and also because his command was at the front, the Chief frequently rode or camped with him. McRae was the kind of soldier Grant liked and trusted to the full.

McRae liked Richard and after one of his daring exploits offered to promote him, but Richard only shook his head. "I haven't the necessary education to command," he said. "I couldn't make out a decent report. I'm doing the work I'm best fitted for."

McRae considered this an excess of diffidence but replied, "All right, Mr. Road-runner, stay where you are."

Richard rejoiced in this nickname. He did not know exactly what a road-runner was but he did know that coming from McRae it was a term of affection, and he returned to his duties with renewed devotion.

He now rode a fine horse, a handsome bay which Clinton's men had taken, and its fleetness and intelligence enabled him on several occasions to escape capture. It was so gentle and so responsive to direction that he exposed it to danger as little as possible. Often he concealed it in a cane-brake and went forward on foot. At night he slept with its picket rope looped about his wrist.

He was entirely scout and courier. He hardly considered the day of the week or the season. He only knew that sometimes it rained and sometimes the sun was hot. In the intensity of his activity he had no time to dwell on visions of home and wife and mother. He ate when he could and slept when no duty called. He was seeing war in very truth. Men were shot down at his side and twice he felt the sting of flying lead; for nearly three weeks he was without change of shirt. He was grimy and gaunt and unshaven, but his spirit never failed of any task.

"How long will this kind of thing keep up?" one weary lad from the prairie demanded.

"Till we win!" replied Richard, to whom this campaign

was only a job, like running a raft through Big Bull Falls. It would end when Grant's object was achieved.

In the performance of his duties he came into knowledge of the fact that every advance command had its scouts. Many of them wore civilian dress and passed for foragers as they came and went between the fields of their activity and the tents of their officers, but there was little communication between these brave and silent men. Each of them inferred that his fellows were on private mission and not to be questioned, only when it became needful (for the sake of co-operation) were they made aware of one another's tasks. Some were hawk-like observers of the movements of troops. Others penetrated deep into the enemy's country in disguise and were liable to be shot upon capture as spies. Richard rode in partial uniform and was not, technically, a spy.

In the service of a commander like Grant, moving in a campaign of unparalleled swiftness from one battlefield to another and in contact with the enemy day and night, the work of such guides is incessant and arduous. They must ride much of the distance twice and sometimes thrice in order to seek out and report to their commanders. They must go without food for long periods and sleep wherever they can find shelter. Some have horses to feed and defend, others depend upon concealment or disguise or fleetness of foot.

It would be putting it too strongly to say that Richard enjoyed these strenuous weeks of his scouting detail, but it remains true to say that he took a characteristic satisfaction in it. Tireless, trained to hardship, keen-eyed, and resourceful, he crowded into those six weeks of service an incredible amount of action. He not only rode, he fought. At times he carried a carbine and shared in an attack, but for the most part he rode solitary, armed only with a revolver.

The Eyes of the Army

Twice he aided in the capture of Confederate scouts and one night he stood guard over a group of officers who had been taken by Clinton's command. In short he experienced almost every phase of the campaign from Milliken's Bend to Champion Hill, and the desperate assault of Vicksburg on the 22nd of May. In this single-hearted absorption in his duties he was typical of Grant's entire command. He was wholly the soldier, the unhesitating scout.

McRae had become his exemplar. His swift action, his resource in battle, and his forgetfulness of self made him an ideal brigade commander.

In the first heavy skirmish after leaving Willow Springs, he received a painful and dangerous wound in his right thigh, but refused to halt longer than to accept the aid of the field-surgeon, who said, "You must go back to the base hospital."

"I can't do that. I can't leave my command."

"You must. You can't ride and you can't walk."

"Then I'll go on a stretcher," retorted McRae. "If I'm to pass out, let it be in the ranks," he said to his staff.

Lying on a stretcher borne by four of his men, he kept his place at the front. His indomitable courage inspired his command to such idolatry that they crowded to win the honour of carrying him on their shoulders. The news of this reached Grant. He made no comment, gave no order, but something in his softened glance indicated his deep feeling for his old comrade. With such subordinates he could not fail of victory.

One by one similar bonds of relationship, based on a common pioneer experience, were being discovered among his other officers, and a noble camaraderie arose. Logan, McPherson, Sherman, these were the men he trusted. His army was the West at war.

One day after they had been on the march nearly two

357

weeks, Clinton said, "Do you know, I believe 'the Old Man' has begun to feel that his army is invincible and that no bullet can touch him. He has lost all sense of fear. He's a wonder! I saw him yesterday, riding in the rain, his poncho spotted with mud, his ragged whiskers dripping with moisture. No parade there! He's hard as nails and as uncomplaining as a Sioux Indian. He's a working General. As McRae says, 'He's as plain as an old stove.'"

A day or two later, while the brigade was massing for an attack, a cheer ran along the lines, an expression of regard which the General's raised hand could not entirely suppress.

He rode lithely, gracefully, like one born to the saddle. Power showed in the lines of his face, and in the light of his keen blue eyes a relentless purpose shone. The men said, "He's our kind, useful but not ornamental."

With Ulysses Grant, war was not a road to glory but a necessary, sorrowful business, a means to an end, the preservation of the Union. He had no hatred, no fury in his heart, but he was resolved to capture Vicksburg. Strangers coming upon him when surrounded by his generals, the resonant Rawlins, the pompous McClernand, the courtly McPherson and the picturesque Logan, were bewildered. It was impossible to believe that this rusty-coated, brown-bearded man who smoked in silence while others harangued, predicted and advised, was the moving spirit of this tremendous campaign. His lack of braid, of military pomp, led some of his subordinates to question his right to leadership, but Sherman and McPherson had no doubts. They knew from whence directing orders came.

He had that mysterious endowment men call genius, a quality which urges to new and original action. He had the Borderman's power of adaptation. He was not dependent on established ruts. He could leave the turnpike of precedent at any time without fear. He was a West

Point man, but he was also a graduate of the lonely barracks school, the school of experience. His motive forces were deep-hid, below consciousness, far below his verbal expression.

His decisions did not arise from reading or from the advice of others; they sprang from something which can not be explained by heredity. A soldier of democracy, he possessed a singular delicacy of feeling, and perception. He had grown with circumstance—as one of his critics was forced to admit.

"He seems to bear a charmed life," Richard heard a staff-officer say, and indeed he rode under fire as if convinced of his immunity.

Whatever his personal philosophy may have been, the facts of this campaign are eloquent of his military skill. In nineteen days his army marched one hundred and eighty miles, defeating the enemy at every point. He drove Johnston out of the city of Jackson and pushed Pemberton back upon Vicksburg, thus preventing their combination, and when at last he and Sherman stood on the high ground overlooking "the Gibralter of the West," the older man took off his hat and said, "General, I didn't believe in your plan when we set out, but I do now."

As the army took position before the Confederate stronghold, Clinton gave Richard a few days release from duty. "You've had a strenuous time, Dick. You've put a year's service into sixty days. You need a rest."

This freedom from active service was very grateful to Richard. He accepted it, not as a favour but as a due. He was tired.

Some of his fellow road-finders had gone to their deaths on this campaign unnoticed and without record, for they were not regularly enrolled, and received only private mention by their commanders. The very nature of their employment forbade their public commendation. Giving an indispensable service, they received no special pay and no promotion. Others, when the army settled down to a siege, were either detailed to field commands or returned to the ranks (as Richard did), without honour or special reward. So far as these pages may speak, I desire to pay them tribute. Richard Graham shall serve as their representative.

CHAPTER X

Within the Lines

IN the first days of his leisure, Richard took occasion to
study the disposition of the troops and the character
of the ground over which they must pass to enter the city.
He located the head-quarters of Grant and also those of
McPherson and other division commanders, awed by the
swiftly assembled armies. It was like witnessing the opening scenes of a colossal play.

All day long, the sound of bugles, the rattle of cannon-
wheels, the blare of drums denoted the arrival of troops
and the placing of batteries. Long rows of tents appeared
on the ridges like strange blooms, and from the ramparts
of the enemy the voices of defiant cannon broke. It was
all so vast, so grandly terrifying that the Wisconsin woodsman forgot all else in the glow of his exultant pride. What
he had done up to this moment seemed of no account. His
heart filled with a wish to do some larger deed. He was
not one to look on while others worked.

Rapidly, in orderly arrangement, the Union forces settled into lines of siege of the stronghold which, defended by a series of ravines and ridges, and by powerful batteries on the highest of these summits, was proof against direct assault. Anxious to spare his men, Grant called upon his engineers to organize a method of warfare new to the world at that time. His plan was to approach by a series of trenches (concealing his men), an approach none the less menacing by reason of its slower progress. Here again he showed himself the military pioneer.

As the railways opened to the north, trains came in laden with recruits and bringing mail and supplies. Men heard from home for the first time since leaving the Bend. Richard had letters not only from Isabel but from his mother, and Addison sent a Chicago newspaper with an editorial on General Grant's daring campaign. David wrote: "The wheat is heading out and the hay crop fine. Faith in your general is reviving," he pencilled on the margin.

At the end of his respite from duty, Richard said to Clinton, "Put me in the ranks. I want to have a hand in this job."

Clinton had intended using him as orderly, but knowing his temperament he now put him in charge of a squad of men and set him to digging, in one of the front line trenches. The pilot, the path-finder became a mole, toiling whole-heartedly among his fellows. His rôle was a minute one, but he made it important by his loyal enthusiasm.

By the 20th of June, the Union Army was remorselessly closing in on the doomed city. No one went in or out. All supplies were cut off and the Northern press was certain that capitulation was near. Grant was not so sure, for he knew that Vicksburg had been a depot of supplies and that Pemberton might be able to hold out for many weeks.

No reliable news came out of the city. All attempts to

penetrate the lines had failed, and captured Confederates, naturally, refused to convey any information favourable to the enemy.

One night late in the month, Richard went to his colonel and said, "Clint, I have a plan for getting into Vicksburg. If you'll give me leave I'll go in and see what the situation is."

Clinton looked at him quizzically. "Up to your old tricks. What is your plan?"

"I don't want even you to know what it is. All I need is your permission, and a foggy night."

"What started you on this?"

"Something McRae said about the general's need of information, and the story goes that a young chap from Illinois went in and got out safely. If he can do it I can."

Clinton laughed. "Now I understand. You hate to take another man's dare." He became serious. "I can't do it, Dick. I can't let you go into almost certain death. In a time like this they would shoot you on capture."

Richard said no more, but his plan was made, and he set about its execution.

To understand his plan you must picture the Union armies as a wide, semi-circular city of tents, extending from the bank of the river on the north to the river-bank to the south. Along a part of the attacking line the men were sheltered in deep trenches. Behind them the main reserves lay in open breastworks with cannon posted above them, pounding away day and night, while from the river, Porter's gunboats ceaselessly heaved destroying shells upon the doomed stronghold.

Richard's design was to seize upon an hour of intense darkness, creep through the Federal pickets, drop into the river above the town, and float down through the enemy lines. He had no doubt of being able to do this; the more difficult problem was concealment after getting there.

You will wonder how a husband and father could bring himself to such a desperate adventure and in after days Richard wondered at it himself. The truth is, he was possessed of the army spirit, an emotion which rendered individual interests of small account. Then, too, it was an act in line with all his experiences. Deeply schooled in taking chances, he took no thought of death. Just as, when river pilot, he had dared the rapids and the whirlpool, so now he rested upon the conviction that he would come safely through this enterprise. It was all a part of the grandiose, dreamlike world of warfare. In the roar of siege-guns, the blare of marching bands, nothing mattered but the action of his comrades and the command of his chief.

He had secured from a negro a Confederate coat and a pair of trousers, and on the first dark night thereafter he put them on and stole through the Union picket-lines down to the edge of the river above the town. Taking off his shoes and hanging them about his neck, he let himself into the water as silently as a mink and struck out toward the deep water. He could see nothing, and for a few minutes he had no current to assist him. Only a few of the besieging cannon were at work, and the gunboats were resting. The Confederate redoubts were without lights except where a flash now and then proclaimed some gunner's sleepless defiance.

For a time the swimmer moved amid chips, weeds, and other slack-water refuse, but once out in the current, there was less to annoy him. The boats on the river were dim masses on his right, and on his left the town rose on its ridge. Slowly he floated on, expecting contacts which did not come, until believing that he was well out of Porter's lines, he turned to the left and struck straight across the current toward the city. The rain was still falling, and as he neared shore he heard it patter on what sounded like a tin roof. Shortly afterward he bumped into a wharf.

Within the Lines

Tired and chilled, he crawled out upon these planks, and lay for a time like a half-drowned rat. At last he rose and peered around him. Little could be seen, but the sound of the rain on a roof promised shelter, and he moved toward it. It appeared to be a deserted warehouse. The roof and one end had been destroyed, but feeling his way he crept cautiously along the wall till he found a dry corner. He stretched out and, wet as he was, went almost instantly to sleep.

When he awoke, lame and stiff, it was daylight and on looking out he saw not far away, under the bank and in the shelter of another ruined building, a post of Confederate pickets sitting about under a piece of canvas. The city was above and to the left. He was at the southern end of the water-front.

Boldness was his natural method of approach. Stepping out into full view, he stood yawning and stretching. The men stared, but made no motion toward their guns as he walked confidently toward them.

"Howdy, boys. Can I taste a drap of your cawfee? I'm feelin' pretty poor."

"Whar'd you-all come from?" asked one of them, eyeing him sharply.

"I been sleepin' in that barn," Richard replied, pointing at the warehouse. "I reckon I had a drap too much last night," he added sheepishly. "You see I met a man I used to know. He offered me a gill and I tuck two."

As it chanced this post was made up of Mississippi men who were not critical of Dick's vernacular. That he could be an enemy did not enter their minds. No one could pass both lines.

"Waal, stranger," said the corporal, "our cawfee is mostly wheat, but you ah welcome to a sip. What regiment air ye from?"

He named one and added, "I'm on sick-leave. Roomatiz."

365

This part of his story was entirely true. He could scarcely put one leg before the other.

The corporal gave him some good advice. "You let whisky alone or you'll be tied into knots. You cain't drink and lie around in the rain and *not* have roomatiz."

Dick admitted this. "I did get powerful chilled lyin' all night on that there floor in that ruin."

A little later a civilian youth came along on some errand and Dick accosted him.

"Hold on, boy, whah ye goin'?"

"Goin' uptown."

"Wait a minute and I'll go with ye." He turned to the corporal. "Much obliged to you-all," he said, and walked off groaning and rubbing his legs.

From below the town looked like a deserted ruin. It was early and nobody was stirring. On every side were evidences of the desolating Federal gun-fire. Embers were smoldering in the cellars of ruined buildings, great holes gaped in the street where the Union shells had exploded.

Suddenly a cannon boomed and his guide shouted, "Look out! Here comes a puff-ball."

A prolonged whistling sound arose and Dick dodged behind a wall just as the shell landed on a brick building across the street. Admiral Porter's men had begun their daily round. Pemberton's guns retorted sharply as if to assure him of their wakefulness and defiant mood.

As he got higher up the street Richard found that the citizens had adjusted themselves to the conditions of the bombardment with heroic courage. Merchants opened their shops and in sheltered places people began to walk about, warily, of course, while others, especially the women, took a stubborn pride in refusing to be driven to cover. They elected to ignore the Yankee cannon.

No one appeared to notice Richard. To them he was merely another gaunt Confederate soldier limping around on sick-leave. All of the citizens talked freely in his presence, and it was all *Grant, Grant, Grant.* That dreaded name had been pounded into their minds night and day for months. "Grant is attacking at Yazoo," "Grant has landed at Bruinsburg," "Grant has beaten our men at Gibson," "Grant has defeated Johnston," "Grant has reached Champion Hill," "Grant has invested the city."

Such had been the successive head-lines of the daily papers, so long as a daily paper could be printed. It was now only a strip of wall-paper with print on the blank side, but it still dealt with Grant. To the women and children, Grant was a monster, a giant, a fierce, relentless demon, entirely responsible for their hunger and their sorrow.

Richard was amused by this talk, realizing that, if Grant were suddenly to appear, none of these speakers would recognize in the kindly, low-voiced, unassuming soldier the ferocious ogre of their imaginations. It was all sorrowful business, even while it caused an inward smile.

All day he wandered about the city, hearing much, seeing more, but as night fell he began to seek a place to sleep. To a friendly trader, he explained that he was on sick-leave and that he'd like to find a real bed. The man directed him to a small frame house, set against the hill on the side toward the river. "Mrs. McFarland used to keep boarders," he explained, and Richard on the chance of finding shelter followed his suggestion.

In answer to his knock a care-worn, middle-aged woman came to the door. "What is it?" she demanded sharply.

"Can I get a bite to eat and a bed?" he asked.

She eyed him suspiciously. "You can not! I haven't enough to feed myself and my boy, let alone a boarder. We'll soon be starvin' entirely. I've only a little corn-male to kape our two souls intil our bodies, and besides we sleep in the cellar. 'Tis not safe here at all."

"But I'm clean done up. I haven't slept in a bed for a year and——"

"What might you be doin' away from yer regiment?"

"I'm on sick-leave, roomatiz."

"Roomatiz," she retorted scornfully. "More like it's the drink."

Dick threw himself on her mercy. "Well, now, maybe I have been taking a bit too much, liquor's plentier than milk," and as she still hesitated, he added, "I've got a little money. I can pay you for a night's lodging anyhow." He offered her a dollar.

She took the coin and studied it closely. "Where did you get this?" she demanded.

"It's a piece I've carried ever since I left home," he explained in the attempt to repair a mistake.

"Where might your home be?"

"Kintucky."

Again she eyed him as no one, not even the picket officers, had done. "All right. Come in," she said shortly. "I'll give ye shelter, anyway."

The house was bare but clean and as he talked she became confidential. "What will we all do? We can't go on anny longer. Our food is gone. We must surrender."

He shook his head like a man disheartened. "Unless President Davis sends help our generals say we can't last a month."

"A month! We'll all be dead in a month. What can President Davis do? His Eastern generals are all busy with their own troubles. They've no men to fight General Grant."

Dick admitted that the outlook was bad, and after he had shared her small corn-cake, he said, "I fell plum beat out. I didn't sleep much last night and if you could let me have a little something to put under my head——"

She stopped him. "I'll give you a bed, but ye may be blown out of it at any minute."

"I'll take the risk," he replied.

After two months of swamp and rain, bellowing alligators and fence-rail mattresses, he slept as a tired farm boy sleeps with complete relaxation, so soundly that nothing but an exploding shell could awaken him and as he came out of his room at sunrise, he said with conviction, "Last night's rest saved my life!"

"What will ye do now?" she asked.

He put on a look of dejection. "I don't know. Go back to my command, I guess, although my sick-leave won't be up for most a week."

"You'd better stay here," she said. Then in a lowered voice she added, "Ye're safer here than in anny other place."

Richard was startled by her manner, but in the pretence that she was referring to his drinking, he protested, "I'll not touch a drop, not if I find it running in the street. You needn't worry about that."

"I'm not worryin'. I'm just wonderin'," she answered with an Irish lilt. Then with a twinkle in her eyes she whispered, "I'm wonderin' where ye caught the Yankee brogue ye have."

For just a moment his blood chilled and his breath caught in his throat, but the smile on the woman's lips reassured him.

"What do you know about a Yankee brogue?"

Her smile broadened. "Sure and didn't I live in Boston meself?"

"Boston! Did you live in Boston? How did you get down into this country?"

Her face clouded. "Niver mind about that. 'Tis a long story and a bitter one. Ye're better off not knowin' it. Ye'll have worries enough of yer own before ye get out of this hole. How ye got here bates the Dutch indade. I do not understand it."

He understood the situation clearly. She knew what he was and had it in her power to destroy him, but her tone indicated loyalty. Trusting in this he said, "You're not a Confed?"

"I *am* not, anny more than you're a soldier boy from Kintucky. I know——"

He held up a warning hand. "Whisper! Don't *say* what you think I am. I don't like the sound of it. I am, just as I said, in the Confederate Army."

She chuckled. "Ye are! In the very belly of it and how do ye expect to get out of it? I dunno. How ye've go so far is a blessed miracle, what with yer 'guesses' and 'worries.'"

He smiled in perfect confidence. "You should be chief of police. You have an ear like a rabbit and an eye like a hawk. I'm at your mercy—no question about that. I came here in the course of my duty and I'm depending on you to help me do it."

While they were still discussing his situation, her son, a boy of ten, came into the room. "A sojer is comin', maw."

She rose and went to the door with an empty dish in her hand and stood there for a moment. "Eddie," she said to the boy, "you skitter out the back door." She turned to Dick. "It's a man I know, a sergeant. You go back to bed. You're a sick man, y'understand?"

He had just time to remove his coat and shoes. The coat he hung on a chair-back, his shoes he put on the floor under the bed. He heard a man's voice at the door. Creeping beneath the sheet he drew it to his chin and assumed the look of a man sleeping heavily. His life was in Biddy's hands.

Lying thus, awaiting arrest, he heard one of Porter's

"swamp angels" bellow from the river's bed. One of Grant's cannon answered it from the east.

He heard his hostess say, "He's in bed, poor divil. All twisted up with roomatiz, so he is."

"What's he doin' h'yar?"

"He's out on sick-leave, and bein' an old friend of me late husband, he came to me. I took him in; how cud I refuse the poor man?"

She opened the door and peered in. "He's still aslape. I hadn't the hairt to disturb him."

Richard understood her hint, and his chest continued to rise and fall in the tranquil heave of slumber.

Through half-closed lids he saw the officer take his coat from the chair. The situation was as clear as it was dangerous. The keen ear of the trader had caught the Northern accent of his speech and had sent an officer to investigate him. "If he takes me to head-quarters, the game is up," he thought.

"You do well to be watchful, serjent," he heard his land-lady say, "but Mr. McIntosh is a fine man and a good soldier, though a sick one."

Richard felt easier as he heard this, for in the coat was a small note-book, greasy and worn, in which the name John McIntosh was scrawled. It might satisfy the officer.

The investigation, though brief, confirmed the woman's report and the officer went away.

CHAPTER XI

Richard Escapes from the City

FOR half an hour Bridget went about her kitchen with the swift step of a busy housekeeper, while Richard pondered the situation. At last she opened the bedroom door and hung his coat back on the chair and remarked, "These spying busy-bodies do always be a nuisance. They take a long time, say much, and do little. You can come out now."

The humorous irritation in this remark revealed to Richard something of the attitude of the officer who had found Biddy and the kitchen attractive. His own heart warmed with admiration of her loyalty. "It's evident that I can't walk about as freely today as I did yesterday. Nevertheless I'm going to try."

When he came out, Biddy said, " 'Tis in sore danger ye are, man. Go away at once."

"I can't go yet."

"What else must ye know? Can I find it out for ye?"

"I want to know how many men Pemberton has, and how much ammunition. I especially want to find out about supplies."

"I know only the talk," she replied. "They do say there is but thirty thousand fighting men. Manny are sick. As for ammunition, you can hear they are not sparin' of it, but each day the provisions are scarcer. The sergeant who was just here wore a long face. He said 'twas a bitter chance now. All the citizens have empty stomachs and some are ready to give up. Them high ginerals know old Grant has 'em by the ears, but they're too proud to surrender. They don't mind how little we have, and besides they're all hopin' President Davis will send an army. But what army has he to send? General Lee has all he can do in the East and I hope they kape 'im that busy he can't even *look* this way."

Richard reflected. "I must chance one more day. I must see a little more."

"You'd better kape under cover till night comes. I told the sergeant I'd seen your sick-leave and that you'd not be able to move around for a day or two. He may get to thinkin' suspicions and come back. I'll go on a jaunt meself and see what I can pick up for ye. When dark comes you'd better get out with what you have."

This wise advice was punctuated by the boom of distant mortars, the sharp crash of near-by exploding shells, and the faint crackle of rifle-fire to the right where some sort of skirmish was going on. It was one of Pemberton's busy days, and the people in their caves and dusty houses wearily entered upon another twelve hours of hot sun, desolating siege, and deepening dismay.

Impatient to get further information, Richard stepped into the street and started slowly walking with a limp, like a wounded elderly soldier. No one troubled him as he made his way down the path which led along the side-hill past a dozen freshly excavated caves in which women were busied with housework, pausing now and then to watch the shells which came soaring up from the gunboats like hand-balls to pop out in snow-white clouds above the roofs. Even as he stood waiting, a huge one struck the ground less than a block away, passing down through the pavement, entirely out of sight for an instant, then spouting like a fountain, the earth leaped high into the air. With a panic which was not entirely simulated, he hurried into a near-by cave where a dozen women and two or three old men stood in patient calm.

They accepted Richard's entrance into their refuge as a perfectly natural action, and for two hours he sat among them, listening to their talk, watching the effect of the bombardment.

The men were openly appalled at their situation. "Why don't General Pemberton give up" one old man demanded. "We'll all starve if he don't."

To this others replied, "He cain't do that. President Davis has ordered him to fight till the last ditch, and he's doing it."

"But what's to become of our wives and children? They mustn't starve just to ease Pemberton's pride. What's the use of going on? Grant is on every side of us and coming closer all the time. He's sure to get us 'fore long. How we goin' to get any more supplies?"

Not all the citizens took this gloomy view. As Richard wandered about he found a general belief that President Davis had already despatched an army. "When that army comes, Grant will be sent whirling. He and all of his soldiers may even be captured."

Slowly, hobbling like a wounded man, Richard, taking advantage of the confusion caused by the terrific bombardment, went poking about. He even helped to move several families from houses which were under fire, and in this way he earned a little bread. Always careful to play the part of a convalescent soldier, he moved slowly and said little.

In this way he met several wounded men, who told him of the failing spirit of the army. One intelligent man said, "I see no help for us. We must surrender or die of starvation."

In his character of simple private, Richard could not ask military questions, but he could listen and observe, and during the long day he secured much of the information he sought and began to plan his escape. Slowly working his way to the southward as darkness fell, he took the road toward the river, intending to go as he came, by swimming. The nearer he got to the bank, the greater his fear of capture became. His hope lay in another dark night and the water. As he came, so he must depart.

The bombardment died away at sunset, and while strongly tempted to stay another day, he decided to let well enough alone. To get out with the information which he had obtained was better than to be captured. In an agony of impatience, but seemingly at leisure, he sat at the door of a cave, in which a family of ragged blacks had taken refuge, and studied the lay of the land. The negroes considered him a Confederate and were not very hospitable, an attitude which gave him renewed confidence in his disguise. They complained of having nothing to eat and were gloomy and querulous, but they answered his questions readily enough.

At ten o'clock, a near-by battery opened fire, and starting to his feet as if in a state of alarm, he limped off down the hill. He met several other blacks who eyed him sourly but said nothing to him. The nearer he got to the river, the more caution he employed. He was so close to freedom! A single false step would destroy him.

He was now below the wharves, on a street which was

hardly more than a muddy country road, and was feeling his way through the picket-posts, when he heard a voice utter a military command. A few moments later he distinguished the sound of a squad of men marching up behind him. Without a moment's hesitation, he took to the water. Slipping over the bank and down to the edge of the river, he slid into its quiet margin as silently as a beaver.

The water was so shallow that his body remained only half-submerged and he dared not move for fear of creating a ripple. With all his care, the Confederates, had they glanced that way, might have seen the wavelets circling out from his head and shoulders, but it was dark and the sound of their feet covered the noise he had made. They passed on and he was free to move.

Taking off his shoes, he turned on his back and with only his nose rising above water, paddled slowly, silently, out into deep water, trusting himself to the current. For a quarter of an hour he drifted without seeing or hearing anything alarming.

Occasionally he lifted his head and took a glance at his surroundings. It was a still night with occasional light clouds, and although it was very dark he could see the shore which was low and displayed no lights, a fact which filled him with confidence. At last he turned toward the land, calculating that he must be below the Confederate lines.

He was in error. A bullet cut the water not two feet from his head, and the report of a musket following it instantly proved he was within the Confederate outposts. Instantly sinking, in imitation of an alligator, he remained below the surface as long as he could hold his breath, and when he came up it was only to poke his nose out for a breath of air.

"The lower I go, the safer my landing will be," he argued. In turning back toward deeper water, he was startled to see a long black object in his path. Was it a log or was it an alligator? If an alligator, nothing was to be gained by turning away. On coming nearer it proved to be a large beam which he accepted as a sign of security. With one arm resting on it, he floated on, enjoying a much-needed rest.

The fact that the river was silent and without sign of Union boats convinced him that he was still within range of Pemberton's cannon. He kept on, very tired and very hungry, for what seemed a long time, then decided to risk a landing. Turning the log toward the shore, he gently urged it forward, careful to keep low on the river side of it.

Soon he saw a campfire and heard a distant familiar bugle call. "Lights out! Lights out!" it said, and it was sweet music in his ears. That he was still in danger he knew, for a Union sentinel might take him for a Confederate and shoot him as he touched shore. Nevertheless, he determined to land and take his chances. He was feeling the strain of his adventure.

Soon he could detect a sentry standing on the bank looking toward the log with exasperating curiosity, and again slowly whirling the log about, he kept on down the current.

Although fully aware of his danger from Union sentries, he once more shouldered the log shoreward, and at last came to anchor in a quiet eddy just below the point of a willow-grown sand-bar. Slowly, silently as an otter, he crawled out of the water, and lay for a few moments on the shelving bank, limp and empty as a wet sack. The sand was gratefuly warm and the wind amiable.

As he lay thus a courier rode by. "I must be well within the Union lines," he reasoned, "but how shall I make myself known without getting a bullet in my head?"

Crawling up the bank, he cautiously peered over it. No one was near him, but the faint glow of a camp-fire showed on the upland to the right, and on the left, only a short distance away, he discerned a man on picket-duty. There was but one thing to do. To rise to his feet and march directly to that picket-post as confidently as his stiff and weary legs would allow.

He straightened himself and set forth, expecting a shout or a shot without the shout. Nothing happened. No one called out, no one appeared to see him or hear him. His confidence returned. Each moment increased his sense of security. His step became firmer. Counting on the psychological effect of a fearless advance, he marched directly toward the smouldering fire.

A voice rang out, "Halt! Who goes there?"

"A friend," he answered boldly, "with a message for the commanding general."

"Advance, friend, and give the countersign."

Richard advanced till he stood at the point of the soldier's bayonet. "I am aide to Colonel Helmstock of the Iron Brigade, and I have messages for the commander-in-chief."

The sentinel was coldly insistent. "Give me the countersign."

"I haven't it. I've been inside Vicksburg for three days."

The soldier eyed him with growing suspicion. "Come with me to the sergeant. Forward, march!"

In the light of the fire, the sergeant in charge of the post was not favourably impressed by the prisoner, who was in his stocking-feet and wore trousers of Confederate grey. "Where do you come from?" he asked.

"From Vicksburg. Take me to head-quarters. I'll explain to your colonel."

The sergeant was disposed to be sarcastic. "You'll go to the colonel, sure thing, and your story will need explaining. It sounds mighty fishy to me."

With musket in hand he marched his prisoner to the

colonel, who had gone to bed and was irritated by the interruption. He listened to the sentry's report, then turned to Richard. "Where've you been?"

"Inside the lines, inside Vicksburg."

The colonel's voice hardened. "Now I know you're lying. It isn't possible for any man to pass in and out of Vicksburg in such manner. I'll put you under guard and in the morning——"

Richard's voice had an angry note in it as he said, "I'm telling you the truth. I volunteered to go inside the city and obtain information. Send me to Colonel Clinton Helmstock of the Illinois Engineers. He knows me. I've been on scout-duty for him before."

Hatless, coatless, and covered with mud as he was, his resolute intonation and the blaze of his grey eyes persuaded the colonel that he had in his hands a prisoner out of the ordinary.

"What is the position of your regiment?"

Richard told him.

"That's some distance from here and not easy to find, but I'll send you there under guard with an order to bring you back in case you have been lying."

"That's all I ask, colonel," replied Richard with sincere gratitude.

"But I can't do it till morning. The men are all asleep and you look as if you need rest yourself."

"If you put me under guard, you might as well send me back to my regiment."

"That's true." Calling an aide he gave order to have a squad of men aroused, and in a few minutes Richard, in the watchful care of a corporal and two armed men, set off on the last segment of his circle. In after years he tried to recall the incidents of that march, but could never do so. He was so tired and his desire to reach his colonel's headquarters so intense, that it was all a huge, incredible dream of white tents, watchful sentries, the boom of cannons, and the rattle of rifle-shots.

He retained his general sense of locality, however, and directed the course of his guards successfully. His knowledge of the various division head-quarters and his eagerness to reach a certain destination were most convincing to the corporal, who became each moment more friendly.

It was after midnight when they reached Clinton's tent, and all was silent. Leaving his guard, Richard walked into the tent. "Clint, wake up! I need your help!"

Clinton raised up. "Who is it? What's wanted?"

"It's Dick. I'm under arrest. I need you."

This put Clinton wide awake. "Dick! By the Lord, I'm glad to hear your voice. I thought we'd lost you. Where've you been? Who arrested you, and what for?"

"I've been inside the lines, just as I told you I would."

Clinton struck a match and lighted a candle. Holding this so that he could look the captive over, he said in a tone of mingled admiration and reproof, "I believe you have! It sounds just like you—and besides, you look the part."

The corporal spoke from the door-way. "I have a note for Colonel Clinton Helmstock from Colonel Nichols."

Clinton read the paper and said, "Present my compliments to Colonel Nichols and report that all is well. This man is one of my scouts."

When they were alone, Clinton remarked coldly, "So you did it in spite of my orders."

"You didn't order me not to do it. You only advised against it."

"Of course you've got a lot to tell, and the general should have your report at once. You look done out or we'd go over there now."

"Give me a chance to clean up and feed up, and I'm ready to go."

Richard Escapes from the City

"Pity the general couldn't see you the way you are. You're most convincing. However, he would be asleep now. We'll wait till morning. Meanwhile you can tell your story to me, and I'll make notes and drawings that will help."

As soon as Richard had shed his muddy clothing and washed his face and hands, he sat down to the task of making out a report. It was easy for him to talk, to write it would have been impossible. A hard-tack and cold coffee gave him heart while Clinton's chuckles and words of amazement and approval spurred him to do his best. He was a mixture of actor and orator. He loved to produce effects like these, and his tale lost nothing in his telling of it, although he did not consciously falsify any part of it. At the end of his moving yet fairly accurate report he said, "And here I am, back on the job with you."

"You old sinner!" exclaimed Clinton affectionately, "you old river rat! This is just in tune with your other exploits. You ought to have a commission for this. The general will recommend you for promotion. Nothing but your customary fool luck brought you back. Well, now, go to sleep. I'll make out a report and in the morning I'll take you over to head-quarters."

In a clean shirt and on his own cot, Richard sank into a slumber which no siege-gun could disturb.

In spite of his deep sleep, he rose with a sense of weakness as well as of languor. A cup of strong coffee offset this feeling, but he was, as he said, "completely let down," like a violin with loosened strings. Instead of rejoicing in the prospect of again meeting the commander, he dreaded it, fearing he might "make a mess of it."

Clinton was confident of the general's approval. "He hasn't had many direct reports of conditions in there. You must tell him everything you can recall."

No one was at head-quarters but an aide and the telegraph operator. Rawlins was at breakfast, and the general was out on a tour of inspection.

"When will he return?"

"I don't know, colonel. He left about daylight with Major Powell."

"Very well. We'll wait."

Within half an hour the general came in accompanied by a short-bearded man of studious look. Both were stained with clay and Grant looked worn and troubled. He smiled as Clinton saluted, but did not speak till he had taken a seat. His action was that of one weary with lack of sleep.

Clinton said, "General, this is Richard Graham, who has been scouting for me."

Again the general's eyes lightened with recognition. "I remember you. I heard from your brother a few days ago."

"General," said Clinton earnestly, "this man has been inside the lines. He spent two days in Vicksburg and has a report to make."

Grant fixed his eyes on Richard without a change of expression, and Clinton went on, "He got in late last night, and I made a brief record of his story." Here he handed out a folded paper.

Still without a word, the general took the report and began to read it with intense preoccupation. Major Powell went out, and at a gesture from Clinton, the aide followed him. Richard standing at attention waited till the general raised his eyes from the papers in his hand, and asked with reflective tone, "You found that Pemberton still has ample supply of ammunition?"

"Yes, general, judging from all I heard, he has more ammunition than food."

"That is likely. Vicksburg was the arsenal for this region. You found the civilians on short rations?"

"Yes. Many of them are actually hungry and the children suffer for lack of milk."

The general became troubled. "Their lot is hard, but Pemberton must assume responsibility for further resistance. The siege must go on."

Grant's eyes were kind, but his lips at the close of that final sentence set in a straight line which expressed his unfaltering resolution. Then with a complete change of mood, he said to Richard, "You've had a hard trip. Tell me about it."

With the aid of Clinton's map, Richard went over his course and told in detail all that he had seen and heard.

The general listened, smoking quietly, asking a question now and then, so intent that the entrance of General Rawlins and others of his staff made no change in his attitude.

At the close of it, he folded the paper and put it in his pocket. "You've earned a rest. If your colonel refuses to allow it, apply to me."

Again Richard left the general with a feeling of duty done, and happily done.

Clinton also insisted on his taking a rest. "Take care of yourself, however. Be careful what you eat. Hundreds of the men are down with some kind of dysentery. It's hot as hell in the open trenches and you'd better keep in the shade for a day or two."

Richard accepted release from trench service with gratitude, for he was "clean beat out." His uniform was heavy and his new shoes hurt his feet. Altogether he was entirely content to go back to his cot.

With this freedom from duty, came a longing for the home which he now felt he might live to see. He permitted himself to think of Isabel and the children. For weeks he had sternly put them out of mind. By means of that merciful, single-minded obsession which rules a soldier, he had kept them in the background. Manifestly while struggling for life in a swamp or in the midst of the hideous welter of battle, it would have been madness to dwell on Hughie's soft little hands or Hattie's rosebud lips. To have visioned Isabel's sweet, imploring face while swimming the Mississippi River would have brought weakness and despair.

It was this habit of mind, this psychology which had enabled him to face for weeks the most appalling dangers with a kind of insensate imperturbability, but now, now that his task was done, he fell into a fit of shivering, of retrospective fear and horror. He recalled with especial disgust the filthy eddy into which he had first lowered himself and wondered at himself for having done it. Visions of snakes, of alligators, the odor of floating carrion, and the menace of up-rooted trees burdened his over-active brain. Dangers which might have been disasters at any stage of his perilous progress returned to plague him.

Morning brought tranquillity, but a lassitude which was as strange as it was disheartening. Hardly able to crawl out of his bed, he listened to the sound of the cannon with languid detachment. It was hardly more to him than the blasting in a stone quarry. He was a bow unstrung. He had a conviction that his participation in the war was at an end.

CHAPTER XII

The Flag of Truce

THE beleaguerment was now an all-developing cordon.
To the east and north the hills were white with tents,
and all day long the music of bands and the sound of
marching troops went on. Hour by hour batteries shifted
ground, and in clouds of dust long lines of infantry wound
their way through the streets of the canvas city which
was more than fifteen miles in length. The heat was intense, and the hospitals were filled with men stricken with
"Yazoo fever" and dysentery.

The Union Army was now so closely entrenched, in lines
parallel to the trenches of the enemy, that the men were
within speaking-distance of one another, and at quiet moments during the night humorous interchanges took place.
Under the light of the sun, the battle-ground appeared solitary; only the ridges of red earth gave evidence of the
human beings digging their way forward.

As night came on, the sky, lit with the flashes of cannon

and starred with exploding shells, was terrifying. It seemed that the city must be beaten into dust by this titanic storm of iron hail.

By raising one side of his tent, Richard could watch the bombs soar up in graceful curves, to burst like rockets just above the town, and the spectacle so moved him that he attempted to describe it in a letter to Isabel. "The sky is all afire. It is only a question of days now. Our army is digging its way right under the Confederate forts and when Vicksburg gives up the South will give up."

Grant's head-quarters swarmed with all kinds and conditions of men, and nothing showed his simple greatness more clearly than his self-command in the midst of this throng of critics, spies, envious officers, and openly antagonistic official observers. He appeared unhurried and unworried, but his natural gravity deepened into a sternly sad mask. His forehead took on lines of pain, the pain which his lips refused to utter. The loss of life, the suffering of the sick and wounded, hurt him sorely.

Late on the night of the third of July, Clinton came to Richard's tent, and said, "Do you feel able to take a little stroll? I'm going to make the rounds of our trenches. There's something going on tonight that will interest you."

Richard rose somewhat stiffly. "I'm not feeling so very gay, but a little exercise may be good for me."

As they set out, Clinton explained that the general had suggested to several of the officers in command of the front line that an order for a general assault was about to be issued, and that it might prove useful if the news of it should leak over into the Confederate trenches. "He wants to test Pemberton's nerve. He wants the news to filter in by various channels. That is to say, he wants Pemberton's subordinates to throw a scare into their chief."

He led the way briskly and Richard followed, forgetting,

in his growing excitement the pain with which he set out. Nothing moved over the surface of the battle-field, yet fifty thousand men were concealed in runways, ready to rise from their pits at a word from "The Old Man." During the lulls in the cannon-fire, multitudinous sounds arose. Words of command, the ring of shovels, and the sound of marching feet ran up and down the lines, as a company of sappers pushed forward to a trench, or some weary, thirsty regiment shifted to the rear. Occasionally, out of a Confederate pit a spiteful musket-shot snapped, to be followed by a vicious rattle in reply.

The night was smotheringly hot and windless, and as they were creeping along behind the men in one of the most advanced positions, a Confederate soldier in a parallel ditch only a few rods away called out, as if addressing the Union lines in general:

"Hello, Yanks!"

Clinton took upon himself to answer. "Hello yourself, Johnny. What's wanted?"

The Confederate's drawling voice was mockingly confidential: "What are you 'uns doing out there, anyhow? Diggin' yo' graves?"

"No, we're digging yours," Clinton retorted and a laugh ran along the trench.

Another Northern voice a little up the line added, "We're guardin' thirty thousand prisoners and lettin' 'em board themselves."

After a short pause, the same Confederate asked, "When are you 'uns goin' to take Vicksburg?"

"Tomorrow," answered Clinton. "We all want to celebrate the Fourth of July in your town, so Grant has ordered a general assault for eight o'clock tomorrow morning."

There was a note of anxiety in a more cultivated voice which came back from the Confederate side. "Is that official?"

Clinton's voice held a note of authority. "You can bet on it. The word is just being passed along. You'd better get ready for trouble. We're going to smoke you fellows out tomorrow morning sure as shootin'."

Richard imagined that he could hear the stir of excitement which the news produced. Clinton whispered, "Similar reports are going on all along the front. They'll give Pemberton something to think about tonight."

Everywhere they went, they heard the men cheering. "We go in tomorrow," and everywhere the news was being flung to the Confederate lines.

Clinton discussed the effect of an assault. "We'll win. We've pierced the Confederate lines at several places and mined them. We can go in any time the chief gives the word. He believes that the Confederates, dreading another assault, will ask for terms."

An hour later, the cannonading began again with unexampled fury. Shells from a hundred mortars, each making a high half-circle, rose like flaming meteors and every flash of light was followed by a jarring report, like a roll of thunder. The sky, lighted into flame colour, glowed as if a devastating conflagration had set in, and Clinton said, "This is the beginning of the end! Think of it all coming from Grant. Two years ago last April I sat with him in his hill-side home in Galena and talked of war, and now think of his power and responsibility."

Returning to his cot, Richard, too excited to sleep, lay in silence watching the desolating rain of fire and listening to the almost incessant rumble of cannon. The heat was especially oppressive by reason of the clouds which overhung the camp and it was nearly morning before he fell into uneasy slumber.

He awoke to the clear sound of bugles and the routine bustle of camp-life. The cannons were at rest, but it seemed to him to be the pause before the hurricane.

388

The Flag of Truce

He was at breakfast with Clinton when an orderly rushed in. "Colonel, a white flag is reported on the enemies' works."

Clinton leaped up. "It's come! Pemberton is finished! We've won!"

Catching up his field-glass he hurried outside. "There it is! You can see it without the glass."

He was right. All could plainly see the fateful flake of white topping one of the central redoubts. The order for an assault would not be given.

Clinton turned to Richard. "Go over to head-quarters and see what's going on."

This suggestion was equivalent to a command to Richard. He followed it out with zest. All the way he found groups of officers and their aides standing in front of regimental and brigade head-quarters, and as he came in sight of Grant's head-quarters, he saw the general standing calmly at the door of his tent surrounded by his staff. "Pemberton is about to ask a parley," he said after a study of the situation.

A little later another Confederate officer appeared on the breastwork and took the flag in his hand and waved it questioningly. Grant turned to his signal-officer. "Answer him. Tell him we consent."

The Union officer moved his flag up and down. Almost immediately, the Confederate messenger, reassured by the sign of acquiescence, left his redoubt and confidently advanced toward the Federal lines.

Grant again turned to his staff and said quietly. "Take a squad of men, meet the messenger, and bring him to me." To his chief of staff he gave an order to cease firing. "Pemberton is about to capitulate."

In a few moments, a group of Union officers set forth upon the desolate, deadly no man's land between the lines.

On approaching the Confederate envoy, they perceived him to be an officer of high rank. He saluted and said,

"General Pemberton has sent me to confer with General Grant."

"You shall be taken to him," replied the officer in command. "But you must be blindfolded."

"Is that necessary?"

"It is customary."

"Very well."

With a broad handkerchief over his eyes, he was led to where Grant was waiting to receive him.

As soon as the bandage was removed, the commander recognized the messenger. He was General Bowen, a man he had known in the army before the war. He greeted him pleasantly. "I am glad to meet you again, general, especially in this capacity."

General Bowen remained stiffly formal. "General Pemberton desires to discuss terms of surrender."

Grant's reply was quietly decisive: "I have no terms to discuss other than those of unconditional surrender," and then added in gentler tone, "You may say, however, that the brave men within the works will be treated with all the respect due to prisoners of war. Present my compliments to General Pemberton and say that I appoint three o'clock this afternoon as an hour convenient for me to meet him."

The envoy was again blindfolded and escorted back to the open space between the lines. There his bandage was removed and in tense silence the officers on both sides watched him return to the redoubt from whence he came.

"What will Pemberton do now? Will he meet you?" asked Rawlins.

"I think he will," replied Grant. "The fact that he sent Bowen is evidence of his anxiety."

Richard hurried back to Clinton with a story of what had taken place. "Everybody says it means the surrender of Pemberton's army."

"Think of the Fourth of July celebration in all the home

towns!" exulted Clinton. "What about the 'decayed ex-captain' now? What will the political generals do now?"

In spite of all order to the contrary, discipline relaxed. The trenches buzzed with talk. Commissioned officers visited one another's positions and compared notes, while the files rested in the blazing sun and commented on the greatness of the impending event. They knew little beyond the orders to cease firing, and the fact that a white flag had been displayed. Many took Richard's point of view, "This ends the war in the West." Talk of home sprang up between comrades. "I hope this lets us out of these God-forsaken trenches," they said. "I don't mind fighting in the open, but this being a dog-goned mole!"

At about three o'clock that afternoon, the commander-in-chief rode out beyond the lines followed by several of his staff. Upon reaching the extreme Union lines he dismounted, and leaving his horse in charge of an aide, proceeded on foot, calmly and slowly, toward the centre of the disputed field. He seemed very small and very defenceless in the midst of that savage battle-ground. "A single shot by a crazy fool might rob us of our chief," Clinton said to McRae. "I don't like his going out there in that way."

McRae was not alarmed. "They're as anxious to protect him as we are."

When, at about the same time, General Pemberton, accompanied by several of his staff, left the Confederate lines and advanced to meet his conqueror, suspense gave way to hope. "The surrender is about to take place," the Union officers said to one another, and so great was the excitement that rank was forgotten.

Instantly from sinister and silent salients and along the top of each battle-ravaged ridge a forest of bayonets sprang until every bleak embankment bristled with a thousand armed and toil-stained warriors. It was as if at some mysterious sign a myriad of subterranean gnomes had risen from their secret passageways to gaze upon some vast and alien drama. The solitary chieftain walking imperturbably forward over soil which had for many weeks been ploughed only by the shrapnels' share by day and the sapper's spade by night, was the centre of all these eyes.

A thrill of awe swept over the civilian onlookers. "Who says the age of chivalry is past?" demanded one of them.

As Grant neared the Confederate group, several of the Union staff officers left their positions and rode forward. Clinton with field-glass in hand reported to his aides that Pemberton saluted, but did not offer to shake hands. "His attitude is stiff and Grant seems waiting for him to begin. . . . There's a hitch somewhere! . . . Pemberton seems to be laying down the law." His tone changed to alarm. "The general has turned away. Pemberton is also going. It's all off! . . . No, it isn't," he added after a pause. "Another general has stepped forward. He appears to be pleading with Pemberton. . . . Pemberton has yielded. . . . He and Grant are moving away from the others. . . . They are taking seats on a bank under an oak tree. Pemberton appears greatly excited and is doing all the talking. Grant seems perfectly calm. He is smoking as usual and patiently listening."

Upon this scene so silent, so tense, so momentous, the boom of a distant cannon broke with startling menace. General Grant sprang to his feet and motioned to one of his staff who set off at full speed back to head-quarters.

"Somebody down on the river has not been told of what is going on up here," remarked Clinton. "He'll find out when that courier reaches him."

Both commanders now rose and walked slowly back toward their officers. After a few minutes' further conference they parted, and each, accompanied by his aides, started on the return to his own lines.

Back into their trenches sank the Union men, not knowing

The Flag of Truce

what the issue of the parley had been. No officer cared to take a chance. The battle might begin again the moment the generals were safely out of range and with redoubled fury.

All that day the men lay in tense expectancy among the trenches. They believed the end of the siege had come but they did not know it. No one knew it—not even Grant, for Pemberton was bitter and might decide to reject the terms, unprecedentedly generous as they were.

"As soon as rolls are made out, and paroles signed by officers and men," Grant had written, "you will be allowed to march out of our lines, the officers taking their side-arms and clothing; the field, staff, and cavalry officers one horse each. The rank and file will be allowed their clothing, but no other property."

These terms, whose leniency amazed certain of Grant's would-be-advisers and infuriated certain War Department officials, won Pemberton's acceptance. He notified the Union commander of his willingness to accede and at ten o'clock the following day, the ragged, emaciated, grey-coated soldiers who had so heroically defended their city marched out of their redoubts in regular order, and at the word of command stacked their arms. After throwing down their knapsacks, bayonets, and belts of cartridges, they tenderly crowned these heaps with festoons of their faded flags, emblems of the brave resistance they had made.

For several hours this movement went on with no derisive cry or exultant gesture on the part of the Federal troops. Grant's personal command had been such as to prevent them: "Nothing that might add to the pain and humiliation of the defeated army should take place," and in truth, his officers had no desire to taunt these stained and tattered veterans whose uniforms contrasted so mournfully with their own blue-clad troops. Grant's words expressed their own feelings. They knew the quality of these lean and ragged warriors. "They were on the wrong side, but they are entitled to respect," Grant feelingly remarked.

In all the correspondence of this strange commander, this ruthless besieger, there is not one word of boasting, scarcely a word of exultation even to his wife. He showed himself once again the most humane as well as the most unassuming of conquerors. He had fought relentlessly and in single-minded purpose, to win, but now that the battle was won, he became the citizen, the sympathetic neighbour. Soldier of democracy that he was, he manifested the chivalry of his feudal forbears. Plain as a farmer in dress and manner, no knight of Arthur's court was more essentially the courteous foe.

A less considerate conqueror would have ridden into the city at the head of his troops, in full uniform, attended by his staff, glittering with gold braid, but Grant never for a moment considered such an entry. He sent General McPherson in to take command and be of service; and when, later, he himself rode in, he did so in such modest guise that few recognized him. He went to see how the inhabitants had protected themselves from the shells, and after a brief inspection returned to head-quarters. If he rode down to the river to water his horse, as he had promised himself to do, it was done so inconspicuously as to escape notice. That victory had been won without a final bloody charge, gave him the keenest satisfaction.

This entire campaign had the audacity of the trail in opposition to the traditional turnpike. Ulysses Grant was not a student of books but of life. No elderly man, no arm-chair general could have won this stronghold. What the military authorities in Washington said he could not do he had accomplished with amazing celerity and with masterly accuracy and coherence of design. It seemed as though all hindering obstacles had been forced aside to permit his advance. In spite of his poverty, notwithstanding his lack of social and political advocates, this borderman had won Belmont, Henry, Donelson, Shiloh, and Vicksburg. In a little over two years he had become the most successful commander of the North.

He would have been inhumanly modest had he not experienced a growing conviction that these achievements were in the order of his destiny. Having reached the point where he now stood, in the light of national fame, after years of hardship, disappointment and privation, he was entitled to a feeling of achievement. All of his detractors were silenced. All opposition was for the moment overborne, and the nation, after applauding, now waited to see in what field the President would employ the demonstrated military genius of "Unconditional Surrender" Grant.

CHAPTER XIII

On the Sick List

ONE of the earliest orders of the Union commander
after the surrender of Vicksburg was a command which
set his soldiers to filling in the trenches and repairing other
damage they had wrought. Having warred (as all great
warriors must) relentlessly, his hand was now applied to
the healing of wounds. Somebody spoke of him as "a
neighbourly kind of a general," and so indeed he was. He
never forgot his humble relationships even in the midst
of a colossal drama such as the siege of Vicksburg had been,
and he did not forget them in the day of victory. These
disheartened people were, after all, his Southern neighbours,
and he set about doing what he could to rid them of their
hates as well as their fears.

In this spirit he issued rations not only to the hungry
troops, but to any civilians who declared themselves in
want. He went further; he forbade any action which might
add to the suffering of soldier or civilians.

On the Sick List

One of the Confederate officers with whom Richard talked, expressed a truth nobly by saying, "General Grant has conquered us twice, first by his military genius, afterward by his magnificent clemency."

Without a touch of pomp or military display, his action during these days possessed a singularly unassuming dignity. He gave no thought, apparently, to the figure he presented to his visitors. Content with his rusty-coated obscurity, he went about his business.

In this self-effacing attitude can be read something modern, something deeply significant. Unimposing, commonplace to many of his observers, he was, to others more discerning, a new kind of conqueror, one whose actions related closely to the spirit and character of Lincoln, and the President, having tried men of fuss and feather, men of gold braid and men of theory, turned to this soldier who fought, and forgave, with a new hope. "Thank God, I have found a general at last," he said to his cabinet and set about measures to make full use of him.

Naturally Grant came in for comment. The rank and file did not hesitate to criticize. The men filling up the trenches felt that "The Old Man" was going a little too far in being helpful. "I didn't mind *fighting* with a spade, but I don't enjoy grading up their door-yard afterwards," said one of Richard's comrades, and in this vigorous remark expressed the feelings of many others who added, "We came down here as soldiers, not as section-hands."

Said still another of these toilers,

"I wouldn't mind the work; it's the climate that gets me."

They were all eager to see what the captured city looked like and every man who could get leave, went in to examine the fortifications they had so long been assaulting. Richard being still free from active duty was among the first to go. He was not only curious to see what was going on; he wanted to be sure Mrs. McFarland was being fed.

He spoke to his colonel about it. "I don't feel much like walking. My legs are two lead pipes, but if I can find a horse, I'd like to ride in and see how Biddy is getting along."

Clinton looked him over carefully. "You better keep quiet for a few days longer. Wait till evening and I'll let you take my horse. I know how you feel about that brave woman, and if she needs anything more tell her to go to head-quarters. I'll tell General MacPherson about her."

An army, any army, is composed of individuals, but the armies under Grant, even after months of discipline and constant marching and fighting, were, after all, only a mixture of farmers, loggers, mechanics, traders, and professional men. You could find among them men who could sew a harness, peg a shoe, mend a watch, survey a plot of ground, or build a bridge. They were just as much citizens as ever, and as a part of the relaxation after the fall of the fortress toward which they had been so long directed, a wave of homesickness swept over them. Many felt, as Richard did, that the war was over and they longed to go back to their homes and their individual affairs. Some like Clinton had left a thriving business which was falling into decay or passing into other hands. The farmers were eager to return to help harvest their wheat, and all were heartily sick of the heat, the flies, and the discipline of camp-life.

Meanwhile the folks at home, rejoicing over the victory and over the fact that their "boys" had come safely through the battle, had no realization that the soldiers' worst enemies are those born of camp-life, and that inactivity is the hardest part. A soldier's life, the army was now again to learn, consists of waiting for orders to move.

From the high vantage of his borrowed horse, Richard

agreed with those who saw the commander had done just the right thing by the soldiers and citizens of Vicksburg, but had he been ordered into the shovel brigade his attitude might have been less magnanimous.

The streets of the sadly battered "Gibraltar of the West" were filled with a crowd of negroes and civilians in which soldiers of both armies mingled, and Richard, making his way through them in search of Mrs. McFarland, was interested to find the work of rebuilding actually, though hesitatingly, beginning. Citizens were moving back into their broken, dusty homes and many of the caves were already given over to sightseers. Aside from its importance as a military centre, it was a village on a hill, a forlorn wreck of a small country town, hardly larger than La Crosse.

No one was in sight at Biddy's cabin as he rode up, but at his call she came to the door apprehensive, yet truculent. "What will a gay soldier lad like you be wantin' of the Widdy McFarland?" she demanded, not recognizing him in his uniform.

"I bring an order from Colonel Helmstock commanding one Widdy McFarland to report at his head-quarters immediately, if not sooner, along with one John McIntosh," he replied in curt official phrase.

She knew him then. "Fer love o'saints!" she exclaimed, then she warningly said, "Man alive! Would you destroy me entirely? Me naybors are all lukin' on." With a wave of her arm she added in a loud voice, "Keep right on over the hill and ye'll find plenty of thim caves."

Richard perceived his blunder. In the warmth of his gratitude, in the excitement of the moment, he had been about to brand his defender as a traitor and so make her an outlaw in the town. Accepting her rebuke, he said, "If you want anything come to me. Ask for Colonel Helmstock of the Iron Brigade. I am on his staff."

Lowering his voice, he said, "I've got some bacon and

flour for you. Let your boy follow me round the corner and I'll drop it on the ground. If you want anything go to the head-quarters of General McPherson tomorrow morning at ten. I'll meet you there."

On his way back to his regiment he felt more and more depressed and at mess found himself without appetite. "I'm in for something hot and heavy," he said to Clinton. "I guess it's Yazoo fever."

"I hope not, Dick, for McRae has received orders to march. Sherman is going against Johnston and my regiment is to be advance-guard again."

Even this news failed to rouse Richard. "I don't feel a bit like marching tonight, Clint. Maybe I can throw it off tomorrow. When do we start?"

"Day after tomorrow. I had a letter from home today. They're all getting rich up there. Wheat and lumber are in great demand."

As they talked on, each realized with a pang of regret that he would never again be the blithe young man he had been at the opening of the war. Even should their service end at Vicksburg, no magic could restore to either of them the joy of youth and the pride of strength with which they had enlisted. It was not a matter of two years' loss of time, in Clinton's case; it was a swift change from the psychology of youth to that of middle age. His boyish faith in the future was dimmed—and yet he was only thirty-five!

"One thing is certain with me, Dick. I shall never handle a cant-hook again. This elbow of mine will always have a kink in it. What luck you've had! You've hardly been singed."

"Yes, I'm all here, in a sense, but I don't feel very gay about myself. I never felt so good-for-nothing in all my life. This heat has got me 'bushed.'"

"Go home for a few weeks. I'll get you a furlough."

On the Sick List

"No, I'll stick it out. I'll go where you go if I can put one foot in front of t'other."

While they were discussing the new campaign, a young soldier in the uniform of a cavalryman rode up and asked, "Is Captain Dick Graham about?"

It was Frank McLane, and Clinton in mock ferocity called out, "Get down off that horse and make a report of yourself, you infernal little scalawag. What are you doing down here?"

With a grave face the boy did as commanded, and his story was soon told. After running away from home, he had enlisted as a musician. His skill had made him regimental bugler, as he was proud and happy to report. Richard could not draw from him a single word of repentance for the manner in which he had left home. "They needed Dave on the farm more than they needed me, and so I pulled out and left him in charge."

"Do they know where you are?"

"Yes; I've written once or twice. I had a letter from Dave last week. That's how I knew where to find you. He said you were on Clint's staff and so the first chance I got I rode over, and here I am!"

As they talked, the battle-field receded swiftly. The smooth hills, flowery meadows, and cool pine forests of the North came back to fill their hearts with longing. Richard's sickle and scythe were awaiting him. His grain was ripening for the harvest whilst he, weak and irresolute, was in the grip of some mysterious disorder.

After the gay young bugler rode away, Richard took to his bed in most unheroic mood. In all his thirteen years of life on the farm and in the forest, he had never been seriously ill; now he lay in the grip of some unseen yet all-powerful enemy within his own body. "I'm pretty near a hospital case, Clint. I'm terribly afraid I can't march when you do."

In this premonition he was confirmed. On the day Clinton broke camp, his scout went to the hospital. After dodging the bullets of innumerable sharpshooters and riding out a rain of lead at Champion Hill and the Big Black, after all the dangers of the scouting detail, Richard had fallen a victim to an enemy too small to be seen, and was in greater peril than at any other time in his career.

In 1863 little was known concerning the office of insects in communicating disease. Bacteriology was hardly more than a word, so far as army surgery and nursing went, and the number of men slain by contagious diseases was greater than the roll of those killed on the battle-field.

Sanitation was deplorably haphazard. Every hospital was a desolating centre of contamination, more dangerous than the enemy troops. Antiseptics were seldom employed, and the soldiers detailed for nursing duty neglected the ordinary rules of cleanliness. "It is a wonder that any of the men came out alive," said a famous surgeon in after years. "We were all children in matters of sanitation. Flies were a nuisance, of course, but no one considered them a source of contagion. No one dreamed that mosquitoes communicated Yazoo fever."

The ignorance, the awkwardness of the nurses, and the careless brutality of the surgeons and their attendants make sorrowful reading to us of today. With no sewage systems, no netting to protect them from the flies, the men lay in rows, communicating one to another all the diseases they had. Only those with wrought-iron constitutions came out alive.

It was typhoid fever which brought Richard low. For many days he lay in the hospital gasping with the heat, too weak to defend himself from insects, despairing, homesick, and at times delirious. He would have given up the struggle right there, had it not been for a visit from General McPherson, his division commander, who came to inspect the hospital one day when Richard was on the point of letting go altogether.

The general came in without warning, looking wonderfully well in a new uniform. His presence sent a wave of excitement through the ward and put new courage into the hearts of the sufferers; even those about to die lifted their hands in feeble yet gallant salute as he passed. Others cheered faintly in heart-felt admiration and gratitude for his interest.

After visiting two or three whom he knew, he came to where Richard lay and, bending over him, asked, "How is the road-runner?"

"Not much good, general, but I guess I'm going to pull through. My hearing is affected. I can hardly hear your voice."

"Shall I send a message to your wife?"

The tears came to Richard's eyes. "If you would send her just a line, general, and tell her that I am getting along all right, I'd be greatly obliged."

The general turned to an aide. "Take this man's name and address." He stood for a moment in thought, and then said, "Colonel Helmstock spoke to me about your case. As soon as you are able to travel I will issue you a furlough with transportation on one of the hospital boats. Your deafness will wear away. Go home and rest for three months. General McRae has recommended you for promotion on the score of bravery and valuable work as a scout. I'm sure it will be approved."

Richard's voice failed him, but he managed to say, "Thank you, general. You've done me more good than any doctor. I shall get out of this soon. I must get out. I want to serve under you again."

With a final word of encouragement, the general turned and walked slowly down the aisle between the cots, with every glance fixed upon him in trust and admiration. When he was gone the men turned toward Richard who had suddenly won great distinction in their regard, as well as in that of the attendants.

One of the unexpected and most disheartening effects of his illness was this impairment of his hearing which had been unusually acute. The world to which he returned was a strange and unsatisfactory world, a world over which a thick, almost sound-proof, curtain had been dropped. He could hear the words of those who bent to speak to him but all distant noises had died away. He heard nothing of the movement of troops, and the sound of the bugle came faintly and in fragmentary notes, a ghostly, far-away voice.

Not merely had the siege ended, the armies had melted away. He could not understand this silence, at first, and when the fact of his deafness was borne in on him he felt suddenly old. He had prided himself on his hearing. He loved sounds, minute sounds of birds and insects. He had been guided by what he heard; now he had a sense of age, of helplessness which no other injury could have produced. The solidity of his world had disappeared. Hesitation, a weakness he had never manifested, now took possession of him. The doctor told him that his affliction was only temporary, but in his weakened state he was not convinced of the surgeon's sincerity. He felt that he was only speaking cheerily for the benefit of a convalescent.

He had but one clear desire now and that was to get back to the cool, sweet North, away from the heat and the flies. "What good is a soldier who can't hear?"

Here I must touch upon a curious, self-protective phase of soldier psychology, one which is not often referred to by military historians. Richard had been away from his home less than a year and yet the figures of his children and the face of his wife were already dim in his memory. His intense interest in the campaign, his incessant danger, his physical activities had blurred their images. The spirit of the army, so coercive, so imperious in its sway, had put his personal affairs out of focus.

So long as there was work to be done, he was the soldier, but now with the promise of a furlough, his mind filled with thoughts of home and the forms he most loved—his wife, his mother, his children—came back with an almost intolerable poignancy of appeal. He became boyishly eager for his discharge from the hospital. It seemed as though he could not endure another day of waiting.

CHAPTER XIV

The Peaceful River

WHILE the folks at home were conceiving of their absent ones in rôles of warriors ceaselessly marching and shooting, the men were actually unhappy because of their inactivity. Soldiering, to them, consisted altogether too largely of drilling, camping, and waiting. Disease was more dreadful to them than conflict. I have heard Richard say that the hardest position he ever held was that of reserve, waiting under fire for the order to charge. To a man of his restless temperament the restrictions and conditions of a camp were almost intolerable.

He resented smells and he had little sympathy for his companions in the hospital and none at all for himself. He was careful to put no hint of his sufferings into his letters. Much as he needed Isabel, he would not permit her to come to him; her place was with the children.

Some of his comrades in misery did send for their wives and many a tender scene was enacted in his ward. There was heroism in the action of these wives and heroism of a

lonely, pitiful sort in those who, like Isabel, only dimly
visioned the sufferings of their men.

Each day some poor fellow went away on an eternal
furlough, while others were permitted to crawl outside the
tent where they could see the sky and trees. This was
regarded as a blessed privilege notwithstanding the hot sun,
and in most cases the change was immediately beneficial.
They began to talk of the cool water and sweet food of
home.

One afternoon, just as Richard had begun his hour of
sitting in the shade, he was surprised and shocked to see
Clinton limping toward him. Though pallid and bent and
carrying one arm in a sling, he waved a greeting with his
free hand and called out, "Hello, man! I'm glad to see
you up and around."

Richard did not smile. After a brief study of his comrade he slowly demanded: "What's happened to *you?*"

Clinton took a seat on a near-by box. "More trouble and
worse of it. My horse fell on me. While I was charging
through a steep ravine, he tripped over a log or a vine
and turned a complete somersault. I landed underneath,
and if I hadn't picked out a soft spot, it would have been
all day with me. As it was, my wounded elbow got
a smash, and one knee was put out of commission, I was
dead to the world when my men picked me up and as soon
as McRae heard of it, he ordered me back to the base
hospital. Said I'd lose my arm and my leg, too, if I remained with the regiment. I tried to argue with him. I
told him that he had set a different example at Port Gibson,
but my plea wouldn't work, and here I am, 'Horse du Combat,' as the Frenchmen say it."

In all their hardships on the river and in the forest,
Richard had never before heard a note of bitterness or complaining from his chum, but now his face was dark as he
resumed, "I hated like hell to fall out of the ranks, Dick,

but the general was right. I couldn't ride, and I couldn't use a sabre, so what was the use. He gave me ninety days' furlough, and now the surgeon advises me to go home and recuperate. I'm going up where it is cool, and where I can get away from flies."

Richard's voice was boyishly eager as he said, "They're going to send me North as soon as I am able to travel. I wish I could go when you do."

"You shall," retorted Clinton emphatically; "I'll tackle the surgeon-general tonight and see if we can't get off on the next boat."

Richard was sorely troubled by Clinton's condition. Without clearly defining it, he put this pallid, limping soldier over against the lithe and handsome boy with whom he had played on the canal-boat thirteen years before and Clinton was equally moved by Richard's weakness. Nothing of this feeling was put into words, however. Their talk was all of the blessed North, of the cool winds and sweet waters of the upper Mississippi, and of joyous meetings with friends and relatives.

Clinton resumed, "We'll take the very next boat no matter what it is. I can look after you and you can bandage my arm for me. The quicker we go, the longer my furlough will be. There's nothing to do here anyhow. The report is, General Grant will go east to take another and more important command. McRae says Chattanooga, but others hint at the Potomac. The President is tremendously pleased with the campaign out here. Grant's capture of Vicksburg offsets the failure of Meade to bag Lee after the Battle of Gettysburg. He wouldn't have gotten back across the river if Grant had been in command. Wherever he goes, I hope to get back on his staff at the end of my furlough."

Later in the afternoon he reported that a St. Louis packet was leaving next day and that he had secured passage on her for Richard as well as for himself. "Here is a furlough for ninety days and the general has recommended your honourable discharge."

Early the following morning Clinton with Richard leaning on his sound arm walked up the gang-plank of the *St. Louis* on his way back to the North. The boat, crowded with passengers, included many wounded soldiers, some of whom were lying on pallets laid along the deck. But Clinton, by reckless expenditure of money, had secured an inside bunk, although during the day they were both glad to sit outside where they could sniff the clean wind, a wind which hinted happily of the region toward which their minds careered like homing eagles.

Here was the side of war which carries very little inspiration for the youthful volunteer. Here were one-armed, one-legged, bandaged, and hollow-eyed veterans, a score or more of them whose share in the war was ended. Having made heavy sacrifices for their country, they were on their way back to familiar scenes and familiar faces with only feeble interest, it must be confessed, in what they were leaving behind them. With eyes directed to home and rest, they had no desire to glance southwards. A few of them were attended by wives or daughters; others, like Clinton and Richard, were travelling without nurses and helping one another.

The steamer, in the judgment of all these home-coming passengers, was the slowest craft afloat. It literally crawled along, loafing unconscionably at every wharf, coughing and wheezing and vacillating in its course like a browsing sea-cow.

Richard was so impatient of all this inconsequential loitering and feebleness that he went all a-strain, "pushing at the dashboard" as he expressed it. But Clinton remained singularly content. He called attention to the cool breezes and praised the comfort of their beds, calling upon Richard to take it easy. "After all," he urged, "your respite has begun. Enjoy it while you can." All this advice he uttered with such an air of cheerful resignation that Richard was not only greatly puzzled but somewhat irritated until on the second day he observed his partner in frequent, absorbed conversation with a young lady, evidently the daughter of a wounded man, a major of cavalry.

Richard had never known Clinton to show quite such intensity of interest in a woman, and though at one time he had hoped that Susan might be the chosen one, he had come to the conclusion that his friend was the confirmed old bachelor which others called him. That he was deeply smitten by this stranger was evident not only to his comrade but to many of his fellow-passengers. Without exactly neglecting Richard he found a great deal of time to walk about with the young lady whom he finally spoke of in a somewhat offhand manner. "She's a Miss Trudo, daughter of Major Trudo of Dubuque. I've seen her a great many times at home, but never had the pleasure of her companionship till now. In fact I never really talked with her till we met on the boat."

Richard was still too weak to say, "You seem to be making up for lost time," but some such thought came into his mind.

Miss Trudo, a tall fair girl, was much more suited to Clinton than slender little Susan, and Richard, though made irritable by the senseless meanderings of the boat, did not complain of neglect. "Clinton is thirty-five years old, middle-aged in fact, and he'd better thank his stars for this slow boat."

In later years, Clinton was accustomed to say to his wife, with a jocular lilt in his voice, "My flag came down on the second day of your siege. It was not a fair contest. You had among the forces on your side the fact that I had rarely spoken to a girl in two years and that I was on my

way home on a furlough with one arm out of commission. What chance had I? Of course," he used to add with elaborate show of fairness, "your youth and good looks had something to do with my early capitulation."

Miss Trudo on her part was in almost equally susceptible mood. She had just been seeing something of the pitiful side of war, and this wounded officer, notably handsome in his colonel's uniform, represented to her the romance and the heroism of the field. He typified for her those of her friends who had volunteered early in the war and had fallen in battle or had perished in camp hospitals, unattended by their wives and daughters.

It was not a gay courtship, but it was beautifully sincere and fine, with a graver sweetness appropriate to the time and the place. They were both so happy in their discovery of mutual interests that all else became of small account, and yet it was a happiness which derived something poetic from the far-spreading shadows of the national storm. It was as if their way were lit by a brief ray of sunshine falling through a rift in the Southern war-cloud, and both made the most of it.

Left much to himself and shut in by his deafness, Richard took comfort in the increasing coolness of the air, and in the growing height of the river-banks with their familiar verdure. To him Cairo was the gate to the North and St. Louis the beginning of home, for it had often been one of the points toward which he had directed his rafts of lumber and logs.

Here the run of the boat on which they had been riding ended and it became necessary to transfer to a smaller craft, one which was accustomed to navigate the upper river, now at low-water stage.

Clinton, notwithstanding the fact that he had been advised by his surgeon in Vicksburg to stop off for treatment in St. Louis, decided to go on. With great magnanimity he said, "I'm going on with you, Dick. I want to see you as far on the way toward your home as possible."

Richard, much improved in health and spirits, was able to smile faintly as he replied, "Don't go any farther on my account, colonel."

Clinton understood him perfectly and his chuckle was frankly revealing as he declared, "I wouldn't miss going on with you for a year's pay. Why, man, it's my job! As an old friend and comrade, it's my duty to stand by you. I'm going to do it if it takes a leg, my wooden leg!"

It chanced that an old acquaintance from Galena was standing at the head of the gang-plank as Clinton and Richard went aboard. Upon recognizing them he called out, "My God, men! What have they been doing to you down there?"

He might well ask this, for they were but poor shadows of the men they had been at that war-meeting in '61. Clinton, however, made humorous answer. "We're a bit the worse for wear, I'll admit. But you should see the other feller! It hasn't been exactly a picnic for Johnny Reb, I'd have you know. We carried away a mouthful of fur, too, you bet!"

The Galena man spoke of Grant. "That man is a wonder. I can't believe he's any relation to the Captain Grant I used to see sitting around Perkins' store."

"He is, though. Same man, only he's found his place."

With a comfortable bunk at night and a seat on deck by day, Richard moved on up the river, rejoicing in the procession of familiar towns and well-known landmarks. The day was heavenly summer, and he was exalted by its almost painful beauty. Knowing that every throb of the engine carried him nearer to Isabel and his children, back into a land wherein no sign of conflict met the eye, he revelled in a sense of deliverance which made speech impossible.

The Peaceful River

At times the river was as wide, as lone, and almost as silent as when the French explorers floated down its peaceful flood. Ragged boys instead of red warriors were paddling about the quiet waters or fishing from the grassy banks on which in other times the clustered tepees stood. The mist which filled the valley was like the veil of memory which the years had dropped into it. It was as if he were re-entering the joyous season of his youth through the medium of a dreamlike flood.

It is probable that Clinton was even more enchanted, for in addition to his love for this great river and the charm of its hills and valleys, he had the delight of a continued companionship with a lovely woman. It did not matter to him that the *War Eagle* grounded on a sand-bar and was nearly ten hours in getting off—or rather it did matter; it gave him secret joy. Of course he was sorry for those who, like Richard, were perishing with homesickness, but so long as worrying could not hurry the process of extricating the boat from her predicament, he was disposed to make full use of the time which this mishap afforded, and in this cheerful acceptance of delay Lucy apparently joined.

Her attitude toward Richard changed markedly. Realizing that he was Clinton's closest friend, she took increasing interest in his welfare and he, on his part, admired her and began to think of her quite definitely as Clinton's wife. She grew younger and gayer as her father's spirits rose. She questioned Richard concerning his home, his wife, and his children with a graceful sincerity of manner which was very pleasing to him, and at last he said, "I hope you'll come up and see us, you and Clinton."

She flushed a little, but answered gravely, "I hope I may, some time."

Her father the major who had been morose and silent for the larger part of the way now took a more gracious attitude toward Clinton. Whether he recognized in him a prospective son-in-law or not, Richard was unable to determine.

After several other delays they arrived at Dubuque in the early morning and again Clinton professed his willingness to go on if Richard desired it.

"No indeed, Clint. I'm all right. You get off here. Don't worry about me; every mile takes me nigher home, makes me stronger. You're just as eager to get home as I am;" here he fetched a faint twist of a smile. "Don't you lose any time over me. Let me know how you prosper, that's all I ask, and bring her up to see Belle."

"I'd bring her next week if she'd come," Clinton shamelessly replied.

So they parted, Clinton assisting Major Trudo to the shore, and Richard returning to his bed, for it was only a little after sunrise.

During the day others of his fellow-travellers dropped off at their home-towns and many touching scenes were enacted on the wharves as the haggard and halting soldiers met their wives and children. One or two of the veterans found no one at all to greet them, and their bewildered loneliness gave Richard a foretaste of what his own landing might be. That he would be wholly unexpected he knew, for he had not been able to tell the name of the boat he would take, nor predict the hour of her arrival. "I must trust to luck," he said with his usual fatalism.

Grand-Daddy Bluff came into view about two o'clock of an August afternoon, and his heart leaped like that of a man returning after years of absence. His incessant activity, the manifold dangers through which he had passed, and especially the devastating sickness which had ended his campaign, and carried him to the crumbling edge of the grave, combined to fill him with tender affection for the looming hills and the small, pleasant valleys opening out between them. His eyes filled with tears. This was his home, the only spot on earth to which he cared to return. The hill-side farm in Maine was an almost forgotten shelter, and Boston a city in a far-off and inaccessible land.

No one recognized him at the landing, and had it not been for the kindness of a fellow-passenger he would have had some trouble in debarking, so overcome was he with excitement.

It was Sunday and a throng of young people had gathered on the shore. Some of them were women expecting returning husbands or sweethearts, but others were merely onlookers. Little of the war spirit was visible, indeed it would have been impossible for a stranger from another country to have discovered that a national conflict was going on. All were gay and well dressed and well fed. None were old.

Pale, bearded, bent and slow-motioned, Richard walked ashore, and there stood till the boat swung out into the stream and moved away. The town he had looked forward to with such longing presented to him a blank, indifferent face. The people turned toward their homes, indifferent to his fortunes.

He was casting about for a drayman to take him to a hotel when he heard a pleasant voice at his elbow, "This is Dick Graham, or I miss my guess."

Richard turned. "I am; what's left of me, and you are Dan Ridgway of Sharpless Valley."

Ridgway, a sturdy, red-bearded man, looked at the soldier pityingly. "You look like a man who has been badly stayed with. Been wounded?"

"Not to hurt, but I've been in the hospital for six weeks; pretty weak yet."

"You're going to need some help about getting home, I take it."

Richard's smile was a bitter grimace. "I don't know how

I'll get there without it. I must find shelter till I can notify my family."

Ridgway gathered up his belongings. "Come along with me. I'll see that you get home. My team is just around the corner."

Richard followed him gratefully, and on the way was cheered by a greeting from one of the merchants who spoke to him not because he knew him, but as a tribute to his uniform.

Ridgway's wagon was heavy and springless, but its seat, balanced on two hickory poles, was a fairly comfortable perch, and Richard, having climbed to it at some risk and with much exertion, asked Ridgway if he could go around by way of Green's Coulee just as well as not. "I hate to bother you."

"Sure thing I can go that way. I can go by way of Onalaska if you want to see the folks there. It's not much out of my way."

Once out of the town Richard discovered that the day had that magic quality which comes along in August at this latitude, a day which marks the change of summer to autumn. The air had a hint of frost in it and yet was delightfully warm and golden. By cupping his hand over his ear he could hear the harvest crickets chirping, and the smell of ripened grass and leaves pervaded the air. The yellow and purple fall flowers were in bloom and the tall marsh grass was turning sere. In the voices of the jay and crow a new and prophetic note had come, a note which harmonized perfectly with the hazy hill-sides and the harvest-fields. To the sick man it was all so sweet, so far away from battle and swamps, cannon-shot and rattle of musketry, that it seemed of another world and time.

Ridgway drove slowly and the sleepy *chuck-chuckle* of the axles mingled with the chirp of the single-trees and the creaking of the seat-springs. At intervals he asked a question and Richard answered briefly, very briefly, loath to bring into this beloved landscape the smoke of battle and the smell of camps. The scenes through which he had passed and which he hoped never to see again were monstrous, unbelievable in the midst of this serene and fruitful valley.

Ridgway's interest it soon appeared was personal. He was facing the question of enlistment. "The draft is going into operation soon and I'm thinking of 'listing before I'm obliged to. I'm a little old for service and I've got one game ankle, but I could drive a team or do something that would free a better man for the ranks. Lincoln is going to need more men to put the war through and I want to do my part."

As they crossed the winding, muddy little La Crosse river, Richard looked away toward the conical hill which marked the eastern boundary of his coulee farm, and remarked, "For a while I had mighty little expectation of ever seeing that bluff again."

"You look as if you'd been in some mighty tight places. It's kindo got around up here that you've been serving as a spy. I give it as it comes to me. A man in Onalasky said he got it from your father."

Richard made no reply to this remark. "If you don't mind, Dan, I *would* like to have you go round by way of Onalaska. I'd like to see my mother for a moment just to let her know I'm alive."

"No trouble in the world, Dick; I'm only too glad to give you the lift."

The saw-mills were silent, but as they came into the village, groups of men around the saloon doors and others sprawling under the trees gave evidence of the prosperity which the war had brought to this lumber town. There was nothing to indicate that hundreds of men had been taken from this industry to carry on the war with the South, and

Richard recalled a conversation he had held with a captured Confederate who had asked, "I suppose you are as badly off for men in the North as we are in the South?" and to which he had answered, in the spirit of a scout, "Captain, if you were to take a trip through the North (as you are likely to do) you wouldn't know that a war is going on." Here, now, was the proof of his boast.

At the door of his father's little cottage, in the shade of a plum tree, his mother was sitting reading a newspaper. She looked up questioningly as she heard the wagon, and for a moment did not recognize in this bearded, gaunt and pale soldier, the son she had sent to the war—then half-rising from her seat, she called in more excitement than he had ever heard in her voice, "Susan, Susan! Here is Richard."

Susan came flying down the path with most unaccustomed haste just in time to help the soldier down from the wagon-wheel. "Oh, Dick," she said as he faced her, "is it really you? How *thin* you are!"

It had never been their habit to kiss each other, but feeling that something out of the ordinary was demanded, he put his arm about her and touched his lips to her cheek. He did the same to his mother as she tremulously rose to meet him.

"My boy! You've been wounded!"

"No, mother, only sick. First, Yazoo fever caught me, then typhoid, and together they got me down pretty low. The thing I mind most is my loss of hearing."

Susan brought a chair for him and another for Ridgway, and sitting beside his mother, he talked on, answering her questions briefly and languidly. "I can't stop but a few minutes, mother. Ridgway is taking me home. Where's father?"

"He's at a church meeting. You can't go before he comes."

"I must. I can't rest till I see Belle and the children, but I'm hungry." He smiled with boyish sweetness. "You know what I'd like? A slice of bread and butter with jelly on it, just as I used to eat it when a boy."

Susan flew to get it while Ridgway helped him back into his high seat and with his luncheon in his hand, he said, "I'll be over again soon. Send word to Dave if you get a chance."

He had a sense of guilt as the horses toiled through the deep sand, and as they went down the hill he said, "Now, Dan, just drop me at the corner, I can manage the rest of the way. I'm feeling stronger every minute."

"I'll drive you all the way up the coulee if you say so."

"No, I don't want you to do that. Truth is, I kind of want to surprise my folks."

"All right. You're the doctor. Hope you find the wife and children well. So long!"

"So long, Dan. I'm much obliged. If you see David or William McLane tell 'em I'm here—what there is left of me."

He stood for a long time absorbing the quiet beauty of his surroundings. On either side of the road, the wheat was standing in shock and the air was filled with the harvest smell, a cool, friendly, fruity smell. The peace of the hour was more than a Sabbath peace; it was a part of the tranquillity of the primitive world to which he naturally belonged. It could not be that he should be called back to the battle-fields. The defeat of Lee at Gettysburg and the capture of Vicksburg were, to him, decisive.

"As soon as I am well enough I will take up the work which the war interrupted. I need a new barn and that marsh must be drained."

His knapsack was a burden, and his steps slow and uncertain, but he set off up the road with returning strength, smiling as he visioned the excitement which his coming would create in Belle and the children. How changed they would be!

He decided not to stop at Green's and, when opposite the gate, hurried a little, keeping his eyes straight ahead, hoping to pass unrecognized. Eager to see his wife's face, he could not spare a moment of time. His knees were unsteady, but he strode sturdily forward with eyes searching the valley.

He was troubled by the fact that a part of his grain was unharvested. "Why hasn't Dave looked after it?" he grumbled. "Isabel can't do it and I'm in no condition to reap." A sense of helplessness such as he had never known came over him. The future which had been so secure in '61 was now a vague and troubled region of storm.

At Roche's gate stood their dog Black Bess who knew him and followed him for a little way. He wondered if his own dog, Rover, would recognize him and come down the road to meet him. He saw his cattle feeding along the side-hill. He could hear old Spot's bell clang as she swung her head against the flies upon her sides. No one was stirring as he came within sight of his cottage. The hens were foraging about the door, and Debby, the cat, was sitting on a fence-post, but the shades of the windows were drawn and all was silent.

The soldier's happy mood chilled. He had counted on the dog's greeting and on finding the children at play in the yard. He had pictured their startled action, and the joyous expression of Isabel's face. Now with the door closed and the curtains down, his home presented a blind and inhospitable face. Tired, bitterly disappointed, he leaned upon the fence, forlornly wondering what had happened to his small family. "Perhaps they are over at David's place," he said to himself. He did not know exactly what to do next. He was too tired to retrace his steps or to go on up the coulee to Crandall's and the sun was going down.

The Peaceful River

Hearing faintly the sound of a voice behind him, he turned his head just as Isabel reached the gate. She was drawing a wooden cart in which her baby boy was seated, and just behind her came Hattie leading her little brother by the hand. Richard saw Isabel hesitate and realized that she was not sure of his identity, then she spoke his name and a look of recognition, of love, of pity swept over her face. How beautiful she was!

As he took her in his arms, she questioned him, "Oh, Dick, have you been wounded?"

"No, nothing to speak of, but I'm just out of the hospital. I've had a poor time for nearly two months. The fever left me hard of hearing. The doctor says it will wear off and I hope it will for I only hear you very faintly now." He turned to the children who stood watching him with wide and curious eyes. Hattie knew him, but the others stood away in fear of him.

As he entered the cottage it seemed to him the sweetest, most restful place in all the world. While Isabel's deft hands prepared his evening meal, he stretched out on the floor the better to rest his weary bones and through the open door he watched the sunset light creep slowly up Old Sugar-Loaf hill. Just as its last rays turned the limestone summit cap to gold, the call to supper came, and in the joy of his reunion with his family, the trail-maker regained something of his native cheerfulness of outlook. His southern circle was rounded and he was at rest.

The children had been put to bed, and the soldier, with his hand on his wife's shoulder was standing in the doorway looking out over his little farm growing dim in the twilight, when the rattle of a wagon and the beat of horse's hooves rapidly approaching, led him to say, "That must be Al Crandall's team. He always drives like a man in a great hurry."

The teamster uttered a musical hail and Isabel exclaimed, "Why, it's Dave!"

"I believe it is! William is with him, and the girls. Ridgway must have gone over to tell them about me."

With another jovial halloo, David brought his team to a stand before the gate and sprang over the edge of the box to the ground as was his boyish habit. William following more sedately, turned to help Mantie and Rachel alight, while David tied his horses to the fence. This action, so familiar, so delightfully characteristic, helped Richard to forget the guerrillas and the swamp-land of the South.

"Hello Dick!" called Rachel as she came up the path. "Dan Ridgway told us you were here, and so we came a-runnin'. How are you?"

Richard met them on the door-stone, so strongly moved that he could scarcely speak, and both girls kissed him, a caress they had never before ventured to give (How pretty, how grown up they both seemed!) and David, almost as shy of emotional utterance as they, first clapped him on the shoulder with his broad palm, then gathered him in the curve of his great right arm. "By the great Horn Spoon, I'm glad to see you!" he declared with a fervor he tried to mask in jocularity.

He paused a moment and studied him closely. "Dan said you'd just got out of the hospital and you feel like it. You're nothing but a rack o' bones."

William, big bearded and impassive, did not speak at all but when they entered the kitchen where the kerosene lamp was burning, a mist in his fine eyes betrayed his tenderness. "I was afraid we'd lost you," he soberly explained; then, to shake off the stress of the moment, he added briskly, "Well now you're here, tell us all about it. Are you home for good?"

"It looks like it, William. I'm not only a rack of bones, as Dave says, but I'm half deaf. I guess my soldiering is over. The war won't last much longer anyway. Vicksburg and Gettysburg have just about put a finish to it. Have you heard from Luke?"

A shadow fell and with it a silence which was finally broken by David. "No, and we've given up hope—all but mother. She still thinks he may be a prisoner somewhere."

"How is Granpap?"

"Well and hearty and still figuring on 'the Great Day.' He fears now that it may not come in his time. Frank wrote that he had seen you at Vicksburg, but didn't say anything about your sickness."

How sweet, how restorative this hour was! With these handsome loyal companions of his early days before him, with Isabel by his side, and the crickets chirping their harvest song from the dusk, the battlefield softly receded. He asked of Adele, of valued neighbours, and was told of other stricken homes, and then for relief the talk turned upon the crops and plans for the autumn.

William said, "Dave and I have bought the newest make of threshing machine, Dick. I hope you'll be ready to join us again in September."

"Maybe I can. I'll be able to drive at least—with a stool to sit on. I must get back to work as soon as I can stagger around."

In such homely, leisurely conversation the evening passed (all too swiftly) and at last William gave the signal for retreat. "Well, Dick," he said as he rose, "we must go. You're tired, and we're all early risers at our house."

Still talking, softly, brokenly, they moved slowly out into the starlit night and down to the gate where they stood for a time reluctant to say good night. There was so much to talk about!

"Mother and Pap are hungry for a sight of you, Dick. We all want to hear more of your story," David urged. "I'll come over tomorrow afternoon and get you."

"I'll come. I won't be of much use in the field but I can sit on the porch and spin yarns."

"That's all we want you to do for a while," Rachel assured him.

With a pleasant chorus of good-byes and admonition to take it easy for a while they rode off down the coulee, leaving the tired, happy scout leaning upon the gate.

"Well, Belle," he finally remarked with a wistful note in his voice, "We're back right where we were a year ago, and I'm a pretty poor specimen, but I'll make up for lost time somehow."

"I don't care for lost time!" Isabel retorted, taking his arm and squeezing it. "I'm so thankful to have you back——" she could not finish. Relying upon her strength he moved slowly toward the lighted doorway.

In the days which followed, the returned soldier took up the tasks and plans which he had dropped in order to serve the Union Flag. Confident that peace was near, his eyes turned once more, in a reviving dream of exploration, to the clear streams and fertile prairies of the farther West. His military service, intense and stirring as it had been, was in truth but an episode, a temporary deflection from the path of his predestined course.